PENGUIN BOO[

VINTAGE THURBER

VOLUME 2

James Thurber was born in 1894 at Columbus, Ohio, where, as he once said, so many awful things happened to him. After university (Ohio State) he worked at the American Embassy in Paris from 1918 to 1920, and then turned to journalism. From 1927 onwards he was on the staff of the *New Yorker*, and first published much of his work in it.

Thurber's art was easy to recognize but hard to define. He created a world in which mournfully sagacious hounds loom over frightened little men who are trying desperately to master life's problems. His drawings and prose alike were marked by economy, wry humour, and an inimitable blend of precision and fantasy. Perhaps his most justly famous character was Walter Mitty, whose *Secret Life* gloriously makes up for the shy young man's failures in competitive real life. Thurberites – and they are many – hardly need reminding that the classic Thurberisms are preserved in *Thurber's Dogs*, *The Thurber Album*, *Thurber Country*, and many more like-minded collections.

In later life James Thurber became increasingly blind. He died in New York in 1961. In an *Observer* appreciation, Paul Jennings wrote that 'he somehow gave us a sense of revelation . . . He created a *genre* and was a giant in it.'

VINTAGE THURBER

A COLLECTION, IN TWO VOLUMES,

OF THE BEST WRITINGS AND DRAWINGS OF

JAMES THURBER

VOLUME 2

PENGUIN BOOKS

Penguin Books Ltd, Harmondsworth, Middlesex, England
Penguin Books, 625 Madison Avenue, New York, New York 10022, U.S.A.
Pengin Books Australia Ltd, Ringwood, Victoria, Australia
Penguin Books Canada Ltd, 2801 John Street, Markham, Ontario, Canada L3R 1B4
Penguin Books (N.Z.) Ltd, 182–190 Wairau Road, Auckland 10, New Zealand

—

First published in Great Britain by Hamish Hamilton 1963
Published in Penguin Books 1983

—

—

Made and printed in Great Britain by
Richard Clay (The Chaucer Press) Ltd,
Bungay, Suffolk

Contents

NOTE

Three pieces in this volume, all in *The Thurber Album*, originally appeared in slightly different versions. 'Adam's Anvil' was originally entitled 'A Good Man' and appeared in *My World and Welcome to It*. This piece, 'Daguerreotype of a Lady' and 'Lavender with a Difference' were all altered when they reappeared in *Alarms and Diversions*. The later versions are followed here in each case.

The Middle-Aged Man on the
Flying Trapeze

FOR

BOB AND ELSA COATES

The Gentleman is Cold

IN THE first chill days of November it was the subject of sharp and rather nasty comment on the part of my friends and colleagues that I went about the draughty streets of town without a hat or overcoat. Once even a stranger who passed me in the street snarled, 'Put on your hat and coat!' It seemed to annoy people. They began to insinuate under their breath, and even come right out and say, that I was simply trying to look strange and different in order to attract attention. This accusation was made with increasing bitterness when my hair, which I always forget to have cut, began to get very long. It was obvious, my friends said, that I walked about the city cold and miserable in the hope that people would nudge their companions and say, 'There goes Jacob Thurman, the eccentric essayist.'

There was, and is, no basis to these charges at all. I have reasons, and good reasons, for not wanting to, for, in fact, not being able to, wear an overcoat. I have just as good reasons about the hat, but I needn't go into them so fully. A week or so ago, however, the smirking remarks and mean innuendoes of my associates forced me one day to put on my overcoat (I couldn't find my hat and I wouldn't buy a new one, because when I try one on and peer in the triplicate mirrors they have in hat shops, I catch unexpected angles of my face which make me look like a slightly ill professor of botany who is also lost). The overcoat, which I bought in 1930, after a brief and losing battle with a sharp-tongued clerk who was taller than I am, does not fit me very well and never did fit me very well. That's one reason I don't like to wear it. Another is that it has no buttons (it didn't have any buttons after the first week) and is extremely difficult to manage in a head wind. In such a wind I used to grab for my hat with both hands, thus letting go the hold I had on my coat to keep it together in front, and the whole thing would belly out all around me. Once, in grabbing for my hat (and missing it, for I was a fraction of a second too late), I knocked my glasses off and was not only caught in a grotesque swirl of overcoat right at the corner of Fifth Avenue and Forty-fourth Street but couldn't see a thing. Several people stopped and watched the struggle without offering to help until finally, when everybody had had his laugh, a woman picked up my glasses and handed them to me. 'Here's your glasses,' she tittered, grinning at me as if I were a policeman's horse with a sunbonnet. I put the glasses on, gathered the coat together, and walked off with as much dignity as I could, leaving my hat swirling along the street under the wheels of traffic.

It was the twentieth of November this winter that I finally put on my over-

3

coat for the first time. It is a heavy grey one, and looks a little like a dog bed because the strap on the inside of the collar broke and the coat had been lying on the floor of my closet for almost a year. I carried it downstairs from my hotel room to the lobby, and didn't start to put it on until I had reached the revolving doors leading to the street. I had just got one arm into a sleeve when I was suddenly grabbed from behind, a hand shot up under the coat, jerked my undercoat sharply down, and I fell backward, choking, into the arms of the hotel doorman, who had come to my assistance. He is a powerfully built man who brooks no denial of, or interference with, his little attentions and services. He didn't exactly throw me, but I took a pretty bad tossing around.

From the hotel I went, in a badly disturbed state of mind, to my barber's, and I was just reaching into a pocket of the overcoat for my cigarettes and matches when the coat was whisked off me from behind. This was done with great firmness but no skill by the coloured porter and bootblack who sneaks up behind people at Joe's barbershop and tears their overcoats off their backs. This porter is not so powerfully built as the doorman at my hotel, but he is sinewy and in excellent condition. Furthermore, he was not wearing an overcoat himself, and the man who *is* wearing an overcoat is at a great disadvantage in a struggle. This porter is also a coat-tugger, belonging to that school of coat-tuggers who reach up under your overcoat after they have helped you on with it and jerk the back of your suit jacket so savagely that the collar of the jacket is pulled away from its proper set around the shoulders and makes you feel loutish and miserable. There is nothing to do about this except give the man a dime.

It wasn't, however, until I went with some fine acquaintances of mine to an excellent restaurant that night that I got into my old familiar plight with the ripped lining of the left sleeve. After dining, the gentlemen in the party were helped on with their coats by one of those slim, silent waiters with the cold and fishy eye of an art critic. He got me adroitly into the right sleeve of my overcoat, and then I stuck my left arm smoothly into the lining of the other sleeve. Running an arm into the ripped lining of an overcoat while people, both acquaintances and strangers, look on and the eye of the struggling waiter gets colder and colder, is one of the most humiliating experiences known to the American male. After it was finally straightened out and I got my arm through the sleeve, I couldn't find any money for a tip; I couldn't even find a dime. I don't like to dwell on that incident.

After leaving the restaurant, we went to a theatre, and there another reason I do not like to wear an overcoat and never will wear an overcoat again reared its terrifying head. In taking off my overcoat to hand it to the unsympathetic hat-check boy, I took off with it the jacket to my dinner clothes and was left standing in the crowded and well-dressed lounge in my shirt-sleeves, with a section of my suspenders plainly visible through the armhole of my waistcoat. So speedily do hat-check boys work that my overcoat and jacket had been whisked to the back of the hat-check room and hung up under a couple of other overcoats before I could do anything about it. The eight or ten seconds that went by before I recovered my dinner jacket were among the worst moments of my life. The only worse experience I can think of was the time my suitcase flopped open on the Madison Avenue car tracks when I was hurrying to make a train at Grand Central.

I tried to pass off the episode of the dinner jacket nonchalantly, but succeeded only in lapsing into that red-faced fixed grin which no truly well-poised man-about-town ever permits himself to lapse into. I reached for my cigarettes, but I found that I had left them in a pocket of my overcoat, so in order to have something to do with my hands – for people were still staring and leering – I gracefully pulled a neatly folded handkerchief from the breast pocket of my dinner jacket, only to discover when I shook it out that it was a clean white silk sock. The last time I had dressed for dinner, I had been unable to find a fresh handkerchief, and after considerable effort had finally folded the sock and tucked it into the pocket of my jacket in such a way that it looked like a handkerchief. Of course, on that occasion I had remembered not to pull the handkerchief out. I had remembered this by grimly repeating it to myself all evening, but that had been several nights before and I had completely forgotten about the sock.

I would never have brought out all these humiliating revelations had it not been for the fact that even those persons who know me best, for a modest, unassuming man, had really come to believe that I went around town without an overcoat in order to make the same kind of impression that Oscar Wilde made with his sunflower or Sean O'Casey with his brown sweater. I simply want to be mentally at ease, and I have found out after years of experience that I cannot be mentally at ease and at the same time wear an overcoat. Going without an overcoat in bitter weather has, God knows, its special humiliations, but having a kindly old lady come up to me on the street and hand me a dime is nothing compared to the horrors I went through when I wore an overcoat, or tried to wear one.

The Departure of Emma Inch

EMMA INCH looked no different from any other middle-aged, thin woman you might glance at in the subway or deal with across the counter of some small store in a country town, and then forget forever. Her hair was drab and unabundant, her face made no impression on you, her voice I don't remember – it was just a voice. She came to us with a letter of recommendation from some acquaintance who knew that we were going to Martha's Vineyard for the summer and wanted a cook. We took her because there was nobody else, and she seemed all right. She had arrived at our hotel in Forty-fifth Street the day before we were going to leave and we got her a room for the night, because she lived way uptown somewhere. She said she really ought to go back and give up her room, but I told her I'd fix that.

Emma Inch had a big scuffed brown suitcase with her, and a Boston bull terrier. His name was Feely. Feely was seventeen years old and he grumbled and growled and snuffled all the time, but we needed a cook and we agreed to take Feely along with Emma Inch, if she would take care of him and keep him out of the way. It turned out to be easy to keep Feely out of the way because he would lie grousing anywhere Emma put him until she came and picked him up again. I never saw him walk. Emma had owned him, she said, since he was a pup. He was all she had in the world, she told us, with a mist in her eyes. I felt embarrassed but not touched. I didn't see how anybody could love Feely.

I didn't lose any sleep about Emma Inch and Feely the night of the day they arrived, but my wife did. She told me next morning that she had lain awake a long time thinking about the cook and her dog, because she felt kind of funny about them. She didn't know why. She just had a feeling that they were kind of funny. When we were all ready to leave – it was about three o'clock in the afternoon, for we had kept putting off the packing – I phoned Emma's room, but she didn't answer. It was getting late and we felt nervous – the Fall River boat would sail in about two hours. We couldn't understand why we hadn't heard anything from Emma and Feely. It wasn't until four o'clock that we did. There was a small rap on the door of our bedroom and I opened it and Emma and Feely were there, Feely in her arms, snuffing and snaffling, as if he had been swimming a long way.

My wife told Emma to get her bag packed, we were leaving in a little while. Emma said her bag *was* packed, except for her electric fan, and she couldn't get that in. 'You won't need an electric fan at the Vineyard,' my wife told her. 'It's cool there, even during the day, and it's almost cold at night. Besides, there is no electricity in the cottage we are going to.' Emma Inch seemed

7

distressed. She studied my wife's face. 'I'll have to think of something else then,' she said. 'Mebbe I could let the water run all night.' We both sat down and looked at her. Feely's asthmatic noises were the only sounds in the room for a while. 'Doesn't that dog ever stop that?' I asked, irritably. 'Oh, he's just talking,' said Emma. 'He talks all the time, but I'll keep him in my room and he won't bother you none.' 'Doesn't he bother you?' I asked. 'He *would* bother

me,' said Emma, 'at night, but I put the electric fan on and keep the light burning. He don't make so much noise when it's light, because he don't snore. The fan kind of keeps me from noticing him. I put a piece of cardboard, like, where the fan hits it and then I don't notice Feely so much. Mebbe I could let the water run in my room all night instead of the fan.' I said 'Hmmm' and got up and mixed a drink for my wife and me – we had decided not to have one till we got on the boat, but I thought we'd better have one now. My wife didn't tell Emma there would be no running water in her room at the Vineyard.

'We've been worried about you, Emma,' I said. 'I phoned your room but you didn't answer.' 'I never answer the phone,' said Emma, 'because I always get a shock. I wasn't there anyways. I couldn't sleep in that room. I went back to Mrs McCoy's on Seventy-eighth Street.' I lowered my glass. 'You went back to Seventy-eighth Street last *night*?' I demanded. 'Yes, sir,' she said. 'I had to tell Mrs McCoy I was going away and wouldn't be there any more for a while – Mrs McCoy's the landlady. Anyways, I never sleep in a hotel.' She looked around the room. 'They burn down,' she told us.

It came out that Emma Inch had not only gone back to Seventy-eighth Street the night before but had walked all the way, carrying Feely. It had taken her an hour or two, because Feely didn't like to be carried very far at a time, so she had had to stop every block or so and put him down on the side-walk for a while. It had taken her just as long to walk back to our hotel, too; Feely, it seems, never got up before afternoon – that's why she was so late. She was sorry. My wife and I finished our drinks, looking at each other, and at Feely.

Emma Inch didn't like the idea of riding to Pier 14 in a taxi, but after ten minutes of cajoling and pleading she finally got in. 'Make it go slow,' she said. We had enough time, so I asked the driver to take it easy. Emma kept getting to her feet and I kept pulling her back onto the seat. 'I never been in an auto-mobile before,' she said. 'It goes awful fast.' Now and then she gave a little squeal of fright. The driver turned his head and grinned. 'You're O.K. wit' me, lady,' he said. Feely growled at him. Emma waited until he had turned away again, and then she leaned over to my wife and whispered. 'They all take cocaine,' she said. Feely began to make a new sound – a kind of high, agonized yelp. 'He's singing,' said Emma. She gave a strange little giggle, but the expression of her face didn't change. 'I wish you had put the Scotch where we could get at it,' said my wife.

If Emma Inch had been afraid of the taxicab, she was terrified by the *Priscilla* of the Fall River Line. 'I don't think I can go,' said Emma. 'I don't think I could get on a boat. I didn't know they were so big.' She stood rooted to the pier, clasping Feely. She must have squeezed him too hard, for he screamed – he screamed like a woman. We all jumped. 'It's his ears,' said Emma. 'His ears hurt.' We finally got her on the boat, and once aboard, in the salon, her terror abated somewhat. Then the three parting blasts of the boat whistle rocked lower Manhattan. Emma Inch leaped to her feet and began to run, letting go of her suitcase (which she had refused to give up to a porter) but holding onto Feely. I caught her just as she reached the gangplank. The ship was on its way when I let go of her arm.

It was a long time before I could get Emma to go to her stateroom, but she went at last. It was an inside stateroom, and she didn't seem to mind it. I think she was surprised to find that it was like a room, and had a bed and a chair and a wash-bowl. She put Feely down on the floor. 'I think you'll have to do some-thing about the dog,' I said. 'I think they put them somewhere and you get them when you get off.' 'No, they don't,' said Emma. I guess, in this case, they didn't. I don't know. I shut the door on Emma Inch and Feely, and went away. My wife was drinking straight Scotch when I got to our stateroom.

The next morning, cold and early, we got Emma and Feely off the *Priscilla* at Fall River and over to New Bedford in a taxi and onto the little boat for Martha's Vineyard. Each move was as difficult as getting a combative drunken man out of the night club in which he fancies he has been insulted. Emma sat in a chair on the Vineyard boat, as far away from sight of the water as she could get, and closed her eyes and held onto Feely. She had thrown a coat over Feely, not only to keep him warm but to prevent any of the ship's officers from taking him away from her. I went in from the deck at intervals to see how she was. She was all right, or at least all right for her, until five minutes before the boat reached the dock at Woods Hole, the only stop between New Bedford and the Vineyard. Then Feely got sick. Or at any rate Emma said he was sick. He didn't seem to me any different from what he always was – his breathing was just as abnormal and irregular. But Emma said he was sick. There were tears in her eyes. 'He's a very sick dog, Mr Thurman,' she said. 'I'll have to take him home.' I knew by the way she said 'home' what she meant. She meant Seventy-eighth Street.

The boat tied up at Woods Hole and was motionless and we could hear the racket of the deckhands on the dock loading freight. 'I'll get off here,' said Emma, firmly, or with more firmness, anyway, than she had shown yet. I explained to her that we would be home in half an hour, that everything would be fine then, everything would be wonderful. I said Feely would be a new dog. I told her people sent sick dogs to Martha's Vineyard to be cured. But it was no good. 'I'll have to take him off here,' said Emma. 'I always have to take him home when he is sick.' I talked to her eloquently about the loveliness of Martha's Vineyard and the nice houses and the nice people and the wonderful accommodations for dogs. But I knew it was useless. I could tell by looking at her. She was going to get off the boat at Woods Hole.

'You really can't do this,' I said, grimly, shaking her arm. Feely snarled weakly. 'You haven't any money and you don't know where you are. You're a long way from New York. Nobody ever got from Woods Hole to New York alone.' She didn't seem to hear me. She began walking toward the stairs leading to the gangplank, crooning to Feely. 'You'll have to go all the way back on boats,' I said, 'or else take a train, and you haven't any money. If you are going to be so stupid and leave us now, I can't give you any money.' 'I don't want any money, Mr Thurman,' she said. 'I haven't earned any money.' I walked along in irritable silence for a moment; then I gave her some money. I made her take it. We got to the gangplank. Feely snaffled and gurgled. I saw now that his eyes were a little red and moist. I knew it would do no good to summon my wife – not when Feely's health was at stake. 'How do you expect to get home from here?' I almost shouted at Emma Inch as she moved down the gangplank. 'You're way out on the end of Massachusetts.' She stopped and turned around. 'We'll walk,' she said. 'We like to walk, Feely and me.' I just stood still and watched her go.

When I went up on deck, the boat was clearing for the Vineyard. 'How's everything?' asked my wife. I waved a hand in the direction of the dock. Emma Inch was standing there, her suitcase at her feet, her dog under one arm, waving goodbye to us with her free hand. I had never seen her smile before, but she was smiling now.

There's an Owl in My Room

I SAW Gertrude Stein on the screen of a newsreel theatre one afternoon and I heard her read that famous passage of hers about pigeons on the grass, alas (the sorrow is, as you know, Miss Stein's). After reading about the pigeons on the grass alas, Miss Stein said, 'This is a simple description of a landscape I have seen many times.' I don't really believe that that is true. Pigeons on the grass alas may be a simple description of Miss Stein's own consciousness, but it is not a simple description of a plot of grass on which pigeons have alighted, are alighting, or are going to alight. A truly simple description of the pigeons alighting on the grass of the Luxembourg Gardens (which, I believe, is where the pigeons alighted) would say of the pigeons alighting there only that they were pigeons alighting. Pigeons that alight anywhere are neither sad pigeons nor gay pigeons, they are simply pigeons.

It is neither just nor accurate to connect the word alas with pigeons. Pigeons are definitely not alas. They have nothing to do with alas and they have nothing to do with hooray (not even when you tie red, white, and blue ribbons on them and let them loose at band concerts); they have nothing to do with mercy me or isn't that fine, either. White rabbits, yes, and Scotch terriers, and bluejays, and even hippopotamuses, but not pigeons. I happen to have studied pigeons very closely and carefully, and I have studied the effect, or rather the lack of effect, of pigeons very carefully. A number of pigeons alight from time to time on the sill of my hotel window when I am eating breakfast and staring out the window. They never alas me, they never make me feel alas; they never make me feel anything.

Nobody and no animal and no other bird can play a scene so far down as a pigeon can. For instance, when a pigeon on my window ledge becomes aware of me sitting there in a chair in my blue polka-dot dressing-gown, worrying, he pokes his head far out from his shoulders and peers sideways at me, for all the world (Miss Stein might surmise) like a timid man peering around the corner of a building trying to ascertain whether he is being followed by some hoofed fiend or only by the echo of his own footsteps. And yet it is *not* for all the world like a timid man peering around the corner of a building trying to ascertain whether he is being followed by a hoofed fiend or only by the echo of his own footsteps, at all. And that is because there is no emotion in the pigeon and no power to arouse emotion. A pigeon looking is just a pigeon looking. When it comes to emotion, a fish, compared to a pigeon, is practically beside himself.

A pigeon peering at me doesn't make me sad or glad or apprehensive or hopeful. With a horse or a cow or a dog it would be different. It would be especially different with a dog. Some dogs peer at me as if I had just gone completely crazy or as if they had just gone completely crazy. I can go so far as to say that most dogs peer at me that way. This creates in the consciousness of both me and the dog a feeling of alarm or downright terror and legitimately permits me to work into a description of the landscape, in which the dog and myself are figures, a note of emotion. Thus I should not have minded if Miss Stein had written: dogs on the grass, look out, dogs on the grass, look out, look out, dogs on the grass, look out Alice. That would be a simple description of dogs on the grass. But when any writer pretends that a pigeon makes him sad, or makes him anything else, I must instantly protest that this is a highly specialized fantastic impression created in an individual consciousness and that therefore it cannot fairly be presented as a simple description of what actually was to be seen.

People who do not understand pigeons – and pigeons can be understood only when you understand that there is nothing to understand about them – should not go around describing pigeons or the effect of pigeons. Pigeons come closer to a zero of impingement than any other birds. Hens embarrass me the way my old Aunt Hattie used to when I was twelve and she still insisted I wasn't big enough to bathe myself; owls disturb me; if I am with an eagle I always pretend that I am not with an eagle; and so on down to swallows at twilight who scare the hell out of me. But pigeons have absolutely no effect on me. They have absolutely no effect on anybody. They couldn't even startle a child. That is why they are selected from among all birds to be let loose, with coloured ribbons attached to them, at band concerts, library dedications, and christenings of new dirigibles. If any body let loose a lot of owls on such an occasion there would be rioting and catcalls and whistling and fainting spells and throwing of chairs and the Lord only knows what else.

From where I am sitting now I can look out the window and see a pigeon being a pigeon on the roof of the Harvard Club. No other thing can be less what it is not than a pigeon can, and Miss Stein, of all people, should understand that simple fact. Behind the pigeon I am looking at, a blank wall of tired grey bricks is stolidly trying to sleep off oblivion; underneath the pigeon the cloistered windows of the Harvard Club are staring in horrified bewilderment at something they have seen across the street. The pigeon is just there on the roof being a pigeon, having been, and being, a pigeon and, what is more, always going to be, too. Nothing could be simpler than that. If you read that sentence aloud you will instantly see what I mean. It is a simple description of a pigeon on a roof. It is only with an effort that I am conscious of the pigeon, but I am acutely aware of a great sulky red iron pipe that is creeping up the side of the building intent on sneaking up on a slightly tipsy chimney which is shouting its head off.

There is nothing a pigeon can do or be that would make me feel sorry for it or for myself or for the people in the world, just as there is nothing I could do or be that would make a pigeon feel sorry for itself. Even if I plucked his feathers out it would not make him feel sorry for himself and it would not make me feel sorry for myself or for him. But try plucking the quills out of a porcupine or even plucking the fur out of a jackrabbit. There is nothing a pigeon could be, or can be, rather, which could get into my consciousness like a fumbling hand in a bureau drawer and disarrange my mind or pull anything out of it. I bar nothing at all. You could dress up a pigeon in a tiny suit of evening clothes and put a tiny silk hat on his head and a tiny gold-headed cane under his wing and send him walking into my room at night. It would make no impression on me. I would not shout, 'Good god almighty, the birds are in charge!' But you could send an owl into my room, dressed only in the feathers it was born with, and no monkey business, and I would pull the covers over my head and scream.

No other thing in the world falls so far short of being able to do what it cannot do as a pigeon does. Of being *unable* to do what it *can* do, too, as far as that goes.

The Topaz Cuff-links Mystery

WHEN the motorcycle cop came roaring up, unexpectedly, out of Never-Never Land (the way motorcycle cops do), the man was on his hands and knees in the long grass beside the road, barking like a dog. The woman was driving slowly along in a car that stopped about eighty feet away; its headlights shone on the man: middle-aged, bewildered, sedentary. He got to his feet.

'What's goin' on here?' asked the cop. The woman giggled. 'Cock-eyed,' thought the cop. He did not glance at her.

'I guess it's gone,' said the man. 'I – ah – could not find it.'

'What was it?'

'What I lost?' the man squinted, unhappily. 'Some – some cuff-links; topazes set in gold.' He hesitated: the cop didn't seem to believe him. 'They were the colour of a fine Moselle,' said the man. He put on a pair of spectacles which he had been holding in his hand. The woman giggled.

'Hunt things better with ya glasses off?' asked the cop. He pulled his motorcycle to the side of the road to let a car pass. 'Better pull over off the concrete, lady,' he said. She drove the car off the roadway.

'I'm nearsighted,' said the man. 'I can hunt things at a distance with my glasses on, but I do better with them off if I am close to something.' The cop kicked his heavy boots through the grass where the man had been crouching.

'He was barking,' ventured the lady in the car, 'so that I could see where he was.' The cop pulled his machine up on its standard; he and the man walked over to the automobile.

'What I don't get,' said the officer, 'is how you lose ya cuff-links a hunderd feet in front of where ya car is; a person usually stops his car *past* the place he loses somethin', not a hunderd feet before he gits *to* the place.'

The lady laughed again; her husband got slowly into the car, as if he were afraid the officer would stop him any moment. The officer studied them.

'Been to a party?' he asked. It was after midnight.

'We're not drunk, if that's what you mean,' said the woman, smiling. The cop tapped his fingers on the door of the car.

'You people didn't lose no topazes,' he said.

'Is it against the law for a man to be down on all fours beside a road, barking in a perfectly civil manner?' demanded the lady.

'No, ma'am,' said the cop. He made no move to get on his motorcycle, however, and go on about his business. There was just the quiet chugging of the cycle engine and the auto engine, for a time.

'I'll tell you how it was, Officer,' said the man, in a crisp, new tone. 'We were settling a bet. O.K.?'

'O.K.,' said the cop. 'Who won?' There was another pulsing silence.

'The lady bet,' said her husband, with dignity, as though he were explaining some important phase of industry to a newly hired clerk, 'the lady bet that my eyes would shine like a cat's do at night, if she came upon me suddenly close to the ground alongside the road. We had passed a cat, whose eyes gleamed. We had passed several persons, whose eyes did *not* gleam –'

'Simply because they were above the light and not under it,' said the lady. 'A man's eyes would gleam like a cat's if people were ordinarily caught by headlights at the same angle as cats are.' The cop walked over to where he had left his motorcycle, picked it up, kicked the standard out, and wheeled it back.

'A cat's eyes,' he said, 'are different than yours and mine. Dogs, cats, skunks, it's all the same. They can see in a dark room.'

'Not in a *totally* dark room,' said the lady.

'Yes, they can,' said the cop.

'No, they can't; not if there is no light at all in the room, not if it's absolutely *black*,' said the lady. 'The question came up the other night; there was a professor there and he said there must be at least a ray of light, no matter how faint.'

'That may be,' said the cop, after a solemn pause, pulling at his gloves. 'But people's eyes don't shine – I go along these roads every night an' pass hunderds of cats and hunderds of people.'

'The people are never close to the ground,' said the lady.

'*I* was close to the ground,' said her husband.

'Look at it this way,' said the cop. 'I've seen wildcats in *trees* at night, and *their* eyes shine.'

'There you are!' said the lady's husband. 'That proves it.'

'I don't see how,' said the lady. There was another silence.

'Because a wildcat in a tree's eyes are higher than the level of a man's,' said her husband. The cop may possibly have followed this, the lady obviously did not, neither one said anything. The cop got on his machine, raced his engine, seemed to be thinking about something, and throttled down. He turned to the man.

'Took ya glasses off so the headlights wouldn't make ya glasses shine, huh?' he asked.

'That's right,' said the man. The cop waved his hand, triumphantly, and roared away. 'Smart guy,' said the man to his wife, irritably.

'I still don't see where the wildcat proves anything,' said his wife. He drove off slowly.

'Look,' he said. 'You claim that the whole thing depends on how *low* a *cat's* eyes are; I –'

'I didn't say that; I said it all depends on how *high* a *man's* eyes . . .'

Casuals of the Keys

IF YOU know the more remote little islands off the Florida coast, you may have met – although I greatly doubt it – Captain Darke. Darrell Darke. His haunted key is, for this reason and that, the most inaccessible of them all. I came upon it quite by chance and doubt that I could find it again. I saw him first that moment when my shining little launch, so impudently summer-resortish, pushed its nose against the lonely pier on which he stood. Tall, dark, melancholy, his white shirt open at the throat, he reminded me instantly of that other solitary wanderer among forgotten islands, the doomed Lord Jim.

I stepped off the boat and he came toward me with a lean brown hand out-thrust. 'I'm Darke,' he said, simply, 'Darrell Darke.' I shook hands with him. He seemed pleased to encounter someone from the outside world. I found out later that no white man had set foot on his remote little key for several years.

He took me to a little thatched hut and waved me to a bamboo chair. It was a pleasant place, with a bed of dried palm leaves, a few withered books, some fishing equipment, and a bright rifle. Darke produced from somewhere a bottle with a greenish heavy liquid in it, and two glasses. 'Opono,' he said, apologetically. 'Made from the sap of the opono tree. Horrible stuff, but kicky.' I asked him if he would care for a touch of Bacardi, of which I had a quart on the launch, and he said he would. I went down and got it. . . .

'A newspaperman, eh?' said Darke, with interest, as I filled up the glasses for the third time. 'You must meet a lot of interesting people.' I really felt that I had met a lot of interesting people and, under slight coaxing, began to tell about them: Gene Tunney, Eddie Rickenbacker, the Grand Duchess Marie, William Gibbs McAdoo. Darke listened to my stories with quick attention, thirsty as he was for news of the colourful civilization which, he told me, he had put behind him twenty years before.

'You must,' I said at last, to be polite, 'have met some interesting people yourself.'

'No,' he said. 'All of a stripe, until you came along. Last chap that put in here, for example, was a little fellow name of Mark Menafee who turned up one day some three years ago in an outboard motor. He was only a trainer of fugitives from justice.' Darke reached for the glass I had filled again.

'I never heard of anyone being that,' I said. 'What did he do?'

'He coached fugitives from justice,' said Darke. 'Seems Menafee could spot one instantly. Take the case of Burt Fredericks he told me about. Fredericks was a bank defaulter from Connecticut. Menafee spotted him on a Havana boat – knew him from his pictures in the papers. "Hello, Burt," says Menafee, casually. Fredericks whirled around. Then he caught himself and stared blankly at Menafee. "My name is Charles Brandon," he says. Menafee won his confidence and for a fee and his expenses engaged to coach Fredericks not to be caught off his guard and answer to the name of Burt. He'd shadow Fredericks from city to city, contriving to come upon him unexpectedly in dining-rooms, men's lounges, bars, and crowded hotel lobbies. "Why Burt!"

Menafee would say, gaily, or "It's old Fredericks!" like someone meeting an old friend after years. Fredericks got so he never let on – unless he was addressed as Charlie or Brandon. Far as I know he was never caught. Menafee made enough to keep going, coaching fugitives, but it was a dullish kind of job.' Darke fell silent. I sat watching him.

'Did you ever meet any other uninteresting people?' I asked.

'There was Harrison Cammery,' said Darke, after a moment. 'He put in here one night in a storm, dressed in full evening clothes. Came from New York – I don't know how. There never was a sign of a boat or anything to show how he got here. He was always that way while he was here, dully incomprehensible. He had the most uninteresting of manias, which is monomania. He was a goldfish-holder.' Darke stopped and seemed inclined to let the story end there.

'What do you mean, a goldfish-holder?' I demanded.

'Cammery had been a professional billiard-player,' said Darke. 'He told me that the strain of developing absolutely nerveless hands finally told on him. He had trained so that he could balance five BB shot on the back of each of his fingers indefinitely. One night, at a party where the host had a bowl of goldfish, the guests got to trying to catch them with one grab of their hand. Nobody could do it until Cammery tried. He caught up one of the fish and held it lightly in his closed hand. He told me that the wettish fluttering of that fish against the palm of his hand became a thing he couldn't forget. He got to snatching up goldfish and holding them, wherever he went. At length he had to have a bowl of them beside the table when he played his billiard matches, and would hold one between innings the way tennis-players take a mouthful of water. The effect finally was to destroy his muscular precision, so he took to the islands. One day he was gone from here – I don't know how. I was glad enough. A singularly one-track and boring fellow.'

'Who else has put in here?' I asked, filling them up again.

'Early in 1913,' said Darke, after a pause in which he seemed to make an effort to recall what he was after, 'early in 1913 an old fellow with a white beard – must have been seventy-five or eighty – walked into this hut one day. He was dripping wet. Said he swam over from the mainland and he probably did. It's fifty miles. Lots of boats can be had for the taking along the main coast, but this fellow was apparently too stupid to take one. He was as dull about everything as about that. Used to recite short stories word for word – said he wrote them himself. He was a writer like you, but he didn't seem to have met any interesting people. Talked only about himself, where he'd come from, what he'd done. I didn't pay any attention to him. I was glad when, one night, he disappeared. His name was . . .' Darke put his head back and stared at the roof of his hut, striving to remember. 'Oh, yes,' he said. 'His name was Bierce. Ambrose Bierce.'

'You say that was in 1913, early in 1913?' I asked, excitedly.

'Yes, I'm sure of it,' said Darke, 'because it was the same year C-18769 showed up here.'

'Who was C-18769?' I asked.

'It was a carrier pigeon,' said Darke. 'Flew in here one night tuckered by the trip from the mainland, and flopped down on that bed with its beak open, panting hard. It was red-eyed and dishevelled. I noticed it had something sizable strapped under its belly and I saw a registration number, on a silver band fastened to its leg: C-18769. When it got rested up it hung around here for quite a while. I didn't pay much attention to it. In those days I used to get the New York papers about once a month off a supply boat that used to put in at an island ten miles from here. I'd row over. One day I saw a notice in one of the papers about this bird. Some concern or other, for a publicity stunt, had arranged to have this bird carry a thousand dollars in hundred-dollar bills from the concern's offices to the place where the bird homed, some five hundred miles away. The bird never got there. The papers had all kinds of theories: the bird had been shot and robbed, it had fallen in the water and drowned, or it had got lost.'

'The last was right,' I said. 'It must have got lost.'

'Lost, hell,' said Darke. 'After I read the stories I caught it up one day, suddenly, and examined the packet strapped to it. It only had four hundred and sixty-five dollars left.'

I felt a little weak. Finally, in a small voice, I asked: 'Did you turn it over to the authorities?'

'Certainly not,' said Darrell Darke. 'A man or a bird's life is his own to lead, down here. I simply figured this pigeon for a fool, and let him go. What could he do, after the money was gone? Nothing.' Darke rolled and lighted a cigarette and smoked a while, silently. 'That's the kind of beings you meet with down here,' he said. 'Stupid, dullish, lacking in common sense, fiddling along aimlessly. Menafee, Cammery, Bierce, C-18769 – all the same. It gets monotonous. Tell me more about this Grand Duchess Marie. She must be a most interesting person.'

A Preface to Dogs

As soon as a wife presents her husband with a child, her capacity for worry becomes acuter: she hears more burglars, she smells more things burning, she begins to wonder, at the theatre or the dance, whether her husband left his service revolver in the nursery. This goes on for years and years. As the child grows older, the mother's original major fear – that the child was exchanged for some other infant at the hospital – gives way to even more magnificent doubts and suspicions: she suspects that the child is not bright, she doubts that it will be happy, she is sure that it will become mixed up with the wrong sort of people.

This insistence of parents on dedicating their lives to their children is carried on year after year in the face of all that dogs have done, and are doing, to prove how much happier the parent-child relationship can become, if managed without sentiment, worry, or dedication. Of course, the theory that dogs have a saner family life than humans is an old one, and it was in order to ascertain whether the notion is pure legend or whether it is based on observable fact that I have for four years made a careful study of the family life of dogs. My conclusions entirely support the theory that dogs have a saner family life than people.

In the first place, the husband leaves on a woodchuck-hunting expedition just as soon as he can, which is very soon, and never comes back. He doesn't write, makes no provision for the care or maintenance of his family, and is not liable to prosecution because he doesn't. The wife doesn't care where he is, never wonders if he is thinking about her, and although she may start at the slightest footstep, doesn't do so because she is hoping against hope that it is he. No lady dog has ever been known to set her friends against her husband, or put detectives on his trail.

This same lack of sentimentality is carried out in the mother dog's relationship to her young. For six weeks – but only six weeks – she looks after them religiously, feeds them (they come clothed), washes their ears, fights off cats, old women, and wasps that come nosing around, makes the bed, and rescues the puppies when they crawl under the floor boards of the barn or get lost in an old boot. She does all these things, however, without fuss, without that loud and elaborate show of solicitude and alarm which a woman displays in rendering some exaggerated service to her child.

At the end of six weeks, the mother dog ceases to lie awake at night harking for ominous sounds; the next morning she snarls at the puppies after break-fast, and routs them all out of the house. 'This is forever,' she informs them, succinctly. 'I have my own life to live, automobiles to chase, grocery boys' shoes to snap at, rabbits to pursue. I can't be washing and feeding a lot of big six-weeks-old dogs any longer. That phase is definitely over.' The family life is thus terminated, and the mother dismisses the children from her mind – fre-quently as many as eleven at one time – as easily as she did her husband. She is now free to devote herself to her career and to the novel and astonishing things of life.

In the case of one family of dogs that I observed, the mother, a large black dog with long ears and a keen zest for living, tempered only by an immoderate fear of toads and turtles, kicked ten puppies out of the house at the end of six weeks to the day – it was a Monday. Fortunately for my observations, the

puppies had no place to go, since they hadn't made any plans, and so they just hung around the barn, now and again trying to patch things up with their mother. She refused, however, to entertain any proposition leading to a re-sumption of home life, pointing out firmly that she was, by inclination, a chaser of bicycles and a hearth-fire watcher, both of which activities would be in-supportably cluttered up by the presence of ten helpers. The bicycle-chasing field was overcrowded, anyway, she explained, and the hearth-fire-watching field even more so. 'We could chase parades together,' suggested one of the dogs, but she refused to be touched, snarled, and drove him off.

It is only for a few weeks that the cast-off puppies make overtures to their mother in regard to the re-establishment of a home. At the end of that time, by some natural miracle that I am unable clearly to understand, the puppies suddenly one day don't recognize their mother any more, and she doesn't recognize them. It is as if they had never met, and is a fine idea, giving both parties a clean break and a chance for a fresh start. Once, some months after this particular family had broken up and the pups had been sold, one of them, named Liza, was brought back to 'the old nest' for a visit. The mother dog of course didn't recognize the puppy and promptly bit her in the hip. They had to be separated, each grumbling something about you never know what kind of dogs you're going to meet. Here was no silly, affecting reunion, no sentimental tears, no bitter intimations of neglect, or forgetfulness, or desertion.

If a pup is not sold or given away, but is brought up in the same household with its mother, the two will fight bitterly, sometimes twenty or thirty times a day, for maybe a month. This is very trying to whoever owns the dogs, particularly if they are sentimentalists who grieve because mother and child don't know each other. The condition finally clears up: the two dogs grow to tolerate each other and, beyond growling a little under their breath about how it takes all kinds of dogs to make up a world, get along fairly well together when their paths cross. I know of one mother dog and her half-grown daughter who sometimes spend the whole day together hunting woodchucks, although they don't speak. Their association is not sentimental, but practical, and is based on the fact that it is safer to hunt woodchucks in pairs than alone. These two dogs start out together in the morning, without a word, and come back together in the evening, when they part, without saying good night, whether they have had any luck or not. Avoidance of farewells, which are always stuffy and sometimes painful, is another thing in which it seems to me dogs have better sense than people.

Well, one day the daughter, a dog about ten months old, seemed, by some prank of nature which again I am unable clearly to understand, for a moment or two, to recognize her mother, after all those months of oblivion. The two had just started out after a fat woodchuck who lives in the orchard. Something got wrong with the daughter's ear – a long, floppy ear. 'Mother,' she said, 'I wish you'd look at my ear.' Instantly the other dog bristled and growled. 'I'm not your mother,' she said, 'I'm a woodchuck-hunter.' The daughter grinned. 'Well,' she said, just to show that there were no hard feelings, 'that's not my ear, it's a motorman's glove.'

Guessing Game

An article was found after your departure in the room which you occupied. Kindly let us know if you have missed such an article, and if so, send us a description and instructions as to what disposition you wish made of same. For lack of space, all Lost and Found articles must be disposed of within two months.

LOST AND FOUND DEPARTMENT
HOTEL LEXINGTON
Lexington Ave. & 48th St., New York
Per R. E. Daley.

Dear Mr Daley:

THIS whole thing is going to be much more complicated than you think. I have waited almost two weeks before answering your postcard notification because I have been unable to figure out what article I left behind. I'm sorry now I didn't just forget the whole business. As a matter of fact, I did try to forget it, but it keeps bobbing up in my mind. I have got into an alphabetical rut about it; at night I lie awake naming articles to myself: bathrobe, bay rum, book, bicycle, belt, baby, etc. Dr Prill, my analyst, has advised me to come right out and meet you on the subject.

So far, I have been able to eliminate, for certain, only two articles. I never remember to take pyjamas or a hairbrush with me, so it couldn't be pyjamas or a hairbrush you found. This does not get us very far. I have, however, ransacked the house and I find that a number of things are missing, but I don't remember which of them, if any, I had with me at the Lexington that night: the vest to my blue suit, my life-insurance policy, my Scotch terrier Jeannie, the jack out of the automobile tool case, the bottle-opener that is supposed to be kept in the kitchen drawer, the glass top to the percolator, a box of aspirin, a letter from my father giving my brother William's new address in Seattle, a roll of films (exposed) for a 2A Kodak, my briefcase (missing since 1927), etc. The article you have on hand might be any of these (with the exception of the briefcase). It would have been entirely possible for me, in the state of mind I was in that Friday, to have gone about all day with the automobile jack in my hand.

The thing that worries me most is the possibility that what I left in my room was something the absence of which I have not yet discovered and may never discover, unless you give me some hint. Is it animal, vegetable, or mineral? Is it as big as I am? Twice as big? Smaller than a man's hand? Does it have a screw-on top? Does it make any kind of regular ticking noise when in operation? Is it worth, new, as much as a hundred dollars? A thousand dollars?

Fifty cents? It isn't a bottle of toothache drops, is it? Or a used razor blade? Because I left them behind on purpose. These questions, it seems to me, are eminently fair. I'm not asking you some others I could think of, such as: Does it go with the pants and coat of a blue suit? Can it bark? Can it lift the wheel of an automobile off the ground? Can it open a bottle? Does it relieve pain? Is it a letter from somebody? Does anybody get any money out of it when I am dead, providing I keep the payments up?

I think you should let me know whether you are willing to answer yes or no to my first set of questions, as in all games of this sort. Because if you are just going to stand there with a silly look on your face and shake your head and keep repeating 'Can't guess what it i-yis, can't guess what it i-yis!', to hell with it. I don't care if it's a diamond ring.

I take it for granted, of course, that I really did leave an article in the room I occupied. If I didn't, and this thing turns out to be merely a guessing game in which the answer is Robert E. Lee's horse, or something, you'll never be able to answer your phone for a whole year without running the chance of it's being me, reserving dozens of rooms in a disguised voice and under various assumed names, reporting a fire on the twenty-third floor, notifying you that your bank balance is overdrawn, pretending, in a husky guttural, that you are the next man the gang is going to put on the spot for the shooting of Joe the Boss over in Brooklyn.

Of course, I'm a little sore about the thing the way it is. If you had been a guest at my house and had gone away leaving your watch or your keyring behind, would I send you a penny postcard asking you to guess what you had left behind? I would now, yes; but I mean before this all happened. Supposing everybody did business that way. Supposing your rich and doting uncle wired you: 'I'm arriving Grand Central some time next month. Meet me.' Or, worse yet, supposing that instead of issuing a summons naming a definite crime or misdemeanour, the courts sent out a postcard reading: 'I know what's going to happen to you-oo!' We'd all be nervous wrecks.

The only thing I see to do right now is comply with your request for a description of the article I left in that room. It is a large and cumbersome iron object, usually kept in a kitchen drawer, entitling my wife, upon my death, to a certain payment of money; it barks when in operation and, unless used when the coffee reaches the boiling point, will allow the liquid to spill out on the stove; it is signed by my father's name, is sensitive to light, relieves neuralgic pains, and is dark blue in colour.

I have, of course, the same suspicion that you seem to have; namely, that maybe the object wasn't left behind by me but by somebody else who occupied the room before I did or who occupied it at the same time I did, without either one of us knowing the other was there. And I'll tell you why. The night that I was at your hotel, the room clerk took a message out of my box when he reached for my key. The message was for a Mr Donovan. I looked at it and said it didn't belong to me. 'You haven't a Mr Donovan with you?' he asked. I said no, but he didn't seem to be convinced. Perhaps whatever was left behind in my room was left behind by Mr Donovan. I have an idea that, after all, Mr Donovan and I may have occupied the same room, since his mail was in my box; perhaps he always arrived just after I had left the room and got out each time just before I came back. It's that kind of city.

I'm glad, anyway, that I have two months before the article is returned to the insurance company or sent to the pound, or whatever. It gives me time to think.

Everything Is Wild

IN THE first place it was a cold and rainy night and the Cortrights lived eighteen miles away, in Bronxville. 'Eighteen hundred miles,' Mr Brush put it, bitterly. He got the car out of the Gramercy Lane garage, snarling savagely at the garage man, an amiable and loquacious fellow who spoke with an accent and who kept talking about winter oil and summer oil, and grinning, and repeating himself. As they drove out, Mrs Brush told her husband that he didn't have to be so mean, the man hadn't done anything to him. 'He kept yelling about oil, didn't he?' demanded Mr Brush. 'I know about oil. Nobody has to tell me about oil.' Mrs Brush kept her voice abnormally low, the way she always did when he was on the verge of a tantrum. 'He wasn't yelling,' she said. 'He'll probably ruin the car some night, the way you acted.'

The drive to Bronxville was as bad as Mr Brush expected it would be. He got lost, and couldn't find Bronxville. When he did find Bronxville, he couldn't find the Woodmere Apartments. 'You'll have to ask somebody where it is,' said Mrs Brush. He didn't want to ask anybody anything, but he stopped in front of a bright little barbershop, got out, and went inside. The barber he encountered turned out to be a garrulous foreigner. Sure, he knew where eez these Woodmare Apartamen. 'Down is street has a concrete breech,' he said. 'It go under but no up to the first raid light. Quick, like this, before turn!' The barber made swift darting angles in the air with his hand. He also turned completely around. 'So not down these light, hah?' he finished up. Mr Brush snarled at him and went outside.

'Well?' asked Mrs Brush. She knew by his silence that he hadn't found out anything. '*I'll* go in and ask next time,' she said. Mr Brush drove on. 'The guy didn't know what he was talking about,' he said. 'He's crazy.' Finally, after many twists and turns, most of them wrong, they drove up in front of the Woodmere. 'Hell of an apartment building,' said Mr Brush. Mrs Brush didn't answer him.

The dinner, fortunately, was quite nice. Mr Brush had expected, indeed he had predicted, that there would be a lot of awful people, but the Brushes were the only guests. The Cortrights were charming, there wasn't a radio, and nobody talked about business or baseball. Also there was, after dinner, Mr Brush's favourite liqueur, and he was just settling comfortably into a soft chair, glass in hand, when the doorbell rang. A man and a woman were brought into the room and introduced – a Mr and Mrs Spreef, as Brush got it. The name turned out to be Spear. Mr Brush didn't like them. They were quite nice, but he never liked anybody he hadn't met before.

After a flurry of trivial talk, during which Spear told a story about a fellow who had been courting a girl for fifteen years, at which everybody laughed but Brush, who grinned fixedly, the hostess wanted to know if people would like to play poker. There were pleased murmurs, a grunt from Brush, and in a twinkling a card table was pulled out from behind something and set up. Mrs Cortright brightly explained that one leg of the table was broken, but she thought it would hold up all right. Mr Brush didn't actually say that he thought it wouldn't, but he looked as if he did.

Mr Spear won the deal. 'This is dealer's choice, Harry,' his hostess told him. 'Change on each deal.' Harry squealed. 'O.K.,' he said. 'How about a little old Duck-in-the-Pond?' The ladies giggled with pleasure. 'Whazzat?' grumbled Brush. He hated any silly variation of the fine old game of poker. He instantly dropped out of the hand and sat staring at Mr Spear. Mr Spear, it came to him, looked like Chevalier. Mr Brush hated Chevalier.

The next deal fell to Brush and he immediately named straight poker as his game. Mrs Spear said she was crazy about Duck-in-the-Pond and why didn't they just keep on playing that?' 'Straight poker,' said Mr Brush, gruffly. 'Oh,' said Mrs Spear, her smile vanishing. Mr Brush won the straight-poker hand with three of a kind.

Mrs Spear was the next dealer. 'Seven-card stud,' she said, 'with the twos and threes wild.' The women all gave little excited screams. Mrs Cortright said she was crazy about seven-card stud with something wild. Mrs Spear said she was, too. Mr Brush said yah. Mrs Spear won the hand with four kings – that is, two kings, a deuce, and a trey. Mr Cortright, the next dealer, announced that they would now play Poison Ivy. This was a nuisance Mr Brush had never heard of. It proved to be a variation of poker in which each player gets four cards, and five others are placed face down on the table to be turned up one at a time. The lowest card, when all are turned up, becomes the wild card. Mr Brush rolled his cigar from one corner of his mouth to the other, and narrowed his eyes. He scowled at Chevalier, because Chevalier kept repeating that Poison Ivy was the nuts. Brush folded up his hand and sat stiffly in his chair, rolling his cigar and grunting. Four aces won that hand, and in doing so had to beat four other aces (there were two fours in the hand on the table, and they were low).

So the game went wildly on, with much exclaiming and giggling, until it came Mr Brush's time to deal again. He sat up very straight in his chair and glared around the table. 'We'll play Soap-in-Your-Eye this time,' he said, grimly. Mrs Spear screeched. 'Oh, I don't know that!' she cried. Brush rolled his cigar at her. 'Out West they call it Kick-in-the-Pants,' he said. Mrs Brush suggested that they better play Duck-in-the-Pond again, or Poison Ivy. 'Soap-in-Your-Eye,' said Brush, without looking at her. 'How does it go?' asked Cortright.

'The red queens, the fours, fives, sixes, and eights are wild,' said Mr Brush. 'I'll show you.' He dealt one card to each person. Then he dealt another one around, face up this time. 'Ah,' he exclaimed, 'Mrs Spear draws a red queen on the second round, so it becomes forfeit. It can be reinstated, however, if on the next round she gets a black four. I'll show you.' Mr Brush was adroit with cards and he contrived it so that Mrs Spear did get a black four on the next round. 'Ho,' said Brush, 'that makes it interesting. Having foured your queen, you can now choose a card, any card, from the deck.' He held up the deck and she selected a card. 'Now if you don't want that card,' continued Brush, 'you can say "Back" or "Right" or "Left," depending on whether you want to put it back in the deck or pass it to the person at your right or the person at your left. If you decide to keep it, you say "Hold." The game, by the way, is sometimes called Hold Back or Right and Left. Get it?'

'I don't think so,' said Mrs Spear. She looked vaguely at the card she had drawn. 'Hold, I guess,' she said.

'Good,' said Brush. 'Now everybody else draws a card.' Everybody did, Mrs Brush trying to catch her husband's eye, but failing. 'Now,' said Brush, 'we each have four cards, two of which everybody has seen, and two of which they haven't. Mrs Spreef, however, has a Hold. That is, having black-foured her red queen, she is privileged to call a jack a queen or a trey a four or any other card just one point under a wild card, a wild card. See?' Nobody, apparently, saw.

'Why don't we just play Poison Ivy again?' asked Mrs Brush. 'Or a round of straight poker?'

'I want to try this,' said Brush. 'I'm crazy about it.' He dealt two more cards around, face down. 'We all have six cards now,' he went on, 'but you can't look at the last two – even after the game is over. All you can look at is the four cards in your hand and this one.' He put a card face down in the middle of the table. 'That card is called Splinter-Under-Your-Thumb and is also wild, whatever it is,' he explained. 'All right, bet.' Everybody was silent for several seconds, and then they all checked to him. Brush bet five chips. Mrs Spear, encouraged in a dim way by the fact that she had black-foured her red queen, thus reinstating it after forfeit, stayed, and so did Mrs Cortright (who always stayed), but the others dropped out. The two ladies put in five chips each, and called Mr Brush. He turned up the card in the middle of the table – the queen of diamonds. 'Hah!' said Brush. 'Well, I got a royal flush in spades!' He laid down the four of diamonds, the eight of hearts, and a pair of sixes. 'I don't see how you have,' said Mrs Spear, dubiously. 'Sure,' said Brush. 'The queen of diamonds is a wild card, so I call it the ace of spades. All my other cards are wild, so I call them king, queen, jack, ten of spades.' The women laid their hands down and looked at Brush. 'Well, you both got royal flushes, too,' he said, 'but mine is spades and is high. You called me, and that gave me the right to name my suit. I win.' He took in the chips.

The Brushes said good night and left shortly after that. They went out to the elevator in silence, and in silence they went out to the car, and in silence they drove off. Mr Brush at last began to chortle. 'Darn good game, Soap-in-Your-

Eye,' he said. Mrs Brush stared at him, evilly, for a full minute. 'You terrible person,' she said. Mr Brush broke into loud and hearty laughter. He ho-hoed all the way down the Grand Concourse. He had had a swell time after all.

The Indian Sign

'MR PINWITHER is doing wonders with the new Cora Allyn letter,' Mrs Bentley told her husband. He winced slightly. Three letters about the old lady hadn't been enough; somebody had had to turn up another one.

'That's fine,' said Mr Bentley, taking off his overcoat and hanging it up in the hall closet.

'It's all about their moving to New Milford – in 1667,' said Mrs Bentley. 'There's nothing new in it, he says, about the Indians.' She seemed disappointed.

'That's fine,' said Mr Bentley again. His wife, on the verge of a new eagerness, apparently didn't hear.

'*And,*' she said, 'Cora learned a new word today!' *This* Cora, Mr Bentley knew, was of course his little daughter. He really meant his 'That's fine' this time. Still, he winced again. He had wanted to name his daughter Rosemary, after a dream. But his wife and all the stern and silly pride of the Allyns had been behind 'Cora.' Since a certain day almost three hundred years ago the first female born into every ramification of the Allyn family had been named Cora: 'After old Cora Cora herself,' as Henry Bentley said at the Comics' Club the night his daughter was born.

The original Cora Allyn, his little girl's great-great-great-great-great-grandmother, had slain nineteen Pequot Indians single-handed in an incredible and dimly authenticated struggle near New London, Connecticut, in 1643, or 1644. The Allyns could never be positive of the year, for the letters bearing upon the incident were almost three centuries old, yellow and brittle and written crisscross, the thrifty and illegible Colonial method of saving postage charges. Two were undated and the date of the other was faded and tricky, like all of the writing in the three priceless heirlooms of the Allyn family. The letters purported to have been written by one Loyal Holgate, supposedly a young divine, and – Bentley had examined them carefully, or as carefully as anyone who was not an Allyn was allowed to – there apparently *were* passages in them about one Cora Allyn's having slain nineteen Indians. Some of the most eminent antiquarians in the country, including Mr Pinwither, had pored over the letters. They had all but one brought out of the vague, faint scrawlings virtually the same story of the early New England lady's heroic deed. The saturnine Murray Kraull had, it is true, doubted that the word 'nineteen' was really 'nineteen' and even that 'Pequots' was 'Pequots.'

He had, indeed, gone so far as to suggest that the phrase might be 'no male peacocks,' for which heresy he had practically been hustled out of Mrs Bentley's mother's house. The other experts had all conformed, however, to the letter – and the number – of the legend. In Henry Bentley's mind, as in Mr Kraull's, there would always remain a doubt.

Mr Bentley, quietly and in secret, had long been elaborating on his doubt. So far as he had been able to find out, there was no record of a Cora Allyn who had slain nineteen Indians. There had been a rather famous incident in which a band of Pequots killed a Mrs Anne Williamson, a Massachusetts woman who had settled near Stamford, but that was all. Once, to make a dinner topic, he had tossed out timidly to his wife that he had come upon an old history of the state at his office and so far had found in it no reference to any woman who had killed nineteen Indians. Mrs Bentley's quick, indignant look had caused him to mumble the rest of his suspicions into his shirt-front. It was the closest he ever came to expressing openly his feeling in the matter.

'The new letter,' said Mrs Bentley, as they walked into the living-room, 'tells some more about Rockbottom Thraillkill, the minister who established the third church in what is now New Milford. It was called Appasottowams then, or something like that. It is all in Mr Pinwither's report.'

'That's close enough,' said Mr Bentley. He strove to change the subject. 'What did my little girl say today?' he asked.

'Cora? She said "telephone".'

'That's fine,' said Mr Bentley. It was terrible the way he allowed the name Cora to affect him. There were literally hundreds of Coras among his wife's connections. They kept recurring, like leaf blight, among the spreading branches of the Allyn family. And scarcely a day went by but what someone alluded to the first, great Cora. He encountered her glib ghost at all family gatherings, on all holidays, and before, during, and after every family ceremony, such as marriage, birth, christening, divorce, and death.

Mrs Bentley talked about the small excitements of her day during dinner. Her husband affected to listen, and now and then gave a sympathetic grunt, but he was quietly contemplating that early American heroine who was so damnably intertwined with his life. Supposing that the story about her *were* true? Why be so insistently conscious and so eternally proud of an ancestor who killed nineteen Indians? Her open-mouthed, wild-eyed gestures during the unmatronly ordeal, the awkwardness of her stance, the disarray of her apparel, must have been disturbingly unattractive. The vision of his little daughter's forebear, who up to her great hour had undoubtedly depended rather charmingly upon a sturdy pioneer husband, suddenly learning that she was more than a match for nineteen males affected Henry Bentley dismally; it saddened him to be continually carried back along the rocky, well-forgotten roads of American life to the prophetic figure of Cora Allyn, standing there against the sky, with her matchlock or her hunting knife or her axe handle, so outrageously and significantly triumphant.

Henry had often tried to get a picture of the famous Cora's husband, old Coppice Allyn. There was little mention of him in the frail letters of almost three centuries ago. Old Coppice was rarely mentioned by the Allyns, either; he remained staunch but indistinct, like a figure in the background of a woodcut. He had cleared away trees, he had built a house, he had dug a well, he had had a touch of brain fever – things like that: no vivid, red, immortal gestures. What must he have thought that April evening (not 'April' but 'apple', Kraull had made it out) when he came home from the fields to find a new gleam in his wife's eyes and nineteen new corpses under her feet? He must have felt some vague, alarming resentment; he must have realized, however dimly, that this was the beginning of a new weave in the fabric of life in the Colonies. Poor old Coppice!

'I want to show you,' said Mrs Bentley after dinner, 'Mr Pinwither's report. Of course it's just a preliminary. Mother sent it over.'

'That's fine,' said Mr Bentley. He watched his wife go out of the room and tried to be glad that she, at least, was not a Cora; her oldest sister held that honour. That was something. Mr Bentley seized the chance, now that he was alone, to reflect upon his latest clandestine delving into the history of the Connecticut Indians. The Pequots, he had discovered in a book that very afternoon, had been woefully incompetent fighters. Some early militarist had written of them that, fighting as they did, they 'couldn't have killed seven people in seven years.' They shot their arrows high into the air: anybody could see them coming and step out of the way. The Colonial militiamen used to pick up the flinted sticks, break them in two, and laugh at their helpless foes. Even when the shafts did get home, they almost never killed; a neckcloth would turn them aside or even, as in the case of one soldier, a piece of cheese carried in one's pocket. Poor, pathetic, stupid old Pequots! Brave they had undeniably been, but dumb. Mr Bentley had suddenly a rather kindly feeling for the Pequots. And he had, at the same time, a new, belittling vision of that grand old lady, the first Cora: he saw her leisurely firing through a chink in the wall of her house, taking all afternoon to knock off nineteen Indians who had no chance against her, who stood on the edge of a clearing firing arrows wistfully into the sky until one of the white woman's blunderbuss slugs – a tenpenny nail or a harness buckle – struck them down. If only they had rushed her! If only one of them had been smart enough to light the end of an arrow and stick it burning in the roof of the Allyn house! They would have finished her off fast enough if they had ever got her outside! Mr Bentley's heart beat faster and his eyes blinked brightly.

'What is it?' asked Mrs Bentley, coming back into the room. Her husband looked so eager and pleased, sitting there.

'I was just thinking,' he said.

Mr Pinwither's preliminary report on the new letter was long and dull. Mr Bentley tried to look interested: he knew better than to appear indifferent to any holy relic connected with the Great Cora.

'Cora's had such a day!' said Mrs Bentley, as they were preparing for bed. 'She went to sleep playing with those toy soldiers and Indians her Uncle Bert gave her.' Mr Bentley had one of his vivid pictures of Uncle Bert. 'Um,' he said, and went downstairs to get his aspirin box out of his coat.

Before he went to bed, Mr Bentley stopped in the nursery to have a goodnight look at his little sleeping daughter. She lay sweetly with her hands curled above her head. Mr Bentley regarded the little girl with sad eyes. The line of her forehead and the curve of her chin were (or so the Allyns hysterically claimed) the unmistakable sign of the Great Cora, the proof of the child's proud heritage, the latest blaze along the trail. He stood above her, thinking, a long time.

When Mr Bentley went back to the bedroom, it was pitch dark; his wife had turned out the light. He tiptoed in. He heard her slow, deep breathing. She was sound asleep.

'Henry?' she called suddenly out of the blackness. Surprised, he did not answer.

'Henry!' she said. There was uneasiness and drowsy bewilderment in her voice.

To Henry Bentley, standing there in the darkness, there came a quick, wild urge. He tried to restrain it, and then, abruptly, he gave way to it, with a profound sense of release. Patting the fingers of his right hand rapidly against his open lips, he gave, at the top of his voice, the Pequot war whoop: 'Ah-wah-wah-wah-wah!'

The Private Life of Mr Bidwell

From where she was sitting, Mrs Bidwell could not see her husband, but she had a curious feeling of tension: she knew he was up to something.

'What are you doing, George?' she demanded, her eyes still on her book.

'Mm?'

'What's the matter with you?'

'Pahhhhh-h-h,' said Mr Bidwell, in a long, pleasurable exhale. 'I was holding my breath.'

Mrs Bidwell twisted creakingly in her chair and looked at him; he was sitting behind her in his favourite place under the parchment lamp with the street scene of old New York on it. 'I was just holding my breath,' he said again.

'Well, please don't do it,' said Mrs Bidwell, and went back to her book. There was silence for five minutes.

'George!' said Mrs Bidwell.

'Bwaaaaaa,' said Mr Bidwell. 'What?'

'Will you please *stop* that?' she said. 'It makes me nervous.'

'I don't see how that bothers you,' he said. 'Can't I breathe?'

'You can breathe without holding your breath like a goop,' said Mrs Bidwell. 'Goop' was a word that she was fond of using; she rather lazily applied it to everything. It annoyed Mr Bidwell.

'Deep breathing,' said Mr Bidwell, in the impatient tone he used when explaining anything to his wife, 'is good exercise. You ought to take more exercise.'

'Well, please don't do it around me,' said Mrs Bidwell, turning again to the pages of Mr Galsworthy.

At the Cowans' party, a week later, the room was full of chattering people when Mrs Bidwell, who was talking to Lida Carroll, suddenly turned around as if she had been summoned. In a chair in a far corner of the room, Mr Bidwell was holding his breath. His chest was expanded, his chin drawn in; there was a strange stare in his eyes, and his face was slightly empurpled. Mrs Bidwell moved into the line of his vision and gave him a sharp, penetrating look. He deflated slowly and looked away.

Later, in the car, after they had driven in silence a mile or more on the way home, Mrs Bidwell said, 'It seems to me you might at least have the kindness not to hold your breath in other people's houses.'

'I wasn't hurting anybody,' said Mr Bidwell.

'You looked silly!' said his wife. 'You looked perfectly crazy!' She was driving and she began to speed up, as she always did when excited or angry. 'What do you suppose people thought – you sitting there all swelled up, with your eyes popping out?'

'I wasn't all swelled up,' he said, angrily.

'You looked like a goop,' she said. The car slowed down, sighed, and came to a complete, despondent stop.

'We're out of gas,' said Mrs Bidwell. It was bitterly cold and nastily sleeting. Mr Bidwell took a long, deep breath.

The breathing situation in the Bidwell family reached a critical point when Mr Bidwell began to inhale in his sleep, slowly, and exhale with a protracted,

growling 'woooooooo.' Mrs Bidwell, ordinarily a sound sleeper (except on nights when she was sure burglars were getting in), would wake up and reach over and shake her husband. 'George!' she would say.

'Hawwwwww,' Mr Bidwell would say, thickly. 'Wahs maa nah, hm?'

After he had turned over and gone back to sleep, Mrs Bidwell would lie awake, thinking.

One morning at breakfast she said, 'George, I'm not going to put up with this another day. If you can't stop blowing up like a grampus, I'm going to leave you.' There was a slight, quick lift in Mr Bidwell's heart, but he tried to look surprised and hurt.

'All right,' he said. 'Let's not talk about it.'

Mrs Bidwell buttered another piece of toast. She described to him the way he sounded in his sleep. He read the paper.

*

With considerable effort, Mr Bidwell kept from inflating his chest for about a week, but one night at the McNallys' he hit on the idea of seeing how many seconds he could hold his breath. He was rather bored by the McNallys' party, anyway. He began timing himself with his wrist-watch in a remote corner of the living-room. Mrs Bidwell, who was in the kitchen talking children and clothes with Bea McNally, left her abruptly and slipped back into the living-room. She stood quietly behind her husband's chair. He knew she was there, and tried to let out his breath imperceptibly.

'I see you,' she said, in a low, cold tone. Mr Bidwell jumped up.

'Why don't you let me alone ?' he demanded.

'Will you please lower your voice ?' she said, smiling so that if anyone were looking he wouldn't think the Bidwells were arguing.

'I'm getting pretty damned tired of this,' said Bidwell in a low voice.

'You've ruined my evening !' she whispered.

'You've ruined mine, too !' he whispered back. They knifed each other, from head to stomach, with their eyes.

'Sitting here like a goop, holding your breath,' said Mrs Bidwell. 'People will think you are an idiot.' She laughed, turning to greet a lady who was approaching them.

Mr Bidwell sat in his office the next afternoon, a black, moist afternoon, tapping a pencil on his desk, and scowling. 'All right, then, get out, get out !' he muttered. 'What do I care ?' He was visualizing the scene when Mrs Bidwell would walk out on him. After going through it several times, he returned to his work, feeling vaguely contented. He made up his mind to breathe any way he wanted to, no matter what she did. And, having come to this decision, he oddly enough, and quite without effort, lost interest in holding his breath.

Everything went rather smoothly at the Bidwells' for a month or so. Mr Bidwell didn't do anything to annoy his wife beyond leaving his razor on her dressing-table and forgetting to turn out the hall light when he went to bed. Then there came the night of the Bentons' party.

Mr Bidwell, bored as usual, was sitting in a far corner of the room, breathing normally. His wife was talking animatedly with Beth Williamson about negligees. Suddenly her voice slowed and an uneasy look came into her eyes: George was up to something. She turned around and sought him out. To anyone but Mrs Bidwell he must have seemed like any husband sitting in a chair. But his wife's lips set tightly. She walked casually over to him.

'What are you doing ?' she demanded.

'Hm ?' he said, looking at her vacantly.

'What are you *doing* ?' she demanded, again. He gave her a harsh, venomous look, which she returned.

'I'm multiplying numbers in my head,' he said, slowly and evenly, 'if you must know.' In the prolonged, probing examination that they silently, without moving any muscles save those of their eyes, gave each other, it became solidly, frozenly apparent to both of them that the end of their endurance had arrived.

The curious bond that held them together snapped – rather more easily than
either had supposed was possible. That night, while undressing for bed, Mr
Bidwell calmly multiplied numbers in his head. Mrs Bidwell stared coldly at
him for a few moments, holding a stocking in her hand; she didn't bother to
berate him. He paid no attention to her. The thing was simply over.

George Bidwell lives alone now (his wife remarried). He never goes to
parties any more, and his old circle of friends rarely sees him. The last time
that any of them did see him, he was walking along a country road with the
halting, uncertain gait of a blind man: he was trying to see how many steps he
could take without opening his eyes.

The Curb in the Sky

WHEN Charlie Deshler announced that he was going to marry Dorothy, someone said he would lose his mind posthaste. 'No,' said a wit who knew them both, 'post hoc.' Dorothy had begun, when she was quite young, to finish sentences for people. Sometimes she finished them wrongly, which annoyed the person who was speaking, and sometimes she finished them correctly, which annoyed the speaker even more.

'When William Howard Taft was – ' some guest in Dorothy's family's home would begin.

'President!' Dorothy would pipe up. The speaker may have meant to say 'President' or he may have meant to say 'young', or 'Chief Justice of the Supreme Court of the United States.' In any case, he would shortly put on his hat and go home. Like most parents, Dorothy's parents did not seem to be conscious that her mannerism was a nuisance. Very likely they thought that it was cute, or even bright. It is even probable that when Dorothy's mother first said 'Come, Dorothy, eat your – ' and Dorothy said 'Spinach, dear,' the former telephoned Dorothy's father at the office and told him about it, and he told everybody he met that day about it – and the next day and the day after.

When Dorothy grew up she became quite pretty and so even more of a menace. Gentlemen became attracted to her and then attached to her. Emotionally she stirred them, but mentally she soon began to wear them down. Even in her late teens she began correcting their English. 'Not "was," Arthur,' she would say, ' "were." "Were prepared." See?' Most of her admirers tolerated this habit because of their interest in her lovely person, but as time went on and her interest in them remained more instructive than sentimental, they slowly drifted away to less captious, if dumber, girls.

Charlie Deshler, however, was an impetuous man, of the sweep-them-off-their-feet persuasion, and he became engaged to Dorothy so quickly and married her in so short a time that, being deaf to the warnings of friends, whose concern he regarded as mere jealousy, he really didn't know anything about Dorothy except that she was pretty and bright-eyed and (to him) desirable.

Dorothy as a wife came, of course, into her great flowering: she took to correcting Charlie's stories. He had travelled widely and experienced greatly and was a truly excellent *raconteur*. Dorothy was, during their courtship, genuinely interested in him and in his stories, and since she had never shared any of the adventures he told about, she could not know when he made mistakes in time or in place or in identities. Beyond suggesting a change here and

41

there in the number of a verb, she more or less let him alone. Charlie spoke rather good English, anyway – he knew when to say 'were' and when to say 'was' after 'if' – and this was another reason he didn't find Dorothy out.

I didn't call on them for quite a while after they were married, because I liked Charlie and I knew I would feel low if I saw him coming out of the anaesthetic of her charms and beginning to feel the first pains of reality. When I did finally call, conditions were, of course, all that I had feared. Charlie began to tell, at dinner, about a motor trip the two had made to this town and that – I never found out for sure what towns, because Dorothy denied almost everything that Charlie said. 'The next day,' he would say, 'we got an early start and drove two hundred miles to Fairview –' 'Well,' Dorothy would say,

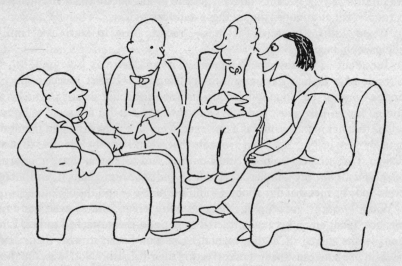

'I wouldn't call it *early*. It wasn't as early as the first day we set out, when we got up about *seven*. And we only drove a hundred and eighty miles, because I remember looking at that mileage thing when we started.'

'Anyway, when we got to Fairview –' Charlie would go on. But Dorothy would stop him. 'Was it Fairview that day, darling?' she would ask. Dorothy often interrupted Charlie by asking him if he were right, instead of telling him that he was wrong, but it amounted to the same thing, for if he would reply: 'Yes, I'm sure it was Fairview,' she would say: 'But it *wasn't*, darling,' and then go on with the story herself. (She called everybody that she differed from 'darling.')

Once or twice, when I called on them or they called on me, Dorothy would let Charlie get almost to the climax of some interesting account of a happening and then, like a tackler from behind, throw him just as he was about to cross the goal-line. There is nothing in life more shocking to the nerves and to the mind than this. Some husbands will sit back amiably – almost it seems, proudly – when their wives interrupt, and let them go on with the story, but these are beaten husbands. Charlie did not become beaten. But his wife's tackles knocked the wind out of him, and he began to realize that he would have to do something. What he did was rather ingenious. At the end of the second year of their marriage, when you visited the Deshlers, Charlie would begin some outlandish story about a dream he had had, knowing that Dorothy could not correct him on his own dreams. They became the only life he had that was his own.

'I thought I was running an airplane,' he would say, 'made out of telephone wires and pieces of old leather. I was trying to make it fly to the moon, taking off from my bedroom. About halfway up to the moon, however, a man who looked like Santa Claus, only he was dressed in the uniform of a customs officer, waved at me to stop – he was in a plane made of telephone wires, too. So I pulled over to a cloud. "Here," he said to me, "you can't go to the moon, if you are the man who invented these wedding cookies." Then he showed me a cookie made in the shape of a man and woman being married – little images of a man and a woman and a minister, made of dough and fastened firmly to a round, crisp cookie base.' So he would go on.

Any psychiatrist will tell you that at the end of the way Charlie was going lies madness in the form of monomania. You can't live in a fantastic dream world, night in and night out and then day in and day out, and remain sane. The substance began to die slowly out of Charlie's life, and he began to live entirely in shadow. And since monomania of this sort is likely to lead in the end to the reiteration of one particular story, Charlie's invention began to grow thin and he eventually took to telling, over and over again, the first dream he had ever described – the story of his curious flight toward the moon in an airplane made of telephone wires. It was extremely painful. It saddened us all.

After a month or two, Charlie finally had to be sent to an asylum. I was out of town when they took him away, but Joe Fultz, who went with him, wrote me about it. 'He seemed to like it up here right away,' Joe wrote. 'He's calmer and his eyes look better.' (Charlie had developed a wild, hunted look.) 'Of course,' concluded Joe, 'he's finally got away from that woman.'

It was a couple of weeks later that I drove up to the asylum to see Charlie. He was lying on a cot on a big screened-in porch, looking wan and thin. Dorothy was sitting on a chair beside his bed, bright-eyed and eager. I was somehow surprised to see her there, having figured that Charlie had, at least, won sanctuary from his wife. He looked quite mad. He began at once to tell me the story of his trip to the moon. He got to the part where the man who looked like Santa Claus waved at him to stop. 'He was in a plane made of telephone wires, too,' said Charlie. 'So I pulled over to a curb –'

'No. You pulled over to a *cloud*,' said Dorothy. 'There aren't any curbs in the *sky*. There *couldn't* be. You pulled over to a cloud.'

Charlie sighed and turned slightly in his bed and looked at me. Dorothy looked at me, too, with her pretty smile.

'He always gets that story wrong,' she said.

Mr Preble Gets Rid of His Wife

MR PREBLE was a plump middle-aged lawyer in Scarsdale. He used to kid with his stenographer about running away with him. 'Let's run away together,' he would say, during a pause in dictation. 'All righty,' she would say.

One rainy Monday afternoon, Mr Preble was more serious about it than usual.

'Let's run away together,' said Mr Preble.

'All righty,' said his stenographer. Mr Preble jingled the keys in his pocket and looked out the window.

'My wife would be glad to get rid of me,' he said.

'Would she give you a divorce?' asked the stenographer.

'I don't suppose so,' he said. The stenographer laughed.

'You'd have to get rid of your wife,' she said.

Mr Preble was unusually silent at dinner that night. About half an hour after coffee, he spoke without looking up from his paper.

'Let's go down in the cellar,' Mr Preble said to his wife.

'What for?' she said, not looking up from her book.

'Oh, I don't know,' he said. 'We never go down in the cellar any more. The way we used to.'

'We never did go down in the cellar that I remember,' said Mrs Preble. 'I could rest easy the balance of my life if I never went down in the cellar.' Mr Preble was silent for several minutes.

'Supposing I said it meant a whole lot to me,' began Mr Preble.

'What's come over you?' his wife demanded. 'It's cold down there and there is absolutely nothing to do.'

'We could pick up pieces of coal,' said Mr Preble. 'We might get up some kind of a game with pieces of coal.'

'I don't want to,' said his wife. 'Anyway, I'm reading.'

'Listen,' said Mr Preble, rising and walking up and down. 'Why won't you come down in the cellar? You can read down there, as far as that goes.'

'There isn't a good enough light down there,' she said, 'and anyway, I'm not going to go down in the cellar. You may as well make up your mind to that.'

'Gee whiz!' said Mr Preble, kicking at the edge of a rug. 'Other people's wives go down in the cellar. Why is it you never want to do anything? I come home worn out from the office and you won't even go down in the cellar with

44

me. God knows it isn't very far – it isn't as if I was asking you to go to the movies or some place.'

'I don't want to *go*!' shouted Mrs Preble. Mr Preble sat down on the edge of a davenport.

'All right, all *right*,' he said. He picked up the newspaper again. 'I wish you'd let me tell you more about it. It's – kind of a surprise.'

'Will you quit harping on that subject?' asked Mrs Preble.

'Listen,' said Mr Preble, leaping to his feet. 'I might as well tell you the truth instead of beating around the bush. I want to get rid of you so I can marry my stenographer. Is there anything especially wrong about that? People do it every day. Love is something you can't control –'

'We've been all over that,' said Mrs Preble. 'I'm not going to go all over that again.'

'I just wanted you to know how things are,' said Mr Preble. 'But you have to take everything so literally. Good Lord, do you suppose I really wanted to go down in the cellar and make up some silly game with pieces of coal?'

'I never believed that for a minute,' said Mrs Preble. 'I knew all along you wanted to get me down there and bury me.'

'You can say that now – after I told you,' said Mr Preble. 'But it would never have occurred to you if I hadn't.'

'You didn't tell me; I got it out of you,' said Mrs Preble. 'Anyway, I'm always two steps ahead of what you're thinking.'

'You're never within a mile of what I'm thinking,' said Mr Preble.

'Is that so? I knew you wanted to bury me the minute you set foot in this house tonight.' Mrs Preble held him with a glare.

'Now that's just plain damn exaggeration,' said Mr Preble, considerably annoyed. 'You knew nothing of the sort. As a matter of fact, I never thought of it till just a few minutes ago.'

'It was in the back of your mind,' said Mrs Preble. 'I suppose this filing woman put you up to it.'

'You needn't get sarcastic,' said Mr Preble. 'I have plenty of people to file without having her file. She doesn't know anything about this. She isn't in on it. I was going to tell her you had gone to visit some friends and fell over a cliff. She wants me to get a divorce.'

'That's a laugh,' said Mrs Preble. '*That's* a laugh. You may bury me, but you'll never get a divorce.'

'She knows that! I told her that,' said Mr Preble. 'I mean – I told her I'd never get a divorce.'

'Oh, you probably told her about burying me, too,' said Mrs Preble.

'That's not true,' said Mr Preble, with dignity. 'That's between you and me. I was never going to tell a soul.'

'You'd blab it to the whole world; don't tell me,' said Mrs Preble. 'I know you.' Mr Preble puffed at his cigar.

'I wish you were buried now and it was all over with,' he said.

'Don't you suppose you would get caught, you crazy thing?' she said. 'They always get caught. Why don't you go to bed? You're just getting yourself all worked up over nothing.'

'I'm not going to bed,' said Mr Preble. 'I'm going to bury you in the cellar. I've got my mind made up to it. I don't know how I could make it any plainer.'

'Listen,' cried Mrs Preble, throwing her book down, 'will you be satisfied and shut up if I go down in the cellar? Can I have a little peace if I go down in the cellar? Will you let me alone then?'

'Yes,' said Mr Preble. 'But you spoil it by taking that attitude.'

'Sure, sure, I always spoil everything. I stop reading right in the middle of a chapter. I'll never know how the story comes out – but that's nothing to you.'

'Did I make you start reading the book?' asked Mr Preble. He opened the cellar door. 'Here, you go first.'

*

'Brrr,' said Mrs Preble, starting down the steps. 'It's *cold* down here! You *would* think of this, at this time of year! Any other husband would have buried his wife in the summer.'

'You can't arrange those things just whenever you want to,' said Mr Preble. 'I didn't fall in love with this girl till late fall.'

'Anybody else would have fallen in love with her long before that. She's been around for years. Why is it you always let other men get in ahead of you? Mercy, but it's dirty down here! What have you got there?'

'I was going to hit you over the head with this shovel,' said Mr Preble.

'You were, huh?' said Mrs Preble. 'Well, get that out of your mind. Do you want to leave a great big clue right here in the middle of everything where the first detective that comes snooping around will find it? Go out in the street and find some piece of iron or something – something that doesn't belong to you.'

'Oh, all right,' said Mr Preble. 'But there won't be any piece of iron in the street. Women always expect to pick up a piece of iron anywhere.'

'If you look in the right place you'll find it,' said Mrs Preble. 'And don't be gone long. Don't you dare stop in at the cigarstore. I'm not going to stand down here in this cold cellar all night and freeze.'

'All right,' said Mr Preble. 'I'll hurry.'

'And shut that *door* behind you!' she screamed after him. 'Where were you born – in a barn?'

The Luck of Jad Peters

AUNT EMMA PETERS, at eighty-three – the year she died – still kept in her unused front parlour, on the table with Jad Peters's collection of lucky souvenirs, a large rough fragment of rock weighing perhaps twenty pounds. The rock stood in the centre of a curious array of odds and ends: a piece of tent canvas, a chip of pine wood, a yellowed telegram, some old newspaper clippings, the cork from a bottle, a bill from a surgeon. Aunt Emma never talked about the strange collection except once, during her last days, when somebody asked her if she wouldn't feel better if the rock were thrown away. 'Let it stay where Lisbeth put it,' she said. All that I know about the souvenirs I have got from other members of the family. A few of them didn't think it was 'decent' that the rock should have been part of the collection, but Aunt Lisbeth, Emma's sister, had insisted that it should be. In fact, it was Aunt Lisbeth Banks who hired a man to lug it to the house and put it on the table with the rest of the things. 'It's as much God's doing as that other clutter-trap,' she would say. And she would rock back and forth in her rocking chair with a grim look. 'You can't taunt the Lord,' she would add. She was a very religious woman. I used to see her now and again at funerals, tall, gaunt, grim, but I never talked to her if I could help it. She liked funerals and she liked to look at corpses, and that made me afraid of her.

Just back of the souvenir table at Aunt Emma's, on the wall, hung a heavy-framed, full-length photograph of Aunt Emma's husband, Jad Peters. It showed him wearing a hat and overcoat and carrying a suitcase. When I was a little boy in the early nineteen-hundreds and was taken to Aunt Emma's house near Sugar Grove, Ohio, I used to wonder about that photograph (I didn't wonder about the rock and the other objects, because they weren't put there till much later). It seemed so funny for anyone to be photographed in a hat and overcoat and carrying a suitcase, and even funnier to have the photograph enlarged to almost life size and put inside so elaborate a frame. When we children would sneak into the front parlour to look at the picture, Aunt Emma would hurry us out again. When we asked her about the picture, she would say, 'Never you mind.' But when I grew up, I learned the story of the big photograph and of how Jad Peters came to be known as Lucky Jad. As a matter of fact, it was Jad who began calling himself that; once when he ran for a county office (and lost) he had 'Lucky Jad Peters' printed on his campaign cards. Nobody else took the name up except in a scoffing way.

It seems that back in 1888, when Jad Peters was about thirty-five, he had a pretty good business of some kind or other which caused him to travel around quite a lot. One week he went to New York with the intention of going on to Newport, later, by ship. Something turned up back home, however, and one of his employees sent him a telegram reading 'Don't go to Newport. Urgent you return here.' Jad's story was that he was on the ship, ready to sail, when the telegram was delivered; it had been sent to his hotel, he said, a few minutes after he had checked out, and an obliging clerk had hustled the messenger boy on down to the dock. That was Jad's story. Most people believed, when they heard the story, that Jad had got the wire at his hotel, probably hours before the ship sailed, for he was a great one at adorning a tale. At any rate, whether or not he rushed off the ship just before the gangplank was hauled up, it sailed without him and some eight or nine hours out of the harbour sank in a storm with the loss of everybody on board. That's why he had the photograph taken and enlarged: it showed him just as he was when he got off the ship, he said. And that is how he came to start his collection of lucky souvenirs. For a few years he kept the telegram, and newspaper clippings of the ship disaster, tucked away in the family Bible, but one day he got them out and put them on the parlour table under a big glass bell.

From 1888 up until 1920, when Jad died, nothing much happened to him. He is remembered in his later years as a garrulous, boring old fellow whose business slowly went to pieces because of his lack of industry and who finally settled down on a small farm near Sugar Grove and barely scraped out an existence. He took to drinking in his sixties, and from then on made Aunt Emma's life miserable. I don't know how she managed to keep up the payments on his life-insurance policy, but some way or other she did. Some of her relatives said among themselves that it would be a blessing if Jad died in one of his frequent fits of nausea. It was pretty well known that Aunt Emma had never liked him very much – she married him because he asked her to twice a week for seven years and because there had been nobody else she cared about; she stayed married to him on account of their children and because her people always stayed married. She grew, in spite of Jad, to be a quiet, kindly old lady as the years went on, although her mouth would take on a strained, tight look when Jad showed up at dinner time from wherever he had been during the day – usually from down at Prentice's store in the village, where he liked to sit around telling about the time he just barely got off the doomed boat in New York harbour in '88 and adding tales, more or less fantastic, of more recent close escapes he had had. There was his appendicitis operation, for one thing: he had come out of the ether, he would say, just when they had given him up. Dr Benham, who had performed the operation, was annoyed when he heard this, and once met Jad in the street and asked him to quit repeating the preposterous story, but Jad added the doctor's bill to his collection of talismans, anyway. And there was the time when he had got up in the night to take a swig of stomach bitters for a bad case of heartburn and had got hold of the carbolic-acid bottle by mistake. Something told him, he would say, to take a look at the bottle before he uncorked it, so he carried it to a lamp, lighted the lamp, and he'd be gol-dam if it wasn't carbolic acid! It was then that he added the cork to his collection.

Old Jad got so that he could figure out lucky escapes for himself in almost every disaster and calamity that happened in and around Sugar Grove. Once, for example, a tent blew down during a wind storm at the Fairfield County Fair, killing two people and injuring a dozen others. Jad hadn't gone to the fair that year for the first time in nine or ten years. Something told him, he would say, to stay away from the fair that year. The fact that he always went to the fair, when he did go, on a Thursday and that the tent blew down on a Saturday didn't make any difference to Jad. He hadn't been there and the tent blew down and two people were killed. After the accident, he went to the fair grounds and cut a piece of canvas from the tent and put it on the parlour table next to the cork from the carbolic-acid bottle. Lucky Jad Peters!

I think Aunt Emma got so that she didn't hear Jad when he was talking, except on evenings when neighbours dropped in, and then she would have to take hold of the conversation and steer it away from any opening that might give Jad a chance to tell of some close escape he had had. But he always got his licks in. He would bide his time, creaking back and forth in his chair, clicking his teeth, and not listening much to the talk about crops and begonias and the latest reports on the Spencers' feeble-minded child, and then, when there was a long pause, he would clear his throat and say that that reminded him of the time he had had a mind to go down to Pullen's lumber yard to fetch home a couple of two-by-fours to shore up the chicken house. Well, sir, he had pottered around the house a little while and was about to set out for Pullen's when something told him not to go a step. And it was that very day that a pile of lumber in the lumber yard let go and crushed Grant Pullen's leg so's it had to be amputated. Well, sir, he would say – but Aunt Emma would cut in on him at this point. 'Everybody's heard that old chestnut,' she would say, with a forced little laugh, fanning herself in quick strokes with an old palm-leaf fan. Jad would go sullen and rock back and forth in his chair, clicking his teeth. He wouldn't get up when the guests rose to go – which they always did at this juncture. The memento of his close escape from the Pullen lumber-yard disaster was, of course, the chip of pine wood.

I think I have accounted for all of Jad's souvenirs that I remember except the big rough fragment of rock. The story of the rock is a strange one. In August, 1920, county engineers were widening the channel of the Hocking River just outside of Sugar Grove and had occasion to do considerable blasting out of river-bed rock. I have never heard Clem Warden tell the story himself, but it has been told to me by people who have. It seems that Clem was walking along the main street of Sugar Grove at about a quarter to four when he saw Jad coming along toward him. Clem was an old crony of Jad's – one of the few men of his own generation who could tolerate Jad – and the two stopped on the sidewalk and talked. Clem figured later that they had talked for about five minutes, and then either he or Jad said something about getting on, so they separated, Jad going on toward Prentice's store, slowly, on account of his rheumatic left hip, and Clem going in the other direction. Clem had taken about a dozen steps when suddenly he heard Jad call to him. 'Say, Clem!' Jad said. Clem stopped and turned around, and here was Jad walking back toward him. Jad had taken about six steps when suddenly he was flung up against the front of Matheny's harness store 'like a sack o' salt,' as Clem put it. By the time Clem could reach him, he was gone. He never knew what hit him, Clem said, and for quite a few minutes nobody else knew what hit him, either. Then somebody in the crowd that gathered found the big muddy rock lying in the road by the gutter. A particularly big shot of dynamite, set off in the river bed, had hurtled the fragment through the air with terrific force. It had come flying over the four-storey Jackson Building like a cannon ball and had struck Jad Peters squarely in the chest.

I suppose old Jad hadn't been in his grave two days before the boys at Prentice's quit shaking their heads solemnly over the accident and began making funny remarks about it. Cal Gregg's was the funniest. 'Well, sir,' said Cal, 'I don't suppose none of us will ever know what it was now, but somethin' must of told Jad to turn around.'

Hell Only Breaks Loose Once

(Written after reading James M. Cain's 'The Postman Always Rings Twice')

I

THEY kicked me out of college when I was about twenty-seven. I went up to see the Dean and tried to hand him a couple of laughs but it was no good. He said he couldn't put me back in college but I could hang around the office and sweep out and wash windows. I figured I better be rambling and I said I had a couple of other offers. He told me to sit down and think it over so I sat down.

Then she came in the room. She was tall and thin and had a white frowning forehead and soft eyes. She wasn't much to look at but she was something to think about. As far as she and I were concerned he wasn't in the room. She leaned over the chair where I was sitting and bit me in the ear. I let her have it right under the heart. It was a good one. It was plenty. She hit the floor like a two-year-old.

'What fell?' asked the Dean, peering over his glasses. I told him nothing fell.

II

After a while I said I guessed I'd hang around and go to work for him. 'Do what?' he asked. He had forgot all about me, but I hung around. I liked him and he liked me but neither one of us cared what happened to the other.

When the Dean went out to lunch I walked into a rear office and she was there. I began to tremble all over like a hooch dancer. She was fussing with some papers but I could see she wasn't really doing anything. I walked close to her. It was like dying and going to Heaven. She was a little like my mother and a little like the time I got my hip busted in a football scrimmage. I reached over and let her have one on the chin and she went down like a tray of dishes. I knew then I would be beating her up the rest of my life. It made me feel like it was April and I was a kid again and had got up on a warm morning and it was all misty outdoors and the birds were singing.

III

'Hi, Dean,' I said to him when he got back from lunch.

'What is it?' he asked. I could tell he thought he had never seen me before. I told him what it was. 'Excellent,' he said, looking surprised. He still didn't know what it was. She came out of the back room and he asked her what she wanted. He never remembered seeing anybody.

I took her out to lunch. It was sweet in the lunchroom and I kicked her under the table and broke her ankle. It was still broken when I carried her back to the Dean's office.

'Who do you wish to see?' he asked, looking over his glasses at us. I wanted to grind his glasses into his skull. She said we both worked there. He said that was excellent, but he wasn't looking for work. I told him to think it over and she and I went into the back room. I let her have one over the eye but it was a glancing blow and didn't knock her out. She cracked down on me with a paperweight and I went out like a light but I took her with me. She broke her head in the fall. We were unconscious for about an hour. A couple of guys were bending over us when we came to. They said they were from a place named Lang's, a cleaning establishment. The Dean had got the idea we were a bear rug and was going to send us out to be dry-cleaned. He was pretty dumb but I liked him.

IV

'What do you want to work for that guy for?'
'I'm his secretary.'
'What do you want to work for him for?'
'I said I'm his secretary.'
'Keep talking.'
'I have to work for him. He's my husband.' I felt pretty sick then.
'That's tough. You oughtn't to be married to him. He doesn't know what it's all about.'
'He lectures in his sleep.'
'That must be swell.'
'I don't want to be his wife. I want to be yours.'
'You are mine.'
'Let me have it again,' she said. I gave her a short left jab on the button. She was dizzy for days.

V

The Dean was too absent-minded to notice she was bruised all the time. It made me sick seeing him sitting at his desk trying to remember what it was all about. One day he began dictating a letter to me but I didn't pay any attention. I went on dusting a chair. Pretty soon he went out to lunch and I went in the back room. She was there and I began to shiver like a tuning fork. I stroked her hair. I had never done that before. It was like going to sleep.

'There is one out for us,' she told me.
'Okay,' I said.

VI

He was sitting at his desk trying to figure out who he was when I hit him over the conk with an auto crank. I thought he would fold up like a leather belt, but he didn't. It didn't faze him. 'Somebody's at the door,' he said. I was shaking a little but I went to the door and opened it. There wasn't anybody there. I stood to one side so he could look out of the door into the hall. It was empty. 'I thought I heard somebody knock,' he said. It made me cold.

VII

We fixed him finally. I got him up on top of the university water tower one night to see the aurora borealis. There wasn't any aurora borealis but he was too dumb to notice that. It was swell up there on the tower. It smelled pretty. It smelled of jasmine. I felt like the first time I ever kissed a girl.

I rigged up one of those double flights of steps like tap-dancers dance up and down on and told him to get up on top of it.

'I don't want to get up on top of that,' he said.

'You want to see the aurora borealis, don't you?'

'Most certainly.'

'Then get up on top of that.'

He got up on top of it and I climbed up after him. The thing was rickety but he didn't notice.

'What are we doing up here?' he asked me.

'Look at the aurora,' I said, pointing at the sky. He looked and while we were standing there she came on top of the steps with us. He didn't pay any attention to her. I swayed from side to side and started the thing teetering. I beat her up a little and then I beat him up a little. He looked like he had been spanked by an old aunt. The thing was swinging bad now, from one side to the other. I knew it was going over.

VIII

We all fell six flights. He was dead when they picked him up. She was dead too. I was near to her, but she was a long way off. I was dying, they told me. So I dictated this to a guy from the D.A.'s office, and here it is. And that's all, except I hope it's pretty in Heaven and smells like when the lilacs first come out on May nights in the Parc Monceau in Paris.

The Man Who Was Wetly

(After reading an Anthology of British Short Stories)

A HALF-DOZEN of us were discussing that curious thing called life and the singular interrelationship between penalty and reward one night in the fireplace of the Cathay Cyclists' Club. 'It seems rather warm in here, you know,' said Empringham, who had, I knew, been wounded four times at Vimy Ridge. We moved out of the fireplace into the club room. It became a little cooler. Masters brought in another large tray of gooseberry wine and spiced walnuts, and for a time we were silent.

'Sitting in that fireplace,' mused Empringham, finally, 'reminded me of a curious adventure I had one night in New York City.'

Lord Burleigh laughed. 'I had supposed,' he said, 'that there were no singular adventures to be had in New York City. How about it, Buell?' This last was addressed to me, as being the only American present.

'Oh,' I said, 'we don't, of course, have your mysterious fog which shrouds London in a – ah –'

'Mysterious fog,' put in little Bailey.

'Precisely,' mused Empringham. 'But I assure you there is mystery also to be found in clear streets. Shall I tell you my story?'

'No,' said the Earl of Leaves, a bald, choleric man, who got up and abruptly left the room.

'Curious chap, Leaves,' mused young Priestley. 'I remember one night in the Sudan. A curious rain had come up and cooled that furnace of a jungle, in which you could hear Snider rifles squibbing wetly. Several of us subalterns were sitting around in our fatigue uniforms, when out of the jungle –'

'Jungle!' cried Empringham, slapping his leg. 'The jungle is a state of mind. Your rain, my dear fellow, was a state of mind, too. Would it surprise you if I said that New York is also a jungle, also a state of mind?'

No one spoke for a minute.

'Let's see, where was I?' began young Priestley, again. 'Oh, yes. It had rained, as I say, and the Sniders were squibbing –'

'Wetly,' I prompted him, for Priestley had been wounded at Nantes and sometimes remembered rather slowly.

'Dear old Wetly!' cried Empringham. 'What a chap he was! I last saw him in Port Said. God, how he had changed! At first I didn't know him. I was pricing some sherids at a native sampan in the marketplace when a fellow seized my shoulder – there in that hustings, that shambles! I supposed, of course, the man was a beggar and I threw off his arm a bit gruffly. 'Have on with you," I said. "Cheero, Empringham," he said, and I saw that it was Wetly.'

'That, of course,' chimed in Leaves, who had returned to the room because he hadn't been able to find anything to do in any of the other rooms, 'that is a decision which, at some time or other, in the lives of all of us, a man must make for himself, all alone – without the help of God or man. Lord, what solitude can encompass a man in the midst of a teeming city!' He held up a curious object for us to look at. It did not seem, at first glance, extraordinary, being only a singular china figurine of a Napoleonic cavalryman standing beside his horse.

'Who is it?' asked Dunleavy, sourly. 'Wetly?' We all fell silent, for it was unusual indeed when Kerry Dunleavy said anything. This was, in point of

fact, the first thing he had said since 1908 when, fresh from Indian service, with the insignia of a subaltern on his shoulders, a pretty wife whom he had married God knows where, and the livid scar of a Sikh tamarinth across one cheek, he walked into the Cyclists' Club, took his old familiar chair, the leather one by the window, and called for a Scotch and soda.

'Damme,' mused Dunleavy, 'it was amazing, I tell you. There hadn't been a sound, except the drip, drip of rain falling from the huge leaves of the pelango trees, which the natives thatch their huts with. I was running over the company accounts at a little table, doing the best I could by the light of a beastly kerosene lamp and smoking that vile native tobacco to fend off the mosquitoes and flet-flet flies, when the door opened and a man wearing the uniform of Her Majesty's Death's Head Hussars staggered into the room. He was ghastly pale and, I could see at a glance, badly wounded at Ypres. Without a word he walked in an uncertain line over to the table and snatched up the champagne glass out of which I had been drinking that fiendish native pongo-pongo, or gluelike liqueur. He stood there wavering, then proposed a toast and –'

'Shattered the glass in his hand!' cried young Priestley.

'Good God!' cried Empringham, pushing back his chair and rising to his feet. We all stared at him.

'Take it easy, old chap,' I said, for I liked Empringham and knew that his old wounds still bothered him.

'I say, what is the matter?' cried young Priestley, who was, as we all knew, too young to know what was the matter.

'Did he give this toast when he shattered that glass?' demanded Empringham, in an odd, strained voice, white as a sheet. 'Did he say, when he broke that glass: "The Queen, God bless her"?' There was a singular, strained silence. We all looked at Dunleavy.

'That,' said Dunleavy in a low, tense voice, 'that is what he said.' Empringham fixed us all in turn with a curious, wide-eyed stare. Outside the rain beat against the windows. Empringham's chair toppled to the floor with a clatter as loud as that of a brass shield falling.

'Gentlemen,' said Empringham, 'that toast has not been drunk for more than one hundred and fifty years.'

'Good God!' cried young Priestley.

'Good God!' muttered little Bailey.

'Good God!' I mused, softly. Old Masters moved over and took up the tray, its wine and walnuts untouched. He was about to turn away when, as if on second thought, he removed the walnut bowl and set it before us.

'Nuts, gentlemen,' said Masters, and withdrew.

If Grant Had Been Drinking at Appomattox

(*Scribner's Magazine* published a series of three articles: 'If Booth Had Missed Lincoln,' 'If Lee Had Not Won The Battle of Gettysburg,' and 'If Napoleon Had Escaped to America.' This is the fourth.)

THE morning of the ninth of April, 1865, dawned beautifully. General Meade was up with the first streaks of crimson in the eastern sky. General Hooker and General Burnside were up, and had breakfasted, by a quarter after eight. The day continued beautiful. It drew on toward eleven o'clock. General Ulysses S. Grant was still not up. He was asleep in his famous old navy hammock, swung high above the floor of his headquarters' bedroom. Headquarters was distressingly disarranged: papers were strewn on the floor; confidential notes from spies scurried here and there in the breeze from an open window; the dregs of an overturned bottle of wine flowed pinkly across an important military map.

Corporal Shultz, of the Sixty-fifth Ohio Volunteer Infantry, aide to General Grant, came into the outer room, looked around him, and sighed. He entered the bedroom and shook the General's hammock roughly. General Ulysses S. Grant opened one eye.

'Pardon, sir,' said Corporal Shultz, 'but this is the day of surrender. You ought to be up, sir.'

'Don't swing me,' said Grant, sharply, for his aide was making the hammock sway gently. 'I feel terrible,' he added, and he turned over and closed his eye again.

'General Lee will be here any minute now,' said the Corporal firmly, swinging the hammock again.

'Will you cut that out!' roared Grant. 'D'ya want to make me sick, or what?' Shultz clicked his heels and saluted. 'What's he coming here for?' asked the General.

'This is the day of surrender, sir,' said Shultz. Grant grunted bitterly.

'Three hundred and fifty generals in the Northern armies,' said Grant, 'and he has to come to *me* about this. What time is it?'

'You're the Commander-in-Chief, that's why,' said Corporal Shultz. 'It's eleven twenty-five, sir.'

'Don't be crazy,' said Grant. 'Lincoln is the Commander-in-Chief. Nobody in the history of the world ever surrendered before lunch. Doesn't he know that an army surrenders on its stomach?' He pulled a blanket up over his head and settled himself again.

'The generals of the Confederacy will be here any minute now,' said the Corporal. 'You really ought to be up, sir.'

Grant stretched his arms above his head and yawned.

'All right, all right,' he said. He rose to a sitting position and stared about the room. 'This place looks awful,' he growled.

'You must have had quite a time of it last night, sir,' ventured Shultz.

'Yeh,' said General Grant, looking around for his clothes. 'I was wrassling some general. Some general with a beard.'

Shultz helped the commander of the Northern armies in the field to find his clothes.

'Where's my other sock?' demanded Grant. Shultz began to look around for it. The General walked uncertainly to a table and poured a drink from a bottle.

'I don't think it wise to drink, sir,' said Shultz.

'Nev' mind about me,' said Grant, helping himself to a second, 'I can take it or let it alone. Didn' ya ever hear the story about the fella went to Lincoln to complain about me drinking too much? "So-and-So says Grant drinks too much," this fella said. "So-and-So is a fool," said Lincoln. So this fella went to What's-His-Name and told him what Lincoln said and he came roarin' to Lincoln about it. "Did you tell So-and-So I was a fool?" he said. "No," said Lincoln, "I thought he knew it." ' The General smiled, reminiscently, and had another drink. '*That's* how I stand with Lincoln,' he said, proudly.

The soft thudding sound of horses' hooves came through the open window. Shultz hurriedly walked over and looked out.

'Hoof steps,' said Grant, with a curious chortle.

'It is General Lee and his staff,' said Shultz.

'Show him in,' said the General, taking another drink. 'And see what the boys in the back room will have.'

Shultz walked smartly over to the door, opened it, saluted, and stood aside. General Lee, dignified against the blue of the April sky, magnificent in his dress uniform, stood for a moment framed in the doorway. He walked in, followed by his staff. They bowed, and stood silent. General Grant stared at them. He only had one boot on and his jacket was unbuttoned.

'I know who you are,' said Grant. 'You're Robert Browning, the poet.'

'This is General Robert E. Lee,' said one of his staff, coldly.

'Oh,' said Grant. 'I thought he was Robert Browning. He certainly looks like Robert Browning. There was a poet for you, Lee: Browning. Did ja ever read "How They Brought the Good News from Ghent to Aix"? "Up Derek, to saddle, up Derek, away; up Dunder, up Blitzen, up Prancer, up Dancer, up Bouncer, up Vixen, up –"'

'Shall we proceed at once to the matter in hand?' asked General Lee, his eyes disdainfully taking in the disordered room.

'Some of the boys was wrassling here last night,' explained Grant. 'I threw Sherman, or some general a whole lot like Sherman. It was pretty dark.' He handed a bottle of Scotch to the commanding officer of the Southern armies, who stood holding it, in amazement and discomfiture. 'Get a glass, somebody,' said Grant, looking straight at General Longstreet. 'Didn't I meet you at Cold Harbour?' he asked. General Longstreet did not answer.

'I should like to have this over with as soon as possible,' said Lee. Grant looked vaguely at Shultz, who walked up close to him, frowning.

'The surrender, sir, the surrender,' said Corporal Shultz in a whisper.

'Oh sure, sure,' said Grant. He took another drink. 'All right,' he said. 'Here we go.' Slowly, sadly, he unbuckled his sword. Then he handed it to the astonished Lee. 'There you are, General,' said Grant. 'We dam' near licked you. If I'd been feeling better we *would* of licked you.'

One More April

(An Effort to Start Another Novel about the Galsworthy Characters, Taking Them Up Where He Left Off)

ON THE second day after the sailing of the transatlantic liner *Picardy* for America, in April, 1935, three English people who were unknown to each other came into the main dining saloon from wholly different staterooms and began to play piquet together. This breach of form affected them all in precisely the same way: each one sat perhaps seven feet from the card table so that, even with arms extended at full length, it was impossible to bring the cards near enough to the playing surface to lay them upon it. One of these three was a young woman of about twenty-two, one a darkish man of perhaps forty-three, and one a man of between ninety-five and a hundred.

The younger man spoke suddenly.

The effect of his breach of form on the others was diverse: the olderish man leaned forward as if to examine the table legs, with a sort of weathered scepticism; the young woman turned a surprised look upon the speaker.

'Didn't I meet you at my wedding?' she queried. 'I am Fleur Desert, the second daughter of Dinny Mont, who married Wilfrid Desert; the first daughter was Celia. There are two brothers, Michael and Michael.' The younger man's mouth lost its disdainful look.

'I am your sister's brother-in-law, Cherrill Desert.'

The older man spoke unexpectedly.

'Forsyte Desert's nephew, eh? Old Derek Mont's cousin. What's become of young Cherrill Desert? Still wandering sallowly about the East, I'll wager, writing verse.'

Desert smiled and shook his head.

'I am Cherrill Desert,' he said. The older man looked surprised.

'And probably died there,' he grunted.

Fleur Desert thought: 'He can't have been home for many years.'

'Cherrill Desert married Dinny Mont's second daughter, Fleur,' she said. 'They have two children, Dinny and Fleur.' A slight colour stained her cheeks. The disdainful look which had been about to return to the young man's lips did not.

'I remember you perfectly,' he said. 'You are Wilfrid Desert's daughter.'

'Old Derek Mont's cousin's wife,' said the older man, with a sort of sceptical weatheredness. 'Forsyte Desert's niece-in-law.'

The other two looked at him with frank surprise.

'I am Uncle Adrian,' said the older man. 'Or his brother, Mark. I cannot always remember which. However, if I'm Mark, he's going to be confoundedly seasick.' He glared about the saloon, which was filled with surprised card tables. 'I like the way these tables stand up,' he said. The ship rocked a bit. 'Mark never had a stomach for the ocean.' He chuckled unexpectedly.

Fleur thought: 'He's Adrian. Uncle Lawrence always said Adrian Mont knew tables.'

The older man gave up his study of the card tables.

'Rather leggish. But they hold up.' He took out a surprised old watch which chimed the days and months and years. It struck April fifth, 1935.

'My goodness! Aunt Sheila's birthday!' cried Fleur. 'And I've forgotten to send her a radiogram!'

The older man smiled and spoke abruptly.

'I was at Somebody Mont's, or her mother's,' he said, 'the day that all these birthday parties started. Ronald Ferse was there, and a small Chinese boy, and Aunt Alison and her youngest, little Anne, and Uncle Hilary and Tony.

Monty Muskham, too – who became Musky Montham. The war turned him around. And Uncle Lawrence, my father's brother. And the Dingo children, Celia and Moriston.' He frowned. 'All scattered now. All scattered then, as far as that goes.'

The disdainful look returned to the younger man's lips.

'Ronald Ferse is in coal and feed, Hilary and Tony's daughter, Jean, went in for one-old-cat behind Government House in Rangoon. I don't know what became of the Chinese boy. Uncle Lawrence is translating the Foreign Office records into Russian for the Soviet – confounded officialism! The Dingo children married each other and broke old Forsyte Dingo's heart.'

'Forsyte Dingo was in love with Celia Dingo, wasn't he?' queried the more weathered of the two men. The dark look deepened on the face of the more disdainful of the two men.

'Forsyte Dingo was her father,' he said. 'And her father-in-law, too – after she married her brother.'

The old man chuckled unexpectedly.

'Like to see old Forsyte again,' he said. 'The two of us could play four-handed bridge.' He looked at Dinny Mont's daughter, for whose mother he had gone away to the East. He wondered who she was. It didn't make much difference. All these women, he understood, were the same woman; he was two men, like old Forsyte Dingo, and outnumbered them all. Perhaps it was what kept him going – that and his nice eye for tables – providing he was Adrian. Mark Mont was never a man for tables. The old man twiddled the setting arrangement of his watch, turning it back to 1894, and suddenly discovered that, except for his shoes and socks, his legs were quite bare. Through some surprising and unexpected oversight he had forgotten to put on his trousers. This breach of form had an immediate effect on the others. Wilfrid Desert's son-in-law arose and so did Dinny Mont's daughter. The older man's face was masked in a sort of shrewd suspicion.

'I for one,' he said, 'shall never leave this spot.' The young man laughed and turned his dark eyes on Fleur.

'Will you have lunch with me tomorrow?' he queried.

'I will. Where?'

'Right here on the ship. It'll be easier. We're two days out, you know.' They crossed the saloon together.

Fleur thought: 'He's as quick as ever. He sees through things.'

The older man sat where he was – where, indeed, he intended always to sit unless they came and carried him away, or brought him the rest of his clothes. 'England, England!' he murmured. It disturbed him that Adrian Mont, the solid one of the two Mont brothers, should lose his pants. Suddenly he began to feel sickish.

With a faint smile of relief, he thought: 'I'm Mark!'

The Funniest Man You Ever Saw

EVERYBODY seemed surprised that I had never met Jack Klohman.
'Judas, I didn't know there was anybody who didn't know Jack
Klohman,' said Mr Potter, who was big and heavy, of body and mind.
'He's funnier'n hell.' Mr Potter laughed and slapped his knee. 'He's the
funniest man you ever saw.'

'He certainly is funny,' said somebody else.

'He's marvellous,' drawled a woman I didn't like. Looking around the
group I discovered I didn't like any of them much, except Joe Mayer. This was
undoubtedly unfair, for Joe was the only one I knew very well. The others had
come over to the table where we were sitting. Somebody had mentioned Jack
Klohman and everybody had begun to laugh.

'Do you know him, Joe?' I asked.

'I know him,' said Joe, without laughing.

'Judas,' went on Potter, 'I'll never forget one night at Jap Rudolph's.
Klohman was marvellous that night. This was a couple years ago, when Ed
Wynn was here in a new show – let's see, what the devil was it? Not "The
Crazy Fool".'

'"The Perfect Fool",' said somebody else.

'Yes. But it wasn't that,' said Potter. 'What the dickens was it? Well, never
mind; anyway there was a scene in it where –'

'Was it "Simple Simon"?' asked the blonde girl who was with Creel.

'No. It was a couple years before that,' said Potter.

'Oh, I know,' said the blonde girl. 'It was – now wait – it was "The Man-
hatters"!'

'Ed Wynn wasn't in that,' said Creel. 'Wynn wasn't in that show.'

'Well, it doesn't make much difference,' said Potter. 'Anyway, in this scene
he has a line where –'

'"Manhattan Mary"!' cried Griswold.

'That's it!' said Potter, slapping his knee. 'Well, in this scene he comes on
with a rope, kind of a lariat –'

'Halter,' said Griswold. 'It was a halter.'

'Yes, that's right,' said Potter. 'Anyway, he comes on with this halter –'

'Who comes on?' asked Joe Mayer. 'Klohman?'

'No, no,' said Potter. 'Wynn comes on with the halter and walks up to the
footlights and some guy asks him what he's got the rope for, what he's doing
with the halter. "Well," says Wynn, 'I've either lost a horse or found a piece
of rope –'

65

'I think he said: "I've either found a piece of rope or lost a horse",' said Griswold. 'Losing the horse coming last is funnier.'

'Well, anyway,' said Potter, 'Jack Klohman used to elaborate on the idea and this night at Jap Rudolph's I thought we'd all pass away.'

'I nearly did,' said Joe Mayer.

'What did this Klohman do?' I asked finally, cutting in on the general laughter.

'Well,' said Potter, 'he'd go out into the kitchen, see, and come in with a Uneeda biscuit and he'd say: "Look, I've either lost a biscuit box or found a cracker" – that's the right order, Gris – "I've either lost a biscuit box or lost" – I mean found – "a cracker".'

'I guess you're right,' said Griswold.

'It sounds right,' said Joe Mayer.

'Then he'd do the same thing with everything he picked up, no matter what,' said Potter. 'Finally he went out of the room and was gone half an hour or so and then he comes down the stairs and holds up this faucet and says: "I've either lost a bathtub or found a faucet." He'd unscrewed a faucet from the bathtub and comes downstairs with this faucet – see what I mean? Laugh? I thought I'd pass away.'

Everybody who had been at Jap Rudolph's that night roared with laughter.

'But that wasn't anything,' said Potter. 'Wait'll you hear. Along about two in the morning he slips out again, see? – all the way out of the house this time. Well, I'll be doggoned if that guy didn't come back carrying part of an honest-to-God chancel rail! He did! I'm telling you! Son-of-a-gun had actually got into a church somehow and wrenched part of this chancel rail loose and there he was standing in the door and he says: "I've either lost a church or found a chancel rail." It was rich. It was the richest thing I ever saw. Helen Rudolph had gone to bed, I remember – she wasn't very well – but we got her up and he did it again. It was rich.'

'Sounds like a swell guy to have around,' I said.

'You'd darn near pass away,' said Potter.

'You really would,' said Joe Mayer.

'He's got a new gag now,' said one of the women. 'He's got a new gag that's as funny as the dickens. He keeps taking things out of his pockets or off of a table or something and says that he's just invented them. He always takes something that's been invented for *years*, say like a lead pencil or something, and goes into this long story about how he thought it up one night. I remember he did it with about twenty different things one night at Jap's –'

'Jap Rudolph's?' I asked.

'Yes,' said the woman. 'He likes to drop in on them, so you can usually find him there, so we usually drop in on them too. Well, this night he took out a package of those Life Savers and handed us each one of the mints and – '

'Oh, yes, I remember that!' said Potter, slapping his knee and guffawing.

'Gave us each one of these mints,' went on the woman, 'and asked us what we thought of them – asked us whether we thought they'd go or not. "It's a little thing I thought up one day," he said. Then he'd go on with a long rig-marole about how he happened to think of the idea, and –'

'And then he'd take a pencil out of his pocket,' cut in Potter, 'and ask you what you thought of the eraser on the end of it. "Just a little gadget I thought

up the other night," he'd say. Then he says he'll show you what it's for, so he makes everybody take a piece of paper and he says: "Now everybody make some pencil marks on the paper; any kind – I won't look,' so then he goes into another room and says to let him know when you're ready. So we all make marks on the pieces of paper and somebody goes and gets him out of the other room –'

'They always go and get him out of the other room,' Joe Mayer said to me.

'Sure,' said Potter. 'So he comes out with his sleeves rolled up, like a magician, and –'

'But the *funniest* thing he does,' began the woman whom Potter had interrupted.

'And he gathers up the papers and erases the marks with the eraser and he says: "Oh, it's just a novelty; I'm not going to try to market it." Laugh? I thought I'd pass away. Of course you really ought to see him do it; the way he does it is a big part of it – solemn and all; he's always solemn, always acts solemn about it.'

'The *funniest* thing he does,' began the interrupted woman again, loudly, 'is fake card tricks. He –'

'Oh, yes!' cried Potter, roaring and slapping his knee. 'He does these fake card tricks. He – ' Here the recollection of the funny man's antics proved too much for Potter and he laughed until he cried. It was several minutes before he could control himself. 'He'll take a pack of cards,' he finally began again. 'He'll take a pack of cards – ' Once more the image of Klohman taking a pack of cards was too much for the narrator and he went off into further gales of laughter. 'He'll take this pack of cards,' Potter eventually said once more, wiping his eyes, 'and ask you to take any card and you take one and then he says: "Put it anywhere in the deck" and you do and then he makes a lot of passes and so on –'

'Like a magician,' said Joe Mayer.

'Yes,' said Potter. 'And then he draws out the wrong card, or maybe he *looks* at your card first and then goes through the whole deck till he finds it and shows it to you or –'

'Sometimes he just lays the pack down and acts as if he'd never started any trick,' said Griswold.

'Does he do imitations?' I asked. Joe Mayer kicked my shins under the table.

'Does he do *imitations*?' bellowed Potter. 'Wait'll I tell you –'

The Black Magic of Barney Haller

I T W A S one of those hot days on which the earth is uninhabitable; even as early as ten o'clock in the morning, even on the hill where I live under the dark maples. The long porch was hot and the wicker chair I sat in complained hotly. My coffee was beginning to wear off and with it the momentary illusion it gives that things are Right and life is Good. There were sultry mutterings of thunder. I had a quick feeling that if I looked up from my book I would see Barney Haller. I looked up, and there he was, coming along the road, lightning playing about his shoulders, thunder following him like a dog.

Barney is (or was) my hired man. He is strong and amiable, sweaty and dependable, slowly and heavily competent. But he is also eerie: he trafficks with the devil. His ears twitch when he talks, but it isn't so much that as the things he says. Once in late June, when all of a moment sabres began to flash brightly in the heavens and bowling balls rumbled, I took refuge in the barn. I always have a feeling that I am going to be struck by lightning and either riven like an old apple tree or left with a foot that aches in rainy weather and a habit of fainting. Those things happen. Barney came in, not to escape the storm to which he is, or pretends to be, indifferent, but to put the scythe away. Suddenly he said the first of those things that made me, when I was with him, faintly creepy. He pointed at the house. 'Once I see dis boat come down de rock,' he said. It is phenomena like that of which I stand in constant dread: boats coming down rocks, people being teleported, statues dripping blood, old regrets and dreams in the form of Luna moths fluttering against the windows at midnight.

Of course I finally figured out what Barney meant – or what I comforted myself with believing he meant: something about a bolt coming down the lightning rod on the house; a commonplace, an utterly natural thing. I should have dismissed it, but it had its effect on me. Here was a stolid man, smelling of hay and leather, who talked like somebody out of Charles Fort's books, or like a traveller back from Oz. And all the time the lightning was zigging and zagging around him.

On this hot morning when I saw Barney coming along with his faithful storm trudging behind him, I went back frowningly to my copy of 'Swann's Way.' I hoped that Barney, seeing me absorbed in a book, would pass by without saying anything. I read: '. . . I myself seemed actually to have become the subject of my book: a church, a quartet, the rivalry between Francis I and Charles V . . .' I could feel Barney standing looking at me, but I didn't look at him.

'Dis morning bime by,' said Barney, 'I go hunt grotches in de voods.'

'That's fine,' I said, and turned a page and pretended to be engrossed in what I was reading. Barney walked on; he had wanted to talk some more, but he walked on. After a paragraph or two, his words began to come between me and the words in the book. 'Bime by I go hunt grotches in de voods.' If you are susceptible to such things, it is not difficult to visualize grotches. They fluttered into my mind: ugly little creatures, about the size of whippoorwills, only covered with blood and honey and the scrapings of church bells. Grotches . . . Who and what, I wondered, really was this thing in the form of a hired man that kept anointing me ominously, in passing, with abracadabra ?

Barney didn't go toward the woods at once; he weeded the corn, he picked apple boughs up off the lawn, he knocked a yellow jacket's nest down out of a plum tree. It was raining now, but he didn't seem to notice it. He kept looking at me out of the corner of his eye, and I kept looking at him out of the corner of my eye. 'Vot dime is it, blease ?' he called to me finally. I put down my book and sauntered out to him. 'When you go for those grotches,' I said, firmly, 'I'll go with you.' I was sure he wouldn't want me to go. I was right; he protested that he could get the grotches himself. 'I'll go with you,' I said, stubbornly. We stood looking at each other. And then, abruptly, just to give *him* something to ponder over, I quoted:

> 'I'm going out to clean the pasture spring;
> I'll only stop to rake the leaves away
> (And wait to watch the water clear, I may):
> I shan't be gone long. – You come too.'

It wasn't, I realized, very good abracadabra, but it served: Barney looked at me in a puzzled way. 'Yes,' he said, vaguely.

'It's five minutes of twelve,' I said, remembering he had asked.

'Den we go,' he said, and we trudged through the rain over to the orchard fence and climbed that, and opened a gate and went out into the meadow that slopes up to the woods. I had a prefiguring of Barney, at some proper spot deep in the woods, prancing around like a goat, casting off his false nature, shedding his hired man's garments, dropping his Teutonic accent, repeating diabolical phrases, conjuring up grotches.

There was a great slash of lightning and a long bumping of thunder as we reached the edge of the woods.

I turned and fled. Glancing over my shoulder, I saw Barney standing and staring after me. . . .

It turned out (on the face of it) to be as simple as the boat that came down the rock. Grotches were 'crotches': crotched saplings which he cut down to use as supports under the peach boughs, because in bearing time they became so heavy with fruit that there was danger of the branches snapping off. I saw Barney later, putting the crotches in place. We didn't have much to say to each other. I can see now that he was beginning to suspect me too.

About six o'clock next evening, I was alone in the house and sleeping upstairs. Barney rapped on the door of the front porch. I knew it was Barney because he called to me. I woke up slowly. It was dark for six o'clock. I heard rumblings and saw flickerings. Barney was standing at the front door with his storm at heel! I had the conviction that it wasn't storming anywhere except around my house. There couldn't, without the intervention of the devil or one of his agents, be so many lightning storms in one neighbourhood.

I had been dreaming of Proust and the church at Combray and *madeleines* dipped in tea, and the rivalry between Francis I and Charles V. My head whirled and I didn't get up. Barney kept on rapping. He called out again. There was a flash, followed by a sharp splitting sound. I leaped up. This time, I thought, he is here to get me. I had a notion that he was standing at the door barefooted, with a wreath of grape leaves around his head, and a wild animal's skin slung over his shoulder. I didn't want to go down, but I did.

He was as usual, solid, amiable, dressed like a hired man. I went out on the porch and looked at the improbable storm, now on in all its fury. 'This is getting pretty bad,' I said, meaningly. Barney looked at the rain placidly. 'Well,' I said, irritably, 'what's up?' Barney turned his little squinty blue eyes on me.

'We go to the garrick now and become warbs,' he said.

'The hell we do!' I thought to myself, quickly. I was uneasy – I was, you might even say, terrified – but I determined not to show it. If he began to chant incantations or to make obscene signs or if he attempted to sling me over his shoulder, I resolved to plunge right out into the storm, lightning and all, and run to the nearest house. I didn't know what they would think at the nearest house when I burst in upon them, or what I would tell them. But I didn't in-tend to accompany this amiable-looking fiend to any garrick and become a warb. I tried to persuade myself that there was some simple explanation, that warbs would turn out to be as innocuous as boats on rocks and grotches in the woods, but the conviction gripped me (in the growling of the thunder) that here at last was the Moment when Barney Haller, or whoever he was, had chosen to get me. I walked toward the steps that lead to the lawn, and turned and faced him, grimly.

'Listen!' I barked, suddenly. 'Did you know that even when it isn't brillig I can produce slithy toves? Did you happen to know that the mome rath never lived that could outgrabe me? Yeah and furthermore I can become anything I want to; even if I were a warb, I wouldn't have to keep on being one if I didn't want to. I can become a playing card at will, too; once I was the jack of clubs, only I forgot to take my glasses off and some guy recognized me. I . . .'

Barney was backing slowly away, toward the petunia box at one end of the porch. His little blue eyes were wide. He saw that I had him. 'I think I go now,' he said. And he walked out into the rain. The rain followed him down the road.

I have a new hired man now. Barney never came back to work for me after that day. Of course I figured out finally what he meant about the garrick and the warbs: he had simply got horribly mixed up in trying to tell me that he was going up to the garret and clear out the wasps, of which I have thousands. The new hired man is afraid of them. Barney could have scooped them up in his hands and thrown them out a window without getting stung. I am sure he trafficked with the devil. But I am sorry I let him go.

The Remarkable Case of Mr Bruhl

SAMUEL O. BRUHL was just an ordinary-looking citizen, like you and me, except for a curious, shoe-shaped scar on his left cheek, which he got when he fell against a wagon-tongue in his youth. He had a good job as treasurer for a syrup-and-fondant concern, a large, devout wife, two tractable daughters, and a nice home in Brooklyn. He worked from nine to five, took in a show occasionally, played a bad, complacent game of golf, and was usually in bed by eleven o'clock. The Bruhls had a dog named Bert, a small circle of friends, and an old sedan. They had made a comfortable, if unexciting, adjustment to life.

There was no reason in the world why Samuel Bruhl shouldn't have lived along quietly until he died of some commonplace malady. He was a man designed by Nature for an uneventful life, an inexpensive but respectable funeral, and a modest stone marker. All this you would have predicted had you observed his colourless comings and goings, his mild manner, the small stature of his dreams. He was, in brief, the sort of average citizen that observers of Judd Gray thought Judd Gray was. And precisely as that mild little family man was abruptly hurled into an incongruous tragedy, so was Samuel Bruhl suddenly picked out of the hundreds of men just like him and marked for an extravagant and unpredictable end. Oddly enough it was the shoe-shaped scar on his left cheek which brought to his heels a Nemesis he had never dreamed of. A blemish on his heart, a tic in his soul would have been different; one would have blamed Bruhl for whatever anguish an emotional or spiritual flaw laid him open to, but it is ironical indeed when the Furies ride down a man who has been guilty of nothing worse than an accident in his childhood.

Samuel O. Bruhl looked very much like George ('Shoescar') Clinigan. Clinigan had that same singular shoe-shaped scar on his left cheek. There was also a general resemblance in height, weight, and complexion. A careful study would have revealed very soon that Clinigan's eyes were shifty and Bruhl's eyes were clear, and that the syrup-and-fondant company's treasurer had a more pleasant mouth and a higher forehead than the gangster and racketeer, but at a glance the similarity was remarkable.

Had Clinigan not become notorious, this prank of Nature would never have been detected, but Clinigan did become notorious and dozens of persons observed that he looked like Bruhl. They saw Clinigan's picture in the papers the day he was shot, and the day after, and the day after that. Presently someone in the syrup-and-fondant concern mentioned to someone else that Clinigan looked like Mr Bruhl, remarkably like Mr Bruhl. Soon everybody in the place had commented on it, among themselves, and to Mr Bruhl.

Mr Bruhl rather laughed it off at first, but one day when Clinigan had been in the hospital a week, a cop peered closely at Mr Bruhl when he was on his way home from work. After that, the little treasurer noticed a number of other strangers staring at him with mingled surprise and alarm. One small, dark man hastily thrust a hand into his coat pocket and paled slightly.

Mr Bruhl began to worry. He began to imagine things. 'I hope this fellow Clinigan doesn't pull through,' he said one morning at breakfast. 'He's a bad actor. He's better off dead.'

'Oh, he'll pull through,' said Mrs Bruhl, who had been reading the morning paper. 'It says here he'll pull through. But it says they'll shoot him again. It says they're sure to shoot him again.'

The morning after the night that Clinigan left the hospital, secretly, by a side door, and disappeared into the town, Bruhl decided not to go to work. 'I don't feel so good today,' he said to his wife. 'Would you call up the office and tell them I'm sick?'

'You don't look well,' said his wife. 'You really don't look well. Get down, Bert,' she added, for the dog had jumped upon her lap and whined. The animal knew that something was wrong.

That evening Bruhl, who had mooned about the house all day, read in the papers that Clinigan had vanished, but was believed to be somewhere in the city. His various rackets required his presence, at least until he made enough money to skip out with; he had left the hospital penniless. Rival gangsters, the papers said, were sure to seek him out, to hunt him down, to give it to him again. 'Give him what again?' asked Mrs Bruhl when she read this. 'Let's talk about something else,' said her husband.

It was little Joey, the office-boy at the syrup-and-fondant company, who first discovered that Mr Bruhl was afraid. Joey, who went about with tennis shoes on, entered the treasurer's office suddenly – flung open the door and started to say something. 'Good God!' cried Mr Bruhl, rising from his chair. 'Why, what's the matter, Mr Bruhl?' asked Joey. Other little things happened. The switchboard girl phoned Mr Bruhl's desk one afternoon and said there was a man waiting to see him, a Mr Globe. 'What's he look like?' asked Bruhl, who didn't know anybody named Globe. 'He's small and dark,' said the girl. 'A small, dark man?' said Bruhl. 'Tell him I'm out. Tell him I've gone to California.' The personnel, comparing notes, decided at length that the treasurer was afraid of being mistaken for Shoescar and put on the spot. They said nothing to Mr Bruhl about this, because they were forbidden to by Ollie Breithofter, a fattish clerk who was a tireless and inventive practical joker and who had an idea.

As the hunt went on for Clinigan and he still wasn't found and killed, Mr Bruhl lost weight and grew extremely fidgety. He began to figure out new ways of getting to work, one requiring the use of two different ferry lines; he ate his lunch in, he wouldn't answer bells, he cried out when anyone dropped anything, and he ran into stores or banks when cruising taxidrivers shouted at him.

One morning, in setting the house to rights, Mrs Bruhl found a revolver under his pillow. 'I found a revolver under your pillow,' she told him that night. 'Burglars are bad in this neighbourhood,' he said. 'You oughtn't to have a revolver,' she said. They argued about it, he irritably, she uneasily, until time for bed. As Bruhl was undressing, after locking and bolting all the doors, the telephone rang. 'It's for you, Sam,' said Mrs Bruhl. Her husband went slowly to the phone, passing Bert on the way. 'I wish I was you,' he said to the dog, and took up the receiver. 'Get this, Shoescar,' said a husky voice. 'We trailed you where you are, see? You're cooked.' The receiver at the other end was hung

up. Bruhl shouted. His wife came running. 'What is it, Sam, what is it?' she cried. Bruhl, pale, sick-looking, had fallen into a chair. 'They got me,' he moaned. 'They got me.' Slowly, deviously, Minnie Bruhl got it out of her husband that he had been mistaken for Clinigan and that he was cooked. Mrs Bruhl was not very quick mentally, but she had a certain intuition and this intuition told her, as she trembled there in her nightgown above her broken husband, that this was the work of Ollie Breithofter. She instantly phoned Ollie Breithofter's wife and, before she hung up, had got the truth out of Mrs Breithofter. It was Ollie who had called.

The treasurer of the Maskonsett Syrup & Fondant Company, Inc., was so relieved to know that the gangs weren't after him that he admitted frankly at the office next day that Ollie had fooled him for a minute. Mr Bruhl even joined in the laughter and wisecracking, which went on all day. After that, for almost a week, the mild little man had comparative peace of mind. The papers said very little about Clinigan now. He had completely disappeared. Gang warfare had died down for the time being.

One Sunday morning Mr Bruhl went for an automobile ride with his wife and daughters. They had driven about a mile through Brooklyn streets when, glancing in the mirror above his head, Mr Bruhl observed a blue sedan just behind him. He turned off into the next side street, and the sedan turned off too. Bruhl made another turn, and the sedan followed him. 'Where are you going, dear?' asked Mrs Bruhl. Mr Bruhl didn't answer her, he speeded up, he drove terrifically fast, he turned corners so wildly that the rear wheels swung around. A traffic cop shrilled at him. The younger daughter screamed. Bruhl drove right on, weaving in and out. Mrs Bruhl began to berate him wildly. 'Have you lost your mind, Sam?' she shouted. Mr Bruhl looked behind him. The sedan was no longer to be seen. He slowed up. 'Let's go home,' he said. 'I've had enough of this.'

A month went by without incident (thanks largely to Mrs Breithofter) and Samuel Bruhl began to be himself again. On the day that he was practically normal once more, sluggy Pensiotta, alias Killer Lewis, alias Stranger Koetschke, was shot. Sluggy was the leader of the gang that had sworn to get Shoescar Clinigan. The papers instantly took up the gang-war story where they had left off. Pictures of Clinigan were published again. The slaying of Pensiotta, said the papers, meant but one thing: it meant that Shoescar Clinigan was cooked. Mr Bruhl, reading this, went gradually to pieces once more.

After another week of skulking about, starting at every noise, and once almost fainting when an automobile backfired near him, Samuel Bruhl began to take on a remarkable new appearance. He talked out of the corner of his mouth, his eyes grew shifty. He looked more and more like Shoescar Clinigan. He snarled at his wife. Once he called her 'Babe,' and he had never called her anything but Minnie. He kissed her in a strange, new way, acting rough, almost brutal. At the office he was mean and overbearing. He used peculiar language. One night when the Bruhls had friends in for bridge – old Mr Creegan and his wife – Bruhl suddenly appeared from upstairs with a pair of scarlet pyjamas on, smoking a cigarette, and gripping his revolver. After a few loud and incoherent remarks of a boastful nature, he let fly at a clock on the mantel, and hit it squarely in the middle. Mrs Bruhl screamed. Mr Creegan fainted. Bert, who was in the kitchen, howled. 'What's the matta you?' snarled Bruhl. 'Ya bunch of softies.'

Quite by accident, Mrs Bruhl discovered, hidden away in a closet, eight or ten books on gangs and gangsters, which Bruhl had put there. They included 'Al Capone,' 'You Can't Win,' '10,000 Public Enemies' and a lot of others; and they were all well thumbed. Mrs Bruhl realized that it was high time something was done, and she determined to have a doctor for her husband. For two or three days Bruhl had not gone to work. He lay around in his bedroom, in his red pyjamas, smoking cigarettes. The office phoned once or twice. When Mrs

Bruhl urged him to get up and dress and go to work, he laughed and patted her roughly on the head. 'It's a knockover, kid,' he said. 'We'll be sitting pretty. To hell with it.'

The doctor who finally came and slipped into Bruhl's bedroom was very grave when he emerged. 'This is a psychosis,' he said, 'a definite psychosis. Your husband is living in a world of fantasy. He has built up a curious defence mechanism against something or other.' The doctor suggested that a psychiatrist be called in, but after he had gone Mrs Bruhl decided to take her husband out of town on a trip. The Maskonsett Syrup & Fondant Company, Inc., was very fine about it. Mr Scully said of course. 'Sam is very valuable to us, Mrs Bruhl,' said Mr Scully, 'and we all hope he'll be all right.' Just the same he had Mr Bruhl's accounts examined, when Mrs Bruhl had gone.

Oddly enough, Samuel Bruhl was amenable to the idea of going away. 'I need a rest,' he said. 'You're right. Let's get the hell out of here.' He seemed normal up to the time they set out for the Grand Central and then he insisted on leaving from the 125th Street station. Mrs Bruhl took exception to this, as being ridiculous, whereupon her doting husband snarled at her. 'God, what a dumb moll *I* picked,' he said to Minnie Bruhl, and he added bitterly that if the heat was put to him it would be his own babe who was to blame. 'And what do you think of *that*?' he said, pushing her to the floor of the cab.

They went to a little inn in the mountains. It wasn't a very nice place, but the rooms were clean and the meals were good. There was no form of entertainment, except a Tom Thumb golf course and an uneven tennis court, but Mr Bruhl didn't mind. He said it was too cold outdoors, anyway. He stayed indoors, reading and smoking. In the evening he played the mechanical piano in the dining-room. He liked to play 'More Than You Know' over and over again. One night, about nine o'clock, he was putting in his seventh or eighth nickel when four men walked into the dining-room. They were silent men, wearing overcoats, and carrying what appeared to be cases for musical instruments. They took out various kinds of guns from their cases, quickly, expertly, and walked over toward Bruhl, keeping step. He turned just in time to see them line up four abreast and aim at him. Nobody else was in the room. There was a cumulative roar and a series of flashes. Mr Bruhl fell and the men walked out in single file, rapidly, nobody having said a word.

Mrs Bruhl, state police, and the hotel manager tried to get the wounded man to talk. Chief Witznitz of the nearest town's police force tried it. It was no good. Bruhl only snarled and told them to go away and let him alone. Finally, Commissioner O'Donnell of the New York City Police Department arrived at the hospital. He asked Bruhl what the men looked like. 'I don't know what they looked like,' snarled Bruhl, 'and if I did know I wouldn't tell you.' He was silent a moment, then: 'Cop!' he added, bitterly. The Commissioner sighed and turned away. 'They're all like that,' he said to the others in the room. 'They never talk.' Hearing this, Mr Bruhl smiled, a pleased smile, and closed his eyes.

Something to Say

Hugh Kingsmill and I stimulated each other to such a pitch that after the first meeting he had a brain storm and I lay sleepless all night and in the morning was on the brink of a nervous breakdown. – William Gerhardi's 'Memoirs of a Polyglot.'

ELLIOT VEREKER was always coming into and going out of my life. He was the only man who ever continuously stimulated me to the brink of a nervous breakdown. I met him first at a party in Amawalk, New York, on the Fourth of July, 1927. He arrived about noon in an old-fashioned horse cab, accompanied by a lady in black velvet whom he introduced as 'my niece, Olga Nethersole.' She was, it turned out, neither his niece nor Olga Nethersole. Vereker was a writer; he was gaunt and emaciated from sitting up all night talking; he wore an admiral's hat which he had stolen from an admiral. Usually he carried with him an old Gladstone bag filled with burned-out electric-light bulbs which it was his pleasure to throw, unexpectedly, against the sides of houses and the walls of rooms. He loved the popping sound they made and the tinkling sprinkle of fine glass that followed. He had an inordinate fondness for echoes. 'Halloooo!' he would bawl, wherever he was, in a terrific booming voice that could have conjured up an echo on a prairie. At the most inopportune and inappropriate moments he would snap out frank four-letter words, such as when he was talking to a little child or the sister of a vicar. He had no reverence and no solicitude. He would litter up your house, burn bedspreads and carpets with lighted cigarette stubs, and as likely as not depart with your girl and three or four of your most prized books and neckties. He was enamoured of breaking phonograph records and phonographs; he liked to tear sheets and pillowcases in two; he would unscrew the doorknobs from your doors so that if you were in you couldn't get out and if you were out you couldn't get in. His was the true artistic fire, the rare gesture of genius. When I first met him, he was working on a novel entitled 'Sue You Have Seen.' He had worked it out, for some obscure reason, from the familiar expression 'See you soon.' He never finished it, nor did he ever finish, or indeed get very far with, any writing, but he was nevertheless, we all felt, one of the great original minds of our generation. That he had 'something to say' was obvious in everything he did.

Vereker could converse brilliantly on literary subjects: Proust, Goethe, Voltaire, Whitman. Basically he felt for them a certain respect, but sometimes, and always when he was drunk, he would belittle their powers and their achievements in strong and pungent language. Proust, I later discovered, he had never read, but he made him seem more clear to me, and less important, than anybody else ever has. Vereker always liked to have an electric fan going

78

while he talked and he would stick a folded newspaper into the fan so that the revolving blades scuttered against it, making a noise like the rattle of machine-gun fire. This exhilarated him and exhilarated me, too, but I suppose that it exhilarated him more than it did me. He seemed, at any rate, to get something out of it that I missed. He would raise his voice so that I could hear him above the racket. Sometimes, even then, I couldn't make out what he was saying. 'What?' I would shout. 'You heard me!' he would yell, his good humour disappearing in an instant.

I had, of course, not heard him at all. There was no reasoning with him, no convincing him. I can still hear the musketry of those fans in my ears. They have done, I think, something to me. But for Vereker, and his great promise, one could endure a great deal. He would talk about the interests implicated in life, the coincidence of desire and realization, the symbols behind art and reality. He was fond of quoting Santayana when he was sober.

'Santayana,' he would say when he was drinking, 'has weight; he's a ton of feathers.' Then he would laugh roaringly; if he was at Tony's, he would flounder out into the kitchen, insulting some movie critic on the way, and repeat his line to whoever was there, and come roaring back.

Vereker had a way of flinging himself at a sofa, kicking one end out of it; or he would drop into a fragile chair like a tired bird dog and something would crack. He never seemed to notice. You would invite him to dinner, or, what happened oftener, he would drop in for dinner uninvited, and while you were shaking up a cocktail in the kitchen he would disappear. He might go upstairs to wrench the bathtub away from the wall ('Breaking lead pipe is one of the truly enchanting adventures in life,' he said once), or he might simply leave for good in one of those inexplicable huffs of his which were a sign of his peculiar genius. He was likely, of course, to come back around two in the morning bringing some awful woman with him, stirring up the fire, talking all night long, knocking things off tables, singing, or counting. I have known him to lie back on a sofa, his eyes closed, and count up to as high as twenty-four thousand by ones, in a bitter, snarling voice. It was his protest against the regularization of a mechanized age. 'Achievement,' he used to say, 'is the fool's gold of idiots.' He never believed in doing anything or in having anything done, either for the benefit of mankind or for individuals. He would have written, but for his philosophical indolence, very great novels indeed. We all knew that, and we treated him with a deference for which, now that he is gone, we are sincerely glad.

Once Vereker invited me to a house which a lady had turned over to him when she went to Paris for a divorce. (She expected to marry Vereker afterward but he would not marry her, nor would he move out of her house until she took legal action. 'American women,' Vereker would say, 'are like American colleges: they have dull, half-dead faculties.') When I arrived at the house Vereker chose to pretend that he did not remember me. It was rather difficult to carry the situation off, for he was in one of his black moods. It was then that he should have written, but never did; instead he would gabble brilliantly about other authors. 'Goethe,' he would say, 'was a wax figure stuffed with hay. When you say that Proust was sick, you have said everything. Shakespeare was a dolt. If there had been no Voltaire, it would not have been necessary to create one.' Etc. I had been invited for the weekend and I intended to stay; none of us ever left Vereker alone when we came upon him in one of his moods. He frequently threatened suicide and six or seven times attempted it but, in every case, there was someone on hand to prevent him. Once, I remember, he got me out of bed late at night at my own apartment. 'I'm going through with it this time,' he said, and darted into the bathroom. He was fumbling

around for some poison in the medicine chest, which fortunately contained none, when I ran in and pleaded with him. 'You have so many things yet to do,' I said to him. 'Yes,' he said, 'and so many people yet to insult.' He talked brilliantly all night long, and drank up a bottle of cognac that I had got to send to my father.

I had gone to the bathroom for a shower, the time he invited me to his lady's house, when he stalked into the room. 'Get out of that tub, you common housebreaker,' he said, 'or I shall summon the police!' I laughed, of course, and went on bathing. I was rubbing myself with a towel when the police arrived – he had sent for them! Vereker would have made an excellent actor;

he convinced the police that he had never seen me before in his life. I was arrested, taken away, and locked up for the night. A few days later I got a note from Vereker. 'I shall never ask you to my house again,' he wrote, 'after the way I acted last Saturday.' His repentances, while whimsical, were always as complete as the erratic charades which called them forth. He was unpredictable and, at times, difficult, but he was always stimulating. Sometimes he keyed you up to a point beyond which, you felt, you could not go.

Vereker had a close escape from death once which I shall never forget. A famous American industrialist had invited a number of American writers and some visiting English men of letters out to his Long Island place. We were to make the trip in a huge bus that had been chartered for the purpose. Vereker came along and insisted, when we reached Long Island, on driving the bus. It was an icy night and he would put on the brakes at a curve, causing the heavy vehicle to skid ponderously. Several times we surged perilously near to a ditch and once the bus snapped off a big tree like a match. I remember that H. G. Bennett was along, and Arnold Wells, the three Sitwells, and four or five Waughs. One of them finally shut off the ignition and another struck Vereker over the head with a crank. His friends were furious. When the car stopped, we carried him outside and put him down on the hard, cold ground. Marvin Deane, the critic, held Vereker's head, which was bleeding profusely, in his lap, looked up at the busload of writers, and said: 'You might have killed him! And he is a greater genius that any of you!' It was superb. Then the amazing Vereker opened his eyes. 'That goes for me, too,' he said, and closed them again.

We hurried him to a hospital, where, in two days, he was on his feet again; he left the hospital without a word to anybody, and we all chipped in to pay the bill. Vereker had some money at the time which his mother had given him but, as he said, he needed it. 'I am glad he is up and out,' I said to the nurse who had taken care of him. 'So am I,' she said. Vereker affected everybody the same way.

Some time after this we all decided to make up a fund and send Vereker to Europe to write. His entire output, I had discovered, consisted of only twenty or thirty pages, most of them bearing the round stain of liquor glasses; one page was the beginning of a play done more or less in the style of Gertrude Stein. It seemed to me as brilliant as anything of its kind.

We got together about fifteen hundred dollars and I was delegated to approach Vereker, as tactfully as possible. We knew that it was folly for him to go on the way he was, dissipating his talent; for weeks he had been in one of his blackest moods: he would call on people, drink up their rye, wrench light-brackets off the walls, hurl scintillating gibes at his friends and at the accepted literary masters of all time, through whose superficiality Vereker saw more clearly, I think, than anybody else I have ever known. He would end up by bursting into tears. 'Here, but for the gracelessness of God,' he would shout, 'stands the greatest writer in the history of the world!' We felt that, despite Vereker's drunken exaggeration, there was more than a grain of truth in what he said: certainly nobody else we ever met had, so utterly, the fire of genius that blazed in Vereker, if outward manifestations meant anything.

He would never try for a Guggenheim fellowship. 'Guggenheim follow-sheep!' he would snarl. 'Fall in line, all you little men! Don't talk to me about Good-in-time fellowships!' He would go on that way, sparklingly, for an hour, his tirade finally culminating in one of those remarkable fits of temper in which he could rip up any apartment at all, no matter whose, in less than fifteen minutes.

Vereker, much to my surprise and gratification, took the fifteen hundred dollars without making a scene. I had suspected that he might denounce us all, that he might go into one of his brilliant philippics against Money, that he might even threaten again to take his life, for it had been several months since he had attempted suicide. But no; he snarled a bit, it is true, but he accepted the money. 'I'm cheap at twice the price,' he said.

It was the most money Vereker had ever had in his life and of course we should have known better than to let him have it all at once. The night of the day I gave it to him he cut a wide swath in the cheaper West Side night clubs and in Harlem, spent three hundred dollars, insulted several women, and figured in fist fights with a policeman, two taxi-drivers, and two husbands, all of whom won. We instantly decided to arrange his passage on a ship that was sailing for Cherbourg three nights later. Somehow or other we kept him out of trouble until the night of the sailing, when we gave a going-away party for him at Marvin Deane's house. Everybody was there: Gene Tunney, Sir Hubert Wilkins, Count von Luckner, Edward Bernays, and the literary and artistic crowd generally. Vereker got frightfully drunk. He denounced every-body at the party and also Hugh Walpole, Joseph Conrad, Crane, Henry James, Hardy, and Meredith. He dwelt on the subject of 'Jude the Obscure.' 'Jude the Obscure,' he would shout, 'Jude the Obscene, June the Obscude, Obs the June Moon.' He combined with his penetrating critical evaluations and his rare creative powers a certain unique fantasy not unlike that of Lewis Carroll. I once told him so. 'Not unlike your goddam grandmother!' he screamed. He was sensitive; he hated to be praised to his face; and then of course he held the works of Carroll in a certain disesteem.

Thus the party went on. Everybody was speechless, spellbound, listening to Elliot Vereker. You could not miss his force. He was always the one person in a room. When it got to be eleven o'clock, I felt that we had better round up Vereker and start for the docks, for the boat sailed at midnight. He was nowhere to be found. We were alarmed. We searched every room, looked under beds, and into closets, but he was gone. Some of us ran downstairs and out into the street, asking cab-drivers and passersby if they had seen him, a gaunt, tall, wild man with his hair in his eyes. Nobody had. It was almost eleven-thirty when somebody thought to look on the roof, to which there was access by a ladder through a trapdoor. Vereker was there. He lay sprawled on his face, the back of his head crushed in by a blow from some heavy instrument, probably a bottle. He was quite dead. 'The world's loss,' murmured Deane, as he looked down at the pitiful dust so lately the most burning genius we had ever been privileged to know, 'is Hell's gain.'

I think we all felt that way.

Snapshot of a Dog

I RAN across a dim photograph of him the other day, going through some old things. He's been dead twenty-five years. His name was Rex (my two brothers and I named him when we were in our early teens) and he was a bull terrier. 'An American bull terrier,' we used to say, proudly; none of your English bulls. He had one brindle eye that sometimes made him look like a clown and sometimes reminded you of a politician with derby hat and cigar. The rest of him was white except for a brindle saddle that always seemed to be slipping off and a brindle stocking on a hind leg. Nevertheless, there was a nobility about him. He was big and muscular and beautifully made. He never lost his dignity even when trying to accomplish the extravagant tasks my brothers and myself used to set for him. One of these was the bringing of a ten-foot wooden rail into the yard through the back gate. We would throw it out into the alley and tell him to go get it. Rex was as powerful as a wrestler, and there were not many things that he couldn't manage somehow to get hold of with his great jaws and lift or drag to wherever he wanted to put them, or wherever we wanted them put. He would catch the rail at the balance and lift it clear of the ground and trot with great confidence toward the gate. Of course, since the gate was only four feet wide or so, he couldn't bring the rail in broadside. He found that out when he got a few terrific jolts, but he wouldn't give up. He finally figured out how to do it, by dragging the rail, holding onto one end, growling. He got a great, wagging satisfaction out of his work. We used to bet kids who had never seen Rex in action that he could catch a baseball thrown as high as they could throw it. He almost never let us down. Rex could hold a baseball with ease in his mouth, in one cheek, as if it were a chew of tobacco.

He was a tremendous fighter, but he never started fights. I don't believe he liked to get into them, despite the fact that he came from a line of fighters. He never went for another dog's throat but for one of its ears (that teaches a dog a lesson), and he would get his grip, close his eyes, and hold on. He could hold on for hours. His longest fight lasted from dusk until almost pitch-dark, one Sunday. It was fought in East Main Street in Columbus with a large, snarly nondescript that belonged to a big coloured man. When Rex finally got his ear grip, the brief whirlwind of snarling turned to screeching. It was frightening to listen to and to watch. The Negro boldly picked the dogs up somehow and began swinging them around his head, and finally let them fly like a hammer in a hammer throw, but although they landed ten feet away with a great plump, Rex still held on.

The two dogs eventually worked their way to the middle of the car tracks, and after a while two or three streetcars were held up by the fight. A motorman tried to pry Rex's jaws open with a switch rod; somebody lighted a fire and made a torch of a stick and held that to Rex's tail, but he paid no attention. In the end, all the residents and storekeepers in the neighbourhood were on hand, shouting this, suggesting that. Rex's joy of battle, when battle was joined, was almost tranquil. He had a kind of pleasant expression during fights, not a vicious one, his eyes closed in what would have seemed to be sleep had it not been for the turmoil of the struggle. The Oak Street Fire Department finally had to be sent for – I don't know why nobody thought of it sooner. Five or six pieces of apparatus arrived, followed by a battalion chief. A hose was attached and a powerful stream of water was turned on the dogs. Rex held on for several moments more while the torrent buffeted him about like a log in a freshet. He was a hundred yards away from where the fight started when he finally let go.

The story of that Homeric fight got all around town, and some of our relatives looked upon the incident as a blot on the family name. They insisted that we get rid of Rex, but we were very happy with him, and nobody could have made us give him up. We would have left town with him first, along any road there was to go. It would have been different, perhaps, if he had ever started fights, or looked for trouble. But he had a gentle disposition. He never bit a person in the ten strenuous years that he lived, nor ever growled at anyone except prowlers. He killed cats, that is true, but quickly and neatly and without especial malice, the way men kill certain animals. It was the only thing he did that we could never cure him of doing. He never killed, or even chased, a squirrel. I don't know why. He had his own philosophy about such things. He never ran barking after wagons or automobiles. He didn't seem to see the idea in pursuing something you couldn't catch, or something you couldn't do anything with, even if you did catch it. A wagon was one of the things he couldn't tug along with his mighty jaws, and he knew it. Wagons, therefore, were not a part of his world.

Swimming was his favourite recreation. The first time he ever saw a body of water (Alum Creek), he trotted nervously along the steep bank for a while, fell to barking wildly, and finally plunged in from a height of eight feet or more. I shall always remember that shining, virgin dive. Then he swam upstream and back just for the pleasure of it, like a man. It was fun to see him battle upstream against a stiff current, struggling and growling every foot of the way. He had as much fun in the water as any person I have known. You didn't have to throw a stick in the water to get him to go in. Of course, he would bring back a stick to you if you did throw one in. He would even have brought back a piano if you had thrown one in.

That reminds me of the night, way after midnight, when he went a-roving in the light of the moon and brought back a small chest of drawers that he found somewhere – how far from the house nobody ever knew; since it was Rex, it could easily have been half a mile. There were no drawers in the chest when he got it home, and it wasn't a good one – he hadn't taken it out of anybody's house; it was just an old cheap piece that somebody had abandoned on a trash heap. Still, it was something he wanted, probably because it presented a nice problem in transportation. It tested his mettle. We first knew about his achievement when, deep in the night, we heard him trying to get the chest up onto the porch. It sounded as if two or three people were trying to tear the house down. We came downstairs and turned on the porch light. Rex was on the top step trying to pull the thing up, but it had caught somehow and he was just holding his own. I suppose he would have held his own till dawn if we hadn't helped him. The next day we carted the chest miles away and threw it out. If we had thrown it out in a nearby alley, he would have brought it home again, as a small token of his integrity in such matters. After all, he had been taught to carry heavy wooden objects about, and he was proud of his prowess.

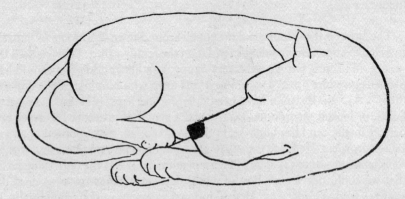

I am glad Rex never saw a trained police dog jump. He was just an amateur jumper himself, but the most daring and tenacious I have ever seen. He would take on any fence we pointed out to him. Six feet was easy for him, and he could do eight by making a tremendous leap and hauling himself over finally by his paws, grunting and straining; but he lived and died without knowing that twelve- and sixteen-foot walls were too much for him. Frequently, after letting him try to go over one for a while, we would have to carry him home. He would never have given up trying.

There was in his world no such thing as the impossible. Even death couldn't beat him down. He died, it is true, but only, as one of his admirers said, after 'straight-arming the death angel' for more than an hour. Late one afternoon he wandered home, too slowly and too uncertainly to be the Rex that had trotted briskly homeward up our avenue for ten years. I think we all knew when he came through the gate that he was dying. He had apparently taken a terrible beating, probably from the owner of some dog that he had got into a fight with. His head and body were scarred. His heavy collar with the teeth marks of many a battle on it was awry; some of the big grass studs in it were sprung loose from the leather. He licked at our hands and, staggering, fell, but got up again. We could see that he was looking for someone. One of his three masters was not home. He did not get home for an hour. During that hour the bull terrier fought against death as he had fought against the cold, strong current of Alum Creek, as he had fought to climb twelve-foot walls. When the person he was waiting for did come through the gate, whistling, ceasing to whistle, Rex walked a few wobbly paces toward him, touched his hand with his muzzle, and fell down again. This time he didn't get up.

The Evening's at Seven

HE HADN'T lighted the upper light in his office all afternoon and now
he turned out the desk lamp. It was a quarter of seven in the evening
and it was dark and raining. He could hear the rattle of taxicabs and
trucks and the sound of horns. Very far off a siren screamed its frenzied scream
and he thought: it's a little like an anguish dying with the years. When it gets
to Third Avenue, or Ninety-fifth Street, he thought, I won't hear it any more.

I'll be home, he said to himself, as he got up slowly and slowly put on his hat
and overcoat (the overcoat was damp), by seven o'clock, if I take a taxicab, I'll
say hello, my dear, and the two yellow lamps will be lighted and my papers
will be on my desk, and I'll say I guess I'll lie down a few minutes before
dinner, and she will say all right and ask two or three small questions about the
day and I'll answer them.

When he got outside of his office, in the street, it was dark and raining and
he lighted a cigarette. A young man went by whistling loudly. Two girls went
by talking gaily, as if it were not raining, as if this were not a time for silence
and for remembering. He called to a taxicab and it stopped and he got in, and
sat there, on the edge of the seat, and the driver finally said where to? He gave
a number he was thinking about.

She was surprised to see him and, he believed, pleased. It was very nice to
be in her apartment again. He faced her, quickly, and it seemed to him as if he
were facing somebody in a tennis game. She would want to know (but wouldn't
ask) why he was, so suddenly, there, and he couldn't exactly say: I gave a
number to a taxi-driver and it was your number. He couldn't say that; and
besides, it wasn't that simple.

It was dark in the room and still raining outside. He lighted a cigarette (not
wanting one) and looked at her. He watched her lovely gestures as of old and
she said he looked tired and he said he wasn't tired and he asked her what she
had been doing and she said oh, nothing much. He talked, sitting awkwardly
on the edge of a chair, and she talked, lying gracefully on a chaise-longue, about
people they had known and hadn't cared about. He was mainly conscious of
the rain outside and of the soft darkness in the room and of other rains and
other darknesses. He got up and walked around the room looking at pictures
but not seeing what they were, and realizing that some old familiar things
gleamed darkly, and he came abruptly face to face with something he had
given her, a trivial and comic thing, and it didn't seem trivial or comic now,
but very large and important and embarrassing, and he turned away from it

and asked after somebody else he didn't care about. Oh, she said, and this and that and so and such (words he wasn't listening to). Yes, he said, absently, I suppose so. Very much, he said (in answer to something else), very much. Oh, she said, laughing at him, not *that* much! He didn't have any idea what they were talking about.

She asked him for a cigarette and he walked over and gave her one, not touching her fingers but very conscious of her fingers. He was remembering a twilight when it had been raining and dark, and he thought of April and kissing and laughter. He noticed a clock on the mantel and it was ten after seven. She said you never used to believe in clocks. He laughed and looked at her for a time and said I have to be at the hotel by seven-thirty, or I don't get anything to eat; it's that sort of hotel. Oh, she said.

He walked to a table and picked up a figurine and set it down again with extreme care, looking out of the corner of his eye at the trivial and comic and gigantic present he had given her. He wondered if he would kiss her and when he would kiss her and if she wanted to be kissed and if she were thinking of it, but she asked him what he would have to eat tonight at his hotel. He said clam chowder. Thursday, he said, they always have clam chowder. Is that the way you know it's Thursday, she said, or is that the way you know it's clam chowder?

He picked up the figurine and put it down again, so that he could look (without her seeing him look) at the clock. It was eighteen minutes after seven and he had the mingled thoughts clocks gave him. You mustn't, she said, miss your meal. (She remembered he hated the word meal.) He turned around quickly and went over quickly and sat beside her and took hold of one of her fingers and she looked at the finger and not at him and he looked at the finger and not at her, both of them as if it were a new and rather remarkable thing.

He got up suddenly and picked up his hat and coat and as suddenly put them down again and took two rapid determined steps toward her, and her eyes seemed a little wider. A bell rang. Oh that, she said, will be Clarice. And they relaxed. He looked a question and she said: my sister; and he said oh, of course. In a minute it was Clarice like a small explosion in the dark and rainy day talking rapidly of this and that: my dear he and this awful and then of all people so nothing loth and I said and he said, if you can imagine that! He picked up his hat and coat and Clarice said hello to him and he said hello and looked at the clock and it was almost twenty-five after seven.

She went to the door with him looking lovely, and it was lovely and dark and raining outside and he laughed and she laughed and she was going to say something but he went out into the rain and waved back at her (not wanting to wave back at her) and she closed the door and was gone. He lighted a cigarette and let his hand get wet in the rain and the cigarette get wet and rain dripped from his hat. A taxicab drove up and the driver spoke to him and he said: what? and: oh, sure. And now he was going home.

He was home by seven-thirty, almost exactly, and he said good evening to old Mrs Spencer (who had the sick husband), and good evening to old Mrs Holmes (who had the sick Pomeranian), and he nodded and smiled and presently he was sitting at his table and the waitress spoke to him. She said: the Mrs will be down, won't she? and he said yes, she will. And the waitress said clam chowder tonight, and consommé: you always take the clam chowder, ain't I right? No, he said, I'll have the consommé.

The Greatest Man in the World

LOOKING back on it now, from the vantage point of 1940, one can only marvel that it hadn't happened long before it did. The United States of America had been, ever since Kitty Hawk, blindly constructing the elaborate petard by which, sooner or later, it must be hoist. It was inevitable that some day there would come roaring out of the skies a national hero of insufficient intelligence, background, and character successfully to endure the mounting orgies of glory prepared for aviators who stayed up a long time or flew a great distance. Both Lindbergh and Byrd, fortunately for national decorum and international amity, had been gentlemen; so had our other famous aviators. They wore their laurels gracefully, withstood the awful weather of publicity, married excellent women, usually of fine family, and quietly retired to private life and the enjoyment of their varying fortunes. No untoward incidents, on a worldwide scale, marred the perfection of their conduct on the perilous heights of fame. The exception to the rule was, however, bound to occur and it did, in July, 1937, when Jack ('Pal') Smurch, erstwhile mechanic's helper in a small garage in Westfield, Iowa, flew a second-hand, single-motored Bresthaven Dragon-Fly III monoplane all the way around the world, without stopping.

Never before in the history of aviation had such a flight as Smurch's ever been dreamed of. No one had even taken seriously the weird floating auxiliary gas tanks, invention of the mad New Hampshire professor of astronomy, Dr Charles Lewis Gresham, upon which Smurch placed full reliance. When the garage worker, a slightly built, surly, unprepossessing young man of twenty-two, appeared at Roosevelt Field early in July, 1937, slowly chewing a great quid of scrap tobacco, and announced 'Nobody ain't seen no flyin' yet,' the newspapers touched briefly and satirically upon his projected twenty-five-thousand-mile flight. Aeronautical and automotive experts dismissed the idea curtly, implying that it was a hoax, a publicity stunt. The rusty, battered, second-hand plane wouldn't go. The Gresham auxiliary tanks wouldn't work. It was simply a cheap joke.

Smurch, however, after calling on a girl in Brooklyn who worked in the flap-folding department of a large paper-box factory, a girl whom he later described as his 'sweet patootie,' climbed nonchalantly into his ridiculous plane at dawn of the memorable seventh of July, 1937, spit a curve of tobacco juice into the still air, and took off, carrying with him only a gallon of bootleg gin and six pounds of salami.

*

When the garage boy thundered out over the ocean the papers were forced to record, in all seriousness, that a mad, unknown young man – his name was variously misspelled – had actually set out upon a preposterous attempt to span the world in a rickety, one-engined contraption, trusting to the long-distance refuelling device of a crazy schoolmaster. When, nine days later, without having stopped once, the tiny plane appeared above San Francisco Bay, headed for New York, spluttering and choking, to be sure, but still magnificently and miraculously aloft, the headlines, which long since had crowded everything else off the front page – even the shooting of the Governor of Illinois by the Vileti gang – swelled to unprecedented size, and the news stories began to run to twenty-five and thirty columns. It was noticeable, however, that the accounts of the epoch-making flight touched rather lightly upon the aviator himself. This was not because facts about the hero as a man were too meagre, but because they were too complete.

Reporters, who had been rushed out to Iowa when Smurch's plane was first sighted over the little French coast town of Serly-le-Mer, to dig up the story of the great man's life, had promptly discovered that the story of his life could not be printed. His mother, a sullen short-order cook in a shack restaurant on the edge of a tourists' camping ground near Westfield, met all inquiries as to her son with an angry 'Ah, the hell with him; I hope he drowns.' His father appeared to be in jail somewhere for stealing spotlights and laprobes from tourists' automobiles; his young brother, a weak-minded lad, had but recently escaped from the Preston, Iowa, Reformatory and was already wanted in several Western towns for the theft of money-order blanks from post offices. These alarming discoveries were still piling up at the very time that Pal Smurch, the greatest hero of the twentieth century, blear-eyed, dead for sleep, half-starved, was piloting his crazy junk-heap high above the region in which the lamentable story of his private life was being unearthed, headed for New York and a greater glory than any man of his time had ever known.

The necessity for printing some account in the papers of the young man's career and personality had led to a remarkable predicament. It was of course impossible to reveal the facts, for a tremendous popular feeling in favour of the young hero had sprung up, like a grass fire, when he was halfway across Europe on his flight around the globe. He was, therefore, described as a modest chap, taciturn, blond, popular with his friends, popular with girls. The only available snapshot of Smurch, taken at the wheel of a phony automobile in a cheap photo studio at an amusement park, was touched up so that the little vulgarian looked quite handsome. His twisted leer was smoothed into a pleasant smile. The truth was, in this way, kept from the youth's ecstatic compatriots; they did not dream that the Smurch family was despised and feared by its neighbours in the obscure Iowa town, nor that the hero himself, because of numerous unsavoury exploits, had come to be regarded in Westfield as a nuisance and a menace. He had, the reporters discovered, once knifed the principal of his high school – not mortally, to be sure, but he had knifed him; and on another occasion, surprised in the act of stealing an altarcloth from a church, he had bashed the sacristan over the head with a pot of Easter lilies; for each of these offences he had served a sentence in the reformatory.

Inwardly, the authorities, both in New York and in Washington, prayed that an understanding Providence might, however awful such a thing seemed, bring disaster to the rusty, battered plane and its illustrious pilot, whose un-heard-of flight had aroused the civilized world to hosannas of hysterical praise. The authorities were convinced that the character of the renowned aviator

was such that the limelight of adulation was bound to reveal him, to all the world, as a congenital hooligan mentally and morally unequipped to cope with his own prodigious fame. 'I trust,' said the Secretary of State, at one of many secret Cabinet meetings called to consider the national dilemma, 'I trust that his mother's prayer will be answered,' by which he referred to Mrs Emma Smurch's wish that her son might be drowned. It was, however, too late for that – Smurch had leaped the Atlantic and then the Pacific as if they were mill-ponds. At three minutes after two o'clock on the afternoon of July 17, 1937, the garage boy brought his idiotic plane into Roosevelt Field for a perfect three-point landing.

It had, of course, been out of the question to arrange a modest little reception for the greatest flier in the history of the world. He was received at Roosevelt Field with such elaborate and pretentious ceremonies as rocked the world. Fortunately, however, the worn and spent hero promptly swooned, had to be removed bodily from his plane, and was spirited from the field without having opened his mouth once. Thus he did not jeopardize the dignity of this first reception, a reception illumined by the presence of the Secretaries of War and the Navy, Mayor Michael J. Moriarity of New York, the Premier of Canada, Governors Fanniman, Groves, McFeely, and Critchfield, and a brilliant array of European diplomats. Smurch did not, in fact, come to in time to take part in the gigantic hullabaloo arranged at City Hall for the next day. He was rushed to a secluded nursing home and confined in bed. It was nine days before he was able to get up, or to be more exact, before he was permitted to get up. Meanwhile the greatest minds in the country, in solemn assembly, had arranged a secret conference of city, state, and government officials, which Smurch was to attend for the purpose of being instructed in the ethics and behaviour of heroism.

On the day that the little mechanic was finally allowed to get up and dress and, for the first time in two weeks, took a great chew of tobacco, he was permitted to receive the newspapermen – this by way of testing him out. Smurch did not wait for questions. 'Youse guys,' he said – and the *Times* man winced – 'youse guys can tell the cock-eyed world dat I put it over on Lindbergh, see? Yeh – an' made an ass o' them two frogs.' The 'two frogs' was a reference to a pair of gallant French fliers who, in attempting a flight only halfway round the world, had, two weeks before, unhappily been lost at sea. The *Times* man was bold enough, at this point, to sketch out for Smurch the accepted formula for interviews in cases of this kind; he explained that there should be no arrogant statements belittling the achievements of other heroes, particularly heroes of foreign nations. 'Ah, the hell with that,' said Smurch. 'I did it, see? I did it, an' I'm talkin' about it.' And he did talk about it.

None of this extraordinary interview was, of course, printed. On the contrary, the newspapers, already under the disciplined direction of a secret directorate created for the occasion and composed of statesmen and editors, gave out to a panting and restless world that 'Jacky,' as he had been arbitrarily nicknamed, would consent to say only that he was very happy and that anyone could have done what he did. 'My achievement has been, I fear, slightly exaggerated,' the *Times* man's article had him protest, with a modest smile. These newspaper stories were kept from the hero, a restriction which did not serve to abate the rising malevolence of his temper. The situation was, indeed, extremely grave, for Pal Smurch was, as he kept insisting, 'rarin' to go.' He could not much longer be kept from a nation clamorous to lionize him. It was the most desperate crisis the United States of America had faced since the sinking of the *Lusitania*.

On the afternoon of the twenty-seventh of July, Smurch was spirited away to a conference-room in which were gathered mayors, governors, government officials, behaviourist psychologists, and editors. He gave them each a limp, moist paw and a brief unlovely grin. 'Hah ya?' he said. When Smurch was seated, the Mayor of New York arose and, with obvious pessimism, attempted to explain what he must say and how he must act when presented to the world, ending his talk with a high tribute to the hero's courage and integrity. The Mayor was followed by Governor Fanniman of New York, who, after a touching declaration of faith, introduced Cameron Spottiswood, Second Secretary of the American Embassy in Paris, the gentleman selected to coach Smurch in the amenities of public ceremonies. Sitting in a chair, with a soiled yellow tie in his hand and his shirt open at the throat, unshaved, smoking a rolled cigarette, Jack Smurch listened with a leer on his lips. 'I get ya, I get ya,' he cut in, nastily. 'Ya want me to ack like a softy, huh? Ya want me to ack like that – – baby-face Lindbergh, huh? Well, nuts to that, see?' Everyone took in his breath sharply; it was a sigh and a hiss. 'Mr Lindbergh,' began a United States Senator, purple with rage, 'and Mr Byrd –' Smurch, who was paring his nails with a jackknife, cut in again. 'Byrd!' he exclaimed. 'Aw fa God's sake, *dat* big –' Somebody shut off his blasphemies with a sharp word. A new-comer had entered the room. Everyone stood up, except Smurch, who, still busy with his nails, did not even glance up. 'Mr Smurch,' said someone, sternly, 'the President of the United States!' It had been thought that the presence of the Chief Executive might have a chastening effect upon the young hero, and the former had been, thanks to the remarkable co-operation of the press, secretly brought to the obscure conference-room.

A great, painful silence fell. Smurch looked up, waved a hand at the President. 'How ya comin'?' he asked, and began rolling a fresh cigarette. The silence deepened. Someone coughed in a strained way. 'Geez, it's hot, ain't it?' said Smurch. He loosened two more shirt buttons, revealing a hairy chest and the tattooed word 'Sadie' enclosed in a stencilled heart. The great and important men in the room, faced by the most serious crisis in recent American history, exchanged worried frowns. Nobody seemed to know how to proceed. 'Come awn, come awn,' said Smurch. 'Let's get the hell out of here! When do I start cuttin' in on de parties, huh? And what's they goin' to be *in* it?' He rubbed a thumb and forefinger together meaningly. 'Money!' exclaimed a state senator, shocked, pale. 'Yeh, money,' said Pal, flipping his cigarette out of a window. 'An' big money.' He began rolling a fresh cigarette. 'Big money,' he repeated, frowning over the rice paper. He tilted back in his chair, and leered at each gentleman, separately, the leer of an animal that knows its power, the leer of a leopard loose in a bird-and-dog shop. 'Aw fa God's sake, let's get some place where it's cooler,' he said. 'I been cooped up plenty for three weeks!'

Smurch stood up and walked over to an open window, where he stood staring down into the street, nine floors below. The faint shouting of newsboys floated up to him. He made out his name. 'Hot dog!' he cried, grinning, ecstatic. He leaned out over the sill. 'You tell 'em, babies!' he shouted down. 'Hot diggity dog!' In the tense little knot of men standing behind him, a quick

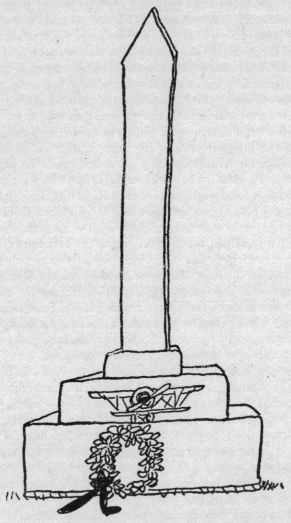

mad impulse flared up. An unspoken word of appeal, of command, seemed to ring through the room. Yet it was deadly silent. Charles K. L. Brand, secretary to the Mayor of New York City, happened to be standing nearest Smurch; he looked inquiringly at the President of the United States. The President, pale, grim, nodded shortly. Brand, a tall, powerfully built man, once a tackle at Rutgers, stepped forward, seized the greatest man in the world by his left shoulder and the seat of his pants, and pushed him out the window.

'My God, he's fallen out the window!' cried a quick-witted editor.

'Get me out of here!' cried the President. Several men sprang to his side and he was hurriedly escorted out of a door toward a side-entrance of the building. The editor of the Associated Press took charge, being used to such things. Crisply he ordered certain men to leave, others to stay; quickly he outlined a story which all the papers were to agree on, sent two men to the street to handle that end of the tragedy, commanded a Senator to sob and two Congressmen to go to pieces nervously. In a word, he skilfully set the stage for the gigantic task that was to follow, the task of breaking to a grief-stricken world the sad story of the untimely, accidental death of its most illustrious and spectacular figure.

The funeral was, as you know, the most elaborate, the finest, the solemnest, and the saddest ever held in the United States of America. The monument in Arlington Cemetery, with its clean white shaft of marble and the simple device of a tiny plane carved on its base, is a place for pilgrims, in deep reverence, to visit. The nations of the world paid lofty tributes to little Jacky Smurch, America's greatest hero. At a given hour there were two minutes of silence throughout the nation. Even the inhabitants of the small, bewildered town of Westfield, Iowa, observed this touching ceremony; agents of the Department of Justice saw to that. One of them was especially assigned to stand grimly in the doorway of a little shack restaurant on the edge of the tourists' camping ground just outside the town. There, under his stern scrutiny, Mrs Emma Smurch bowed her head above two hamburger steaks sizzling on her grill – bowed her head and turned away, so that the Secret Service man could not see the twisted, strangely familiar, leer on her lips.

One Is a Wanderer

THE walk up Fifth Avenue through the slush of the sidewalks and the dankness of the air had tired him. The dark was coming quickly down, the dark of a February Sunday evening, and that vaguely perturbed him. He didn't want to go 'home,' though, and get out of it. It would be gloomy and close in his hotel room, and his soiled shirts would be piled on the floor of the closet where he had been flinging them for weeks, where he had been flinging them for months, and his papers would be disarranged on the tops of the tables and on the desk, and his pipes would be lying around, the pipes he had smoked determinedly for a while only to give them up, as he always did, to go back to cigarettes. He turned into the street leading to his hotel, walking slowly, trying to decide what to do with the night. He had had too many nights alone. Once he had enjoyed being alone. Now it was hard to be alone. He couldn't read any more, or write, at night. Books he tossed aside after nervously flipping through them; the writing he tried to do turned into spirals and circles and squares and empty faces.

I'll just stop in, he thought, and see if there are any messages; I'll see if there have been any phone calls. He hadn't been back to the hotel, after all, for – let's see – for almost five hours; just wandering around. There might be some messages. I'll just stop in, he thought, and see; and maybe I'll have one brandy. I don't want to sit there in the lobby again and drink brandy; I don't want to do that.

He didn't go through the revolving doors of the hotel, though. He went on past the hotel and over to Broadway. A man asked him for some money. A shabbily dressed woman walked by, muttering. She had what he called the New York Mouth, a grim, set mouth, a strained, querulous mouth, a mouth that told of suffering and discontent. He looked in the window of a cane-and-umbrella shop and in the window of a cheap restaurant, a window holding artificial pie and cake, a cup of cold coffee, a plate of artificial vegetables. He got into the shoving and pushing and halting and slow flowing of Broadway. A big cop with a red face was striking his hands together and kidding with a couple of girls whom he had kept from crossing the street against a red light. A thin man in a thin overcoat watched them out of thin, emotionless eyes.

It was a momentary diversion to stand in front of the book counter in the drugstore at Forty-fifth Street and Broadway and look at the books, cheap editions of ancient favourites, movie editions of fairly recent best-sellers. He picked up some of the books and opened them and put them down again, but there was nothing he wanted to read. He walked over to the soda counter and sat down and asked for hot chocolate. It warmed him up a little and he thought about going to the movie at the Paramount; it was a movie with action and guns and airplanes, and Myrna Loy, the kind of movie that didn't bother you. He walked down to the theatre and stood there a minute, but he didn't buy a ticket. After all, he had been to one movie that day. He thought about going to the office. It would be quiet there, nobody would be there; maybe he could get some work done; maybe he could answer some of the letters he had been putting off for so long.

It was too gloomy, it was too lonely. He looked around the office for a while, sat down at his typewriter, tapped out the alphabet on a sheet of paper, took a paper-clip, straightened it, cleaned the 'e' and the 'o' on the typewriter, and put the cover over it. He never remembered to put the cover over the typewriter when he left in the evening. I never, as a matter of fact, remember anything, he thought. It is because I keep trying not to; I keep trying not to remember anything. It is an empty and cowardly thing, not to remember. It might lead you anywhere; no, it might stop you, it might stop you from getting anywhere. Out of remembrance comes everything; out of remembrance comes a great deal, anyway. You can't do anything if you don't let yourself remember things. He began to whistle a song because he found himself about to remember things, and he knew what things they would be, things that would bring a grimace to his mouth and to his eyes, disturbing fragments of old sentences, old scenes and gestures, hours, and rooms, and tones of voice, and the sound of a voice crying. All voices cry differently; there are no two voices in the whole world that cry alike; they're like footsteps and fingerprints and the faces of friends . . .

He became conscious of the song he was whistling. He got up from the chair in front of his covered typewriter, turned out the light, and walked out of the room to the elevator, and there he began to sing the last part of the song, waiting for the elevator. 'Make my bed and light the light, for I'll be home late tonight, blackbird, bye bye.' He walked over to his hotel through the slush and the damp gloom and sat down in a chair in the lobby, without taking off his overcoat. He didn't want to sit there long.

'Good evening, sir,' said the waiter who looked after the guests in the lobby. 'How are you?'

'I'm fine, thank you,' he said. 'I'm fine. I'll have a brandy, with water on the side.'

He had several brandies. Nobody came into the lobby that he knew. People were gone to all kinds of places Sunday night. He hadn't looked at his letter box back of the clerk's desk when he came in, to see if there were any messages there. That was a kind of game he played, or something. He never looked for messages until after he had had a brandy. He'd look now after he had another brandy. He had another brandy and looked. 'Nothing,' said the clerk at the desk, looking too.

He went back to his chair in the lobby and began to think about calling up people. He thought of the Graysons. He saw the Graysons, not as they would be, sitting in their apartment, close together and warmly, but as he and Lydia had seen them in another place and another year. The four had shared a bright vacation once. He remembered various attitudes and angles and lights and colours of that vacation. There is something about four people, two couples, that like each other and get along; that have a swell time; that grow in intimacy and understanding. One's life is made up of twos, and of fours. The Graysons understood the nice little arrangements of living, the twos and fours. Two is company, four is a party, three is a crowd. One is a wanderer.

No, not the Graysons. Somebody would be there on Sunday night, some couple, some two; somebody he knew, somebody they had known. That is the way life is arranged. One arranges one's life – no, two arrange their life – in terms of twos, and fours, and sixes. Marriage does not make two people one, it makes two people two. It's sweeter that way, and simpler. All this, he thought, summoning the waiter, is probably very silly and sentimental. I must look out that I don't get to that state of tipsiness where all silly and lugubrious things seem brilliant divinations of mine, sound and original ideas and theories. What I must remember is that such things are sentimental and tiresome and grow out of not working enough and out of too much brandy. That's what I must remember. It is no good remembering that it takes four to make a party, two to make a house.

People living alone, after all, have made a great many things. Let's see, what have people living alone made? Not love, of course, but a great many other things: money, for example, and black marks on white paper. 'Make this one a double brandy,' he told the waiter. Let's see, who that I *know* has made something alone, who that I know *of* has made something alone? Robert Browning? No, not Robert Browning. Odd, that Robert Browning would be the first person he thought of. 'And had you only heard me play one tune, or viewed me from a window, not so soon with you would such things fade as with the rest.' He had written that line of Browning's in a book once for Lydia, or Lydia had written it in a book for him; or they had both written it in a book for each other. 'Not so soon with you would such things fade as with the rest.' Maybe he didn't have it exactly right; it was hard to remember now, after so long a time. It didn't matter. 'Not so soon with you would such things fade as with the rest.' The fact is that all things do fade; with twos, and with fours; all bright things, all attitudes and angles and lights and colours, all growing in intimacy and understanding.

I think maybe I'll call the Bradleys, he thought, getting up out of his chair. And don't, he said to himself, standing still a moment, don't tell me you're not cockeyed now, because you are cockeyed now, just as you said you wouldn't be when you got up this morning and had orange juice and coffee and determined to get some work done, a whole lot of work done; just as you said you wouldn't be but you knew you would be, all right. You knew you would be, all right.

The Bradleys, he thought, as he walked slowly around the lobby, avoiding the phone booths, glancing at the headlines of the papers on the newsstand, the Bradleys have that four-square thing, that two-square thing – that two-square thing, God damn them! Somebody described it once in a short story that he had read: an intimacy that you could feel, that you could almost take hold of, when you went into such a house, when you went into where such people were, a warming thing, a nice thing to be in, like being in warm sea water; a little embarrassing, too, yes, damned embarrassing, too. He would only take a damp blanket into that warmth. That's what I'd take into that warmth, he told himself, a damp blanket. They know it, too. Here comes old Kirk again with his damp blanket. It isn't because I'm so damned unhappy – I'm not so damned unhappy – it's because they're so damned happy, damn them. Why don't they know that? Why don't they do something about it? What right have they got to flaunt it at me, for God's sake? . . . Look here now, he told himself, you're getting too cockeyed now; you're getting into one of those states, you're getting into one of those states that Marianne keeps telling you about, one of those states when people don't like to have you around . . . Marianne, he thought. He went back to his chair, ordered another brandy, and thought about Marianne.

She doesn't know how I start my days, he thought, she only knows how I end them. She doesn't even know how I started my life. She only knows me when night gets me. If I could only be the person she wants me to be, why, then I would be fine, I would be the person she wants me to be. Like ordering a new dress from a shop, a new dress that nobody ever wore, a new dress that nobody's ever going to wear but you. I wouldn't get mad suddenly, about nothing. I wouldn't walk out of places suddenly, about nothing. I wouldn't snarl at nice people. About what she says is nothing. I wouldn't be 'unbearable.' Her word, 'unbearable.' A female word, female as a cat. Well, she's right, too, I am unbearable. 'George,' he said to the waiter, 'I am unbearable, did you know that?' 'No, sir, I did not, sir,' said the waiter. 'I would not call you unbearable, Mr Kirk.' 'Well, you don't know, George,' he said. 'It just happens that I am unbearable. It just happened that way. It's a long story.' 'Yes, sir,' said the waiter.

I could call up the Mortons, he thought. They'll have twos and fours there, too, but they're not so damned happy that they're unbearable. The Mortons are all right. Now look, the Mortons had said to him, if you and Marianne would only stop fighting and arguing and forever analyzing yourselves and forever analyzing everything, you'd be fine. You'd be fine if you got married and just shut up, just shut up and got married. That would be fine. Yes, sir, that would be fine. Everything would work out all right. You just shut up and get married, you just get married and shut up. Everybody knows that. It is practically the simplest thing in the world. . . . Well, it would be, too, if you were twenty-five maybe; it would be if you were twenty-five, and not forty.

'George,' he said, when the waiter walked over for his empty glass, 'I will be forty-one next November.' 'But that's not old, sir, and that's a long way off,' said George. 'No, it isn't,' he said. 'It's almost here. So is forty-two and forty-three and fifty, and here I am trying to be – do you know what I'm trying to be, George? I'm trying to be happy.' 'We all want to be happy, sir,' said George. 'I would like to see you happy, sir.' 'Oh, you will,' he said. 'You will, George. There's a simple trick to it. You just shut up and get married. But you see, George, I am an analyzer. I am also a rememberer. I have a pocketful of old used years. You put all those things together and they sit in a lobby getting silly and old.' 'I'm very sorry, sir,' said George.

'And I'll have one more drink, George,' he called after the waiter.

He had one more drink. When he looked up at the clock in the lobby it was only 9.30. He went up to his room and, feeling sleepy, he lay down on his bed without turning out the overhead light. When he woke up it was 12.30 by his wristwatch. He got up and washed his face and brushed his teeth and put on a clean shirt and another suit and went back down into the lobby, without looking at the disarranged papers on the tables and on the desk. He went into the dining-room and had some soup and a lamb chop and a glass of milk. There was nobody there he knew. He began to realize that he had to see somebody he knew. He paid his check and went out and got into a cab and gave the driver an address on Fifty-third Street.

There were several people in Dick and Joe's that he knew. There were Dick and Joe, for two – or, rather, for one, because he always thought of them as one; he could never tell them apart. There were Bill Vardon and Mary Wells. Bill Vardon and Mary Wells were a little drunk and gay. He didn't know them very well, but he could sit down with them. . . .

It was after three o'clock when he left the place and got into a cab. 'How are you tonight, Mr Kirk?' asked the driver. The driver's name was Willie. 'I'm fine tonight, Willie,' he said. 'You want to go on somewhere else?' asked Willie. 'Not tonight, Willie,' he said. 'I'm going home.' 'Well,' said Willie, 'I guess you're right there, Mr Kirk. I guess you're right about that. These places is all right for what they are – you know what I mean – it's O.K. to kick around in 'em for a while and maybe have a few drinks with your friends, but when you come right down to it, home is the best place there is. Now, you take me, I'm hackin' for ten years, mostly up around here – because why? Because all these places know me; you know that, Mr Kirk. I can get into 'em you might say the same way you do, Mr Kirk – I have a couple drinks in Dick and Joe's maybe or in Tony's or anywheres else I want to go into – hell, I've had drinks in 'em with you, Mr Kirk – like on Christmas night, remember? But I got a home over in Brooklyn and a wife and a couple kids and, boy, I'm tellin' you that's the best place, you know what I mean?'

'You're right, Willie,' he said. 'You're absolutely right, there.'

'You're darn tootin' I am,' said Willie. 'These joints is all right when a man wants a couple drinks or maybe even get a little tight with his friends, that's O.K. with me –'

'Getting tight with friends is O.K. with me, too,' he said to Willie.

'But when a man gets fed up on that kind of stuff, a man wants to go home. Am I right, Mr Kirk?'

'You're absolutely right, Willie,' he said. 'A man wants to go home.'

'Well, here we are, Mr Kirk. Home it is.'

He got out of the cab and gave the driver a dollar and told him to keep the change and went into the lobby of the hotel. The night clerk gave him his key and then put two fingers into the recesses of the letter box. 'Nothing,' said the night clerk.

When he got to his room, he lay down on the bed a while and smoked a cigarette. He found himself feeling drowsy and he got up. He began to take his clothes off, feeling drowsily contented, mistily contented. He began to sing, not loudly, because the man in 711 would complain. The man in 711 was a grey-haired man, living alone . . . an analyzer . . . a rememberer . . .

'Make my bed and light the light, for I'll be home late tonight . . .'

A Box to Hide In

I WAITED till the large woman with the awful hat took up her sack of groceries and went out, peering at the tomatoes and lettuce on her way. The clerk asked me what mine was.

'Have you got a box,' I asked, 'a large box? I want a box to hide in.'

'You want a box?' he asked.

'I want a box to hide in,' I said.

'Whatta you mean?' he said. 'You mean a big box?'

I said I meant a big box, big enough to hold me.

'I haven't got any boxes,' he said. 'Only cartons that cans come in.'

I tried several other groceries and none of them had a box big enough for me to hide in. There was nothing for it but to face life out. I didn't feel strong, and I'd had this overpowering desire to hide in a box for a long time.

'Whatta you mean you want to hide in this box?' one grocer asked me.

'It's a form of escape,' I told him, 'hiding in a box. It circumscribes your worries and the range of your anguish. You don't see people, either.'

'How in the hell do you eat when you're in this box?' asked the grocer. 'How in the hell do you get anything to eat?' I said I had never been in a box and didn't know, but that that would take care of itself.

'Well,' he said, finally, 'I haven't got any boxes, only some pasteboard cartons that cans come in.'

It was the same every place. I gave up when it got dark and the groceries closed, and hid in my room again. I turned out the light and lay on the bed. You feel better when it gets dark. I could have hid in a closet, I suppose, but people are always opening doors. Somebody would find you in a closet. They would be startled and you'd have to tell them why you were in the closet. Nobody pays any attention to a big box lying on the floor. You could stay in it for days and nobody'd think to look in it, not even the cleaning-woman.

My cleaning-woman came the next morning and woke me up. I was still feeling bad. I asked her if she knew where I could get a large box.

'How big a box you want?' she asked.

'I want a box big enough for me to get inside of,' I said. She looked at me with big, dim eyes. There's something wrong with her glands. She's awful but she has a big heart, which makes it worse. She's unbearable, her husband is sick and her children are sick and she is sick too. I got to thinking how pleasant it would be if I were in a box now, and didn't have to see her. I would be in a box right there in the room and she wouldn't know. I wondered if you have a desire to bark or laugh when someone who doesn't know walks by the box you are in. Maybe she would have a spell with her heart, if I did that, and would die right there. The officers and the elevatorman and Mr Gramadge would find us. 'Funny doggone thing happened at the building last night,' the doorman would say to his wife. 'I let in this woman to clean up 10-F and she never come out, see? She's never there more'n an hour, but she never come out, see? So when it got to be time for me to go off duty, why I says to Crennick, who was on the elevator, I says what the hell you suppose has happened to that woman cleans 10-F? He says he didn't know; he says he never seen her after he took her up. So I spoke to Mr Gramadge about it. "I'm sorry to bother you, Mr Gramadge," I says, "but there's something funny about that woman cleans 10-F." So I told him. So he said we better have a look and we all three goes up and knocks on the door and rings the bell, see, and nobody answers so he said we'd have to walk in so Crennick opened the door and we walked in and here was this woman cleans the apartment dead as a herring on the floor and the gentleman that lives there was in a box.' . . .

The cleaning-woman kept looking at me. It was hard to realize she wasn't dead. 'It's a form of escape,' I murmured. 'What say?' she asked, dully.

'You don't know of any large packing boxes, do you?' I asked.

'No, I don't,' she said.

I haven't found one yet, but I still have this overpowering urge to hide in a box. Maybe it will go away, maybe I'll be all right. Maybe it will get worse. It's hard to say.

The Last Flower

A PARABLE IN PICTURES

FOR

ROSEMARY

IN THE WISTFUL HOPE THAT HER

WORLD WILL BE BETTER THAN MINE

WORLD WAR XII, AS EVERYBODY KNOWS,

BROUGHT ABOUT THE COLLAPSE OF CIVILIZATION

TOWNS, CITIES, AND VILLAGES DISAPPEARED
FROM THE EARTH

ALL THE GROVES AND FORESTS WERE
DESTROYED

AND ALL THE GARDENS

AND ALL THE WORKS OF ART

MEN, WOMEN, AND CHILDREN BECAME LOWER
THAN THE LOWER ANIMALS

DISCOURAGED AND DISILLUSIONED, DOGS DESERTED
THEIR FALLEN MASTERS

EMBOLDENED BY THE PITIFUL CONDITION
OF THE FORMER LORDS OF THE EARTH,
RABBITS DESCENDED UPON THEM

BOOKS, PAINTINGS, AND MUSIC DISAPPEARED
FROM THE EARTH, AND HUMAN BEINGS
JUST SAT AROUND, DOING NOTHING

YEARS AND YEARS WENT BY

EVEN THE FEW GENERALS WHO WERE LEFT
FORGOT WHAT THE LAST WAR HAD DECIDED

BOYS AND GIRLS GREW UP TO STARE AT EACH OTHER
BLANKLY, FOR LOVE HAD PASSED FROM THE EARTH

ONE DAY A YOUNG GIRL WHO HAD NEVER
SEEN A FLOWER CHANCED TO COME
UPON THE LAST ONE IN THE WORLD

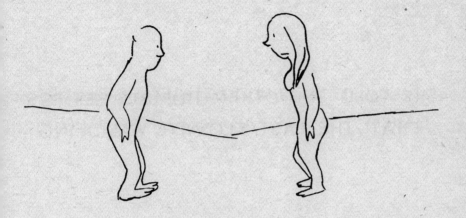

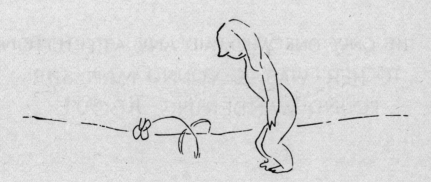

SHE TOLD THE OTHER HUMAN BEINGS
THAT THE LAST FLOWER WAS DYING

THE ONLY ONE WHO PAID ANY ATTENTION
TO HER WAS A YOUNG MAN SHE
FOUND WANDERING ABOUT

TOGETHER THE YOUNG MAN AND THE GIRL
NURTURED THE FLOWER AND IT BEGAN
TO LIVE AGAIN

ONE DAY A BEE VISITED THE FLOWER,
AND A HUMMINGBIRD

BEFORE LONG THERE WERE TWO FLOWERS, AND
THEN FOUR, AND THEN A GREAT MANY

GROVES AND FORESTS FLOURISHED AGAIN

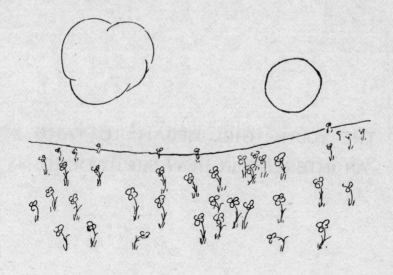

THE YOUNG GIRL BEGAN TO TAKE
AN INTEREST IN HOW SHE LOOKED

THE YOUNG MAN DISCOVERED THAT
TOUCHING THE GIRL WAS PLEASURABLE

LOVE WAS REBORN INTO THE WORLD

THEIR CHILDREN GREW UP STRONG AND HEALTHY
AND LEARNED TO RUN AND LAUGH

DOGS CAME OUT OF THEIR EXILE

THE YOUNG MAN DISCOVERED, BY PUTTING ONE
STONE UPON ANOTHER, HOW TO BUILD A SHELTER

PRETTY SOON EVERYBODY WAS BUILDING SHELTERS

TOWNS, CITIES, AND VILLAGES SPRANG UP

SONG CAME BACK INTO THE WORLD

AND TROUBADOURS AND JUGGLERS

AND TAILORS AND COBBLERS

AND PAINTERS AND POETS

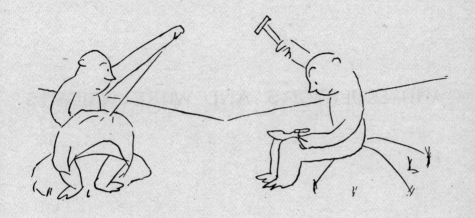

AND SCULPTORS AND WHEELWRIGHTS

AND SOLDIERS

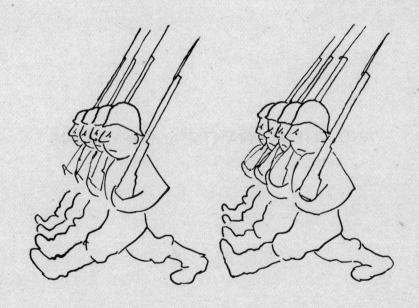

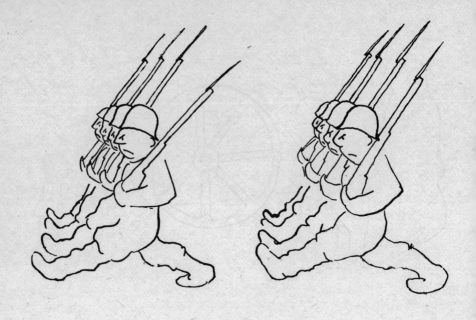

AND LIEUTENANTS AND CAPTAINS

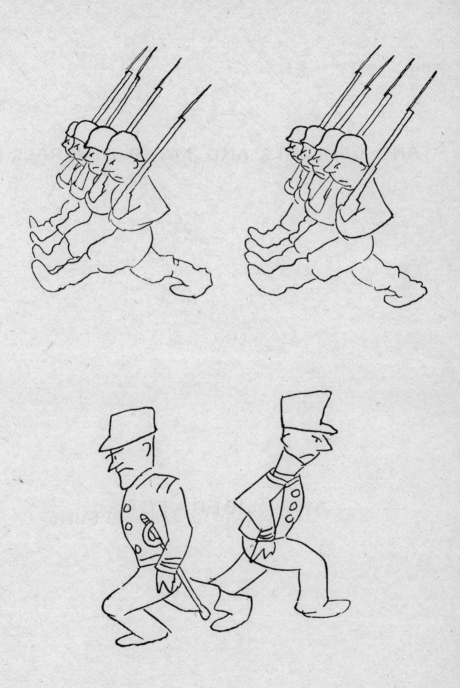

AND GENERALS AND MAJOR-GENERALS

AND LIBERATORS

SOME PEOPLE WENT TO ONE PLACE TO LIVE,
AND SOME TO ANOTHER

BEFORE LONG, THOSE WHO WENT TO LIVE IN THE VALLEYS
WISHED THEY HAD GONE TO LIVE IN THE HILLS

AND THOSE WHO HAD GONE TO LIVE IN THE HILLS
WISHED THEY HAD GONE TO LIVE IN THE VALLEYS

THE LIBERATORS, UNDER THE GUIDANCE OF GOD,
SET FIRE TO THE DISCONTENT

SO PRESENTLY THE WORLD WAS AT WAR AGAIN

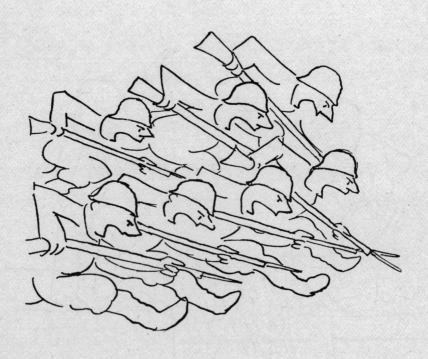

THIS TIME THE DESTRUCTION WAS SO COMPLETE...

THAT NOTHING AT ALL WAS LEFT IN THE WORLD

EXCEPT ONE MAN

AND ONE WOMAN

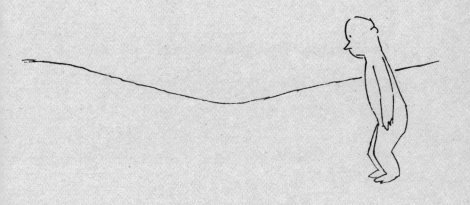

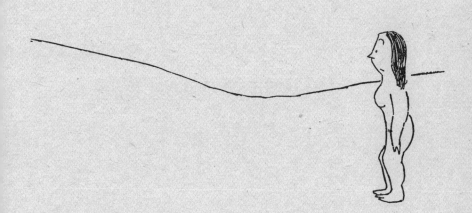

AND ONE FLOWER

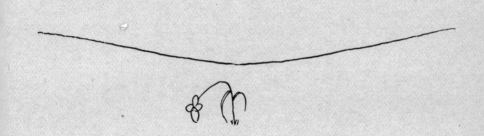

My Life and Hard Times

FOR

MARY A. THURBER

One woman climbed up into the 'These Are My Jewels' statue

The Night the Bed Fell

I SUPPOSE that the high-water mark of my youth in Columbus, Ohio, was the night the bed fell on my father. It makes a better recitation (unless, as some friends of mine have said, one has heard it five or six times) than it does a piece of writing, for it is almost necessary to throw furniture around, shake doors, and bark like a dog, to lend the proper atmosphere and verisimilitude to what is admittedly a somewhat incredible tale. Still, it did take place.

It happened, then, that my father had decided to sleep in the attic one night, to be away where he could think. My mother opposed the notion strongly because, she said, the old wooden bed up there was unsafe: it was wobbly and the heavy headboard would crash down on father's head in case the bed fell, and kill him. There was no dissuading him, however, and at a quarter past ten he closed the attic door behind him and went up the narrow twisting stairs. We later heard ominous creakings as he crawled into bed. Grandfather, who usually slept in the attic bed when he was with us, had disappeared some days before. (On these occasions he was usually gone six or eight days and returned growling and out of temper, with the news that the federal Union was run by a passel of blockheads and that the Army of the Potomac didn't have any more chance than a fiddler's bitch.)

We had visiting us at this time a nervous first cousin of mine named Briggs Beall, who believed that he was likely to cease breathing when he was asleep. It was his feeling that if he were not awakened every hour during the night, he might die of suffocation. He had been accustomed to setting an alarm clock to ring at intervals until morning, but I persuaded him to abandon this. He slept in my room and I told him that I was such a light sleeper that if anybody quit breathing in the same room with me, I would wake instantly. He tested me the first night – which I had suspected he would – by holding his breath after my regular breathing had convinced him I was asleep. I was not asleep, however, and called to him. This seemed to allay his fears a little, but he took the precaution of putting a glass of spirits of camphor on a little table at the head of his bed. In case I didn't arouse him until he was almost gone, he said, he would sniff the camphor, a powerful reviver. Briggs was not the only member of his family who had his crotchets. Old Aunt Melissa Beall (who could whistle like a man, with two fingers in her mouth) suffered under the premonition that she was destined to die on South High Street, because she had been born on South High Street and married on South High Street. Then there was Aunt Sarah Shoaf, who never went to bed at night without the fear that a burglar was going to get in and blow chloroform under her door through a tube. To avert this calamity – for she was in greater dread of anaesthetics than of losing her household goods – she always piled her money, silverware, and other valuables in a neat stack just outside her bedroom, with a note reading: 'This is all I have. Please take it and do not use your chloroform, as this is all I have.' Aunt Gracie Shoaf also had a burglar phobia, but she met it with more fortitude. She was confident that burglars had been getting into her house every night for forty years. The fact that she never missed anything was to her no proof to the contrary. She always claimed that she scared them off before

Some nights she threw them all

they could take anything, by throwing shoes down the hallway. When she went to bed she piled, where she could get at them handily, all the shoes there were about her house. Five minutes after she had turned off the light, she would sit up in bed and say 'Hark!' Her husband, who had learned to ignore the whole situation as long ago as 1903, would either be sound asleep or pretend to be sound asleep. In either case he would not respond to her tugging and pulling, so that presently she would arise, tiptoe to the door, open it slightly and heave a shoe down the hall in one direction, and its mate down the hall in the other direction. Some nights she threw them all, some nights only a couple of pair.

He came to the conclusion that he was suffocating

But I am straying from the remarkable incidents that took place during the night that the bed fell on father. By midnight we were all in bed. The layout of the rooms and the disposition of their occupants is important to an understanding of what later occurred. In the front room upstairs (just under father's attic bedroom) were my mother and my brother Herman, who sometimes sang in his sleep, usually 'Marching Through Georgia' or 'Onward, Christian Soldiers.' Briggs Beall and myself were in a room adjoining this one. My brother Roy was in a room across the hall from ours. Our bull terrier, Rex, slept in the hall.

My bed was an army cot, one of those affairs which are made wide enough to sleep on comfortably only by putting up, flat with the middle section, the two sides which ordinarily hang down like the sideboards of a drop-leaf table. When these sides are up, it is perilous to roll too far toward the edge, for then the cot is likely to tip completely over, bringing the whole bed down on top of one, with a tremendous banging crash. This, in fact, is precisely what happened, about two o'clock in the morning. (It was my mother who, in recalling the scene later, first referred to it as 'the night the bed fell on your father.')

Always a deep sleeper, slow to arouse (I had lied to Briggs), I was at first unconscious of what had happened when the iron cot rolled me onto the floor and toppled over on me. It left me still warmly bundled up and unhurt, for the bed rested above me like a canopy. Hence I did not wake up, only reached the edge of consciousness and went back. The racket, however, instantly awakened my mother, in the next room, who came to the immediate conclusion that her worst dread was realized: the big wooden bed upstairs had fallen on father. She therefore screamed, 'Let's go to your poor father!' It was this shout, rather than the noise of my cot falling, that awakened Herman, in the same room with her. He thought that mother had become, for no apparent reason, hysterical. 'You're all right, Mamma!' he shouted, trying to calm her. They exchanged shout for shout for perhaps ten seconds: 'Let's go to your poor father!' and 'You're all right!' That woke up Briggs. By this time I was conscious of what was going on, in a vague way, but did not yet realize that I was under my bed instead of on it. Briggs, awakening in the midst of loud shouts of fear and apprehension, came to the quick conclusion that he was suffocating and that we were all trying to 'bring him out.' With a low moan, he grasped the glass of camphor at the head of his bed and instead of sniffing it poured it over himself. The room reeked of camphor. 'Ugf, ahfg,' choked Briggs, like a drowning man, for he had almost succeeded in stopping his breath under the deluge of pungent spirits. He leaped out of bed and groped toward the open window, but he came up against one that was closed. With his hand, he beat out the glass, and I could hear it crash and tinkle on the alleyway below. It was at this juncture that I, in trying to get up, had the uncanny sensation of feeling my bed above me! Foggy with sleep, I now suspected, in my turn, that the whole uproar was being made in a frantic endeavour to extricate me from what must be an unheard-of and perilous situation. 'Get me out of this!' I bawled. 'Get me out!' I think I had the nightmarish belief that I was entombed in a mine. 'Gugh,' gasped Briggs, floundering in his camphor.

By this time my mother, still shouting, pursued by Herman, still shouting, was trying to open the door to the attic, in order to go up and get my father's body out of the wreckage. The door was stuck, however, and wouldn't yield. Her frantic pulls on it only added to the general banging and confusion. Roy and the dog were now up, the one shouting questions, the other barking.

Father, farthest away and soundest sleeper of all, had by this time been awakened by the battering on the attic door. He decided that the house was on fire. 'I'm coming, I'm coming!' he wailed in a slow, sleepy voice – it took him many minutes to regain full consciousness. My mother, still believing he was caught under the bed, detected in his 'I'm coming!' the mournful, resigned note of one who is preparing to meet his Maker. 'He's dying!' she shouted.

'I'm all right!' Briggs yelled to reassure her. 'I'm all right!' He still believed that it was his own closeness to death that was worrying mother. I found at last the light switch in my room, unlocked the door, and Briggs and I joined the others at the attic door. The dog, who never did like Briggs, jumped for him – assuming that he was the culprit in whatever was going on – and Roy had to throw Rex and hold him. We could hear father crawling out of bed

Roy had to throw Rex

upstairs. Roy pulled the attic door open, with a mighty jerk, and father came down the stairs, sleepy and irritable but safe and sound. My mother began to weep when she saw him. Rex began to howl. 'What in the name of God is going on here?' asked father.

The situation was finally put together like a gigantic jigsaw puzzle. Father caught a cold prowling around in his bare feet but there were no other bad results. 'I'm glad,' said mother, who always looked on the bright side of things, 'that your grandfather wasn't here.'

The Car We Had to Push

MANY autobiographers, among them Lincoln Steffens and Gertrude Atherton, describe earthquakes their families have been in. I am unable to do this because my family was never in an earthquake, but we went through a number of things in Columbus that were a great deal like earthquakes. I remember in particular some of the repercussions of an old Reo we had that wouldn't go unless you pushed it for quite a way and suddenly let your clutch out. Once, we had been able to start the engine easily by cranking it, but we had had the car for so many years that finally it wouldn't go unless you pushed it and let your clutch out. Of course, it took more than one person to do this; it took sometimes as many as five or six, depending on the grade of the roadway and conditions underfoot. The car was unusual in that the clutch and brake were on the same pedal, making it quite easy to stall the engine after it got started, so that the car would have to be pushed again.

It took sometimes as many as five or six

My father used to get sick at his stomach pushing the car, and very often was unable to go to work. He had never liked the machine, even when it was good, sharing my ignorance and suspicion of all automobiles of twenty years ago and longer. The boys I went to school with used to be able to identify every car as it passed by: Thomas Flyer, Firestone-Columbus, Stevens Duryea, Rambler, Winton, White Steamer, etc. I never could. The only car I was really interested in was one that the Get-Ready Man, as we called him, rode around town in: a big Red Devil with a door in the back. The Get-Ready Man was a lank unkempt elderly gentleman with wild eyes and a deep voice who used to go about shouting at people through a megaphone to prepare for the end of the world. 'GET READY! GET READ-Y!' he would bellow. 'THE WORLLLD IS COMING TO AN END!' His startling exhortations would come up, like summer thunder, at the most unexpected times and in the most surprising places. I remember once during Mantell's production of 'King Lear' at the Colonial Theatre, that the Get-Ready Man added his bawlings to the squealing of Edgar and the ranting of the King and the mouthing of the Fool, rising from somewhere in the

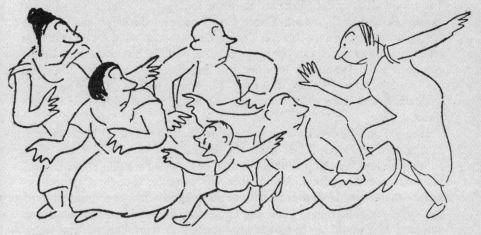

The Get-Ready Man

balcony to join in. The theatre was in absolute darkness and there were rumblings of thunder and flashes of lightning offstage. Neither father nor I, who were there, ever completely got over the scene, which went something like this:

Edgar: Tom's a-cold. – O, do de, do de, do de! – Bless thee from whirlwinds, star-blasting, and taking . . . the foul fiend vexes!

(Thunder off.

Lear: What! Have his daughters brought him to this pass? –
Get-Ready Man: Get ready! Get ready!
Edgar: Pillicock sat on Pillicock-hill: –

Halloo, halloo, loo, loo!
(Lightning flashes.

Get-Ready Man: The Worllld is com-ing to an End!
Fool: This cold night will turn us all to fools and madmen!
Edgar: Take heed o' the foul fiend: obey thy paren –
Get-Ready Man: Get *Rea*-dy!
Edgar: Tom's a-*cold*!
Get-Ready Man: The *Worr*-uld is coming to an end! . . .

They found him finally, and ejected him, still shouting. The Theatre, in our time, has known few such moments.

But to get back to the automobile. One of my happiest memories of it was when, in its eighth year, my brother Roy got together a great many articles from the kitchen, placed them in a square of canvas, and swung this under the car with a string attached to it so that, at a twitch, the canvas would give way and the steel and tin things would clatter to the street. This was a little scheme of Roy's to frighten father, who had always expected the car might explode. It worked perfectly. That was twenty-five years ago, but it is one of the few things in my life I would like to live over again if I could. I don't suppose that I can, now. Roy twitched the string in the middle of a lovely afternoon, on Bryden Road near Eighteenth Street. Father had closed his eyes and, with his hat off, was enjoying a cool breeze. The clatter on the asphalt was tremendously effective: knives, forks, can-openers, pie pans, pot lids, biscuit-cutters, ladles, egg-beaters fell, beautifully together, in a lingering, clamant crash. 'Stop the *car*!' shouted father. 'I can't,' Roy said. 'The engine fell out.' 'God Almighty!' said father, who knew what *that* meant, or knew what it sounded as if it might mean.

It ended unhappily, of course, because we finally had to drive back and pick up the stuff and even father knew the difference between the works of an automobile and the equipment of a pantry. My mother wouldn't have known, however, nor *her* mother. My mother, for instance, thought – or, rather, knew – that it was dangerous to drive an automobile without gasoline: it fried the valves, or something. 'Now don't you dare drive all over town without gasoline!' she would say to us when we started off. Gasoline, oil, and water were much the same to her, a fact that made her life both confusing and perilous. Her greatest dread, however, was the Victrola – we had a very early one, back in the 'Come Josephine in My Flying Machine' days. She had an idea that the Victrola might blow up. It alarmed her, rather than reassured her, to explain that the phonograph was run neither by gasoline nor by electricity. She could only suppose that it was propelled by some newfangled and untested apparatus which was likely to let go at any minute, making us all the victims and martyrs of the wild-eyed Edison's dangerous experiments. The telephone she was comparatively at peace with, except, of course, during storms, when for some reason or other she always took the receiver off the hook and let it hang. She came naturally by her confused and groundless fears, for her own mother lived the latter years of her life in the horrible suspicion that electricity was dripping invisibly all over the house. It leaked, she contended, out of empty sockets if the wall switch had been left on. She would go around screwing in bulbs, and if they lighted up she would hastily and fearfully turn off the wall switch and go back to her *Pearson's* or *Everybody's*, happy in the satisfaction that she had stopped not only a costly but a dangerous leakage. Nothing could ever clear this up for her.

Our poor old Reo came to a horrible end, finally. We had parked it too far from the curb on a street with a car line. It was late at night and the street was

Electricity was leaking all over the house

dark. The first streetcar that came along couldn't get by. It picked up the tired old automobile as a terrier might seize a rabbit and drubbed it unmercifully, losing its hold now and then but catching a new grip a second later. Tyres booped and whooshed, the fenders queeled and graked, the steering-wheel rose up like a spectre and disappeared in the direction of Franklin Avenue with a melancholy whistling sound, bolts and gadgets flew like sparks from a Catherine wheel. It was a splendid spectacle but, of course, saddening to everybody (except the motorman of the streetcar, who was sore). I think some of us broke down and wept. It must have been the weeping that caused grandfather to take on so terribly. Time was all mixed up in his mind; automobiles and the like he never remembered having seen. He apparently gathered, from the talk and excitement and weeping, that somebody had died. Nor did he let go of this delusion. He insisted, in fact, after almost a week in which we strove mightily to divert him, that it was a sin and a shame and a disgrace on the family to put the funeral off any longer. 'Nobody is dead! The automobile is smashed!' shouted my father, trying for the thirtieth time to explain the situation to the old man. 'Was he drunk?' demanded grandfather, sternly. 'Was who drunk?' asked father. 'Zenas,' said grandfather. He had a name for the corpse now: it was his brother Zenas, who, as it happened, *was* dead, but not from driving an automobile while intoxicated. Zenas had died in 1866. A sensitive, rather poetical boy of twenty-one when the Civil War broke out, Zenas had gone to South America – 'just', as he wrote back, 'until it blows over.' Returning after the war had blown over, he caught the same disease that was killing off the chestnut trees in those years, and passed away. It was the only case in history where a tree doctor had to be called in to spray a person, and our family had felt it very keenly; nobody else in the United States caught the blight. Some of us have looked upon Zenas' fate as a kind of poetic justice.

Now that grandfather knew, so to speak, who was dead, it became increasingly awkward to go on living in the same house with him as if nothing had happened. He would go into towering rages in which he threatened to write to the Board of Health unless the funeral were held at once. We realized that something had to be done. Eventually, we persuaded a friend of father's, named George Martin, to dress up in the manner and costume of the eighteen-sixties and pretend to be Uncle Zenas, in order to set grandfather's mind at rest. The impostor looked fine and impressive in sideburns and a high beaver hat, and not unlike the daguerreotypes of Zenas in our album. I shall never forget the night, just after dinner, when this Zenas walked into the living-room. Grandfather was stomping up and down, tall, hawk-nosed, round-oathed. The newcomer held out both his hands.'Clem!' he cried to grandfather. Grandfather turned slowly, looked at the intruder, and snorted. 'Who air *you*?' he demanded in his deep, resonant voice. 'I'm Zenas!' cried Martin. 'Your brother Zenas, fit as a fiddle and sound as a dollar!' 'Zenas, my foot!' said grandfather. 'Zenas died of the chestnut blight in '66!'

Grandfather was given to these sudden, unexpected, and extremely lucid moments; they were generally more embarrassing than his other moments.

He comprehended before he went to bed that night that the old automobile had been destroyed and that its destruction had caused all the turmoil in the house. 'It flew all to pieces, Pa,' my mother told him, in graphically describing the accident. 'I knew 'twould,' growled grandfather. 'I allus told ye to git a Pope-Toledo.'

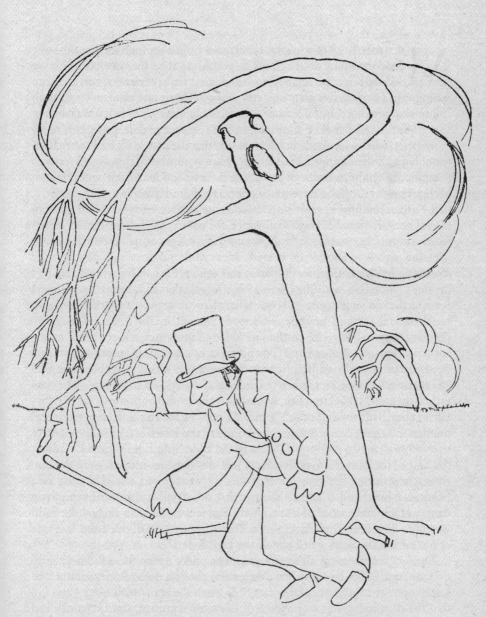

He caught the same disease that was killing the chestnut trees

The Day the Dam Broke

MY MEMORIES of what my family and I went through during the 1913 flood in Ohio I would gladly forget. And yet neither the hardships we endured nor the turmoil and confusion we experienced can alter my feeling toward my native state and city. I am having a fine time now and wish Columbus were here, but if anyone ever wished a city was in hell it was during that frightful and perilous afternoon in 1913 when the dam broke, or, to be more exact, when everybody in town *thought* that the dam broke. We were both ennobled and demoralized by the experience. Grandfather especially rose to magnificent heights which can never lose their splendour for me, even though his reactions to the flood were based upon a profound misconception; namely, that Nathan Bedford Forrest's cavalry was the menace we were called upon to face. The only possible means of escape for us was to flee the house, a step which grandfather sternly forbade, brandishing his old army sabre in his hand. 'Let the sons – – come!' he roared. Meanwhile hundreds of people were streaming by our house in wild panic, screaming 'Go east! Go east!' We had to stun grandfather with the ironing board. Impeded as we were by the inert form of the old gentleman – he was taller than six feet and weighed almost a hundred and seventy pounds – we were passed, in the first half-mile, by practically everybody else in the city. Had grandfather not come to, at the corner of Parsons Avenue and Town Street, we would unquestionably have been overtaken and engulfed by the roaring waters – that is, if there had *been* any roaring waters. Later, when the panic had died down and people had gone rather sheepishly back to their homes and their offices, minimizing the distances they had run and offering various reasons for running, city engineers pointed out that even if the dam had broken, the water level would not have risen more than two additional inches in the West Side. The West Side was, at the time of the dam scare, under thirty feet of water – as, indeed, were all Ohio river towns during the great spring floods of twenty years ago. The East Side (where we lived and where all the running occurred) had never been in any danger at all. Only a rise of some ninety-five feet could have caused the flood waters to flow over High Street – the thoroughfare that divided the east side of town from the west – and engulf the East Side.

The fact that we were all as safe as kittens under a cookstove did not, however, assuage in the least the fine despair and the grotesque desperation which seized upon the residents of the East Side when the cry spread like a grass fire that the dam had given way. Some of the most dignified, staid, cynical, and clear-thinking men in town abandoned their wives, stenographers, homes, and offices and ran east. There are few alarms in the world more terrifying than 'The dam has broken!' There are few persons capable of stopping to reason when that clarion cry strikes upon their ears, even persons who live in towns no nearer than five hundred miles to a dam.

The Columbus, Ohio, broken-dam rumour began, as I recall it, about noon of March 12, 1913. High Street, the main canyon of trade, was loud with the placid hum of business and the buzzing of placid businessmen arguing, computing, wheedling, offering, refusing, compromising. Darius Conningway, one of the foremost corporation lawyers in the Middle-West, was telling the

Two thousand people were in full flight

Public Utilities Commission in the language of Julius Caesar that they might as well try to move the Northern star as to move him. Other men were making their little boasts and their little gestures. Suddenly somebody began to run. It may be that he had simply remembered, all of a moment, an engagement to meet his wife, for which he was now frightfully late. Whatever it was, he ran east on Broad Street (probably toward the Maramor Restaurant, a favourite place for a man to meet his wife). Somebody else began to run, perhaps a newsboy in high spirits. Another man, a portly gentleman of affairs, broke into a trot. Inside of ten minutes, everybody on High Street, from the Union Depot to the Courthouse, was running. A loud mumble gradually crystallized into the dread word 'dam.' 'The dam has broke!' The fear was put into words by a little old lady in an electric, or by a traffic cop, or by a small boy: nobody knows who, nor does it now really matter. Two thousand people were abruptly in full flight. 'Go east!' was the cry that arose – east away from the river, east to safety. 'Go east! Go east! Go east!'

Black streams of people flowed eastward down all the streets leading in that direction; these streams, whose headwaters were in the dry-goods stores, office buildings, harness shops, movie theatres, were fed by trickles of house-wives, children, cripples, servants, dogs, and cats, slipping out of the houses past which the main streams flowed, shouting and screaming. People ran out leaving fires burning and food cooking and doors wide open. I remember, however, that my mother turned out all the fires and that she took with her a dozen eggs and two loaves of bread. It was her plan to make Memorial Hall, just two blocks away, and take refuge somewhere in the top of it, in one of the dusty rooms where war veterans met and where old battle flags and stage scenery were stored. But the seething throngs, shouting 'Go east!' drew her along and the rest of us with her. When grandfather regained full conscious-ness, at Parsons Avenue, he turned upon the retreating mob like a vengeful prophet and exhorted the men to form ranks and stand off the Rebel dogs, but at length he, too, got the idea that the dam had broken and, roaring 'Go east!' in his powerful voice, he caught up in one arm a small child and in the other a slight clerkish man of perhaps forty-two and we slowly began to gain on those ahead of us.

A scattering of firemen, policemen, and army officers in dress uniforms – there had been a review at Fort Hayes, in the northern part of town – added colour to the surging billows of people. 'Go east!' cried a little child in a piping voice, as she ran past a porch on which drowsed a lieutenant-colonel of in-fantry. Used to quick decisions, trained to immediate obedience, the officer bounded off the porch and, running at full tilt, soon passed the child, bawling 'Go east!' The two of them emptied rapidly the houses of the little street they were on. 'What is it? What is it?' demanded a fat, waddling man who inter-cepted the colonel. The officer dropped behind and asked the little child what it was. 'The dam has broke!' gasped the girl. 'The dam has broke!' roared the colonel. 'Go east! Go east! Go east!' He was soon leading, with the ex-hausted child in his arms, a fleeing company of three hundred persons who had gathered around him from living-rooms, shops, garages, backyards, and basements.

Nobody has ever been able to compute with any exactness how many people took part in the great rout of 1913, for the panic, which extended from the Winslow Bottling Works in the south end to Clintonville, six miles north, ended as abruptly as it began and the bobtail and rag-tag and velvet-gowned groups of refugees melted away and slunk home, leaving the streets peaceful and deserted. The shouting, weeping, tangled evacuation of the city lasted not more than two hours in all. Some few people got as far east as Reynoldsburg, twelve miles away; fifty or more reached the Country Club, eight miles away; most of the others gave up, exhausted, or climbed trees in Franklin Park, four

miles out. Order was restored and fear dispelled finally by means of militiamen riding about in motor lorries bawling through megaphones: 'The dam
has *not* broken!' At first this tended only to add to the confusion and increase
the panic, for many stampeders thought the soldiers were bellowing 'The dam
has now broken!' thus setting an official seal of authentication on the calamity.

All the time, the sun shone quietly and there was nowhere any sign of on-
coming waters. A visitor in an airplane, looking down on the straggling,
agitated masses of people below, would have been hard put to it to divine a
reason for the phenomenon. It must have inspired, in such an observer, a
peculiar kind of terror, like the sight of the *Marie Celeste*, abandoned at sea, its
galley fires peacefully burning, its tranquil decks bright in the sunlight.

An aunt of mine, Aunt Edith Taylor, was in a movie theatre on High Street
when, over and above the sound of the piano in the pit (a W. S. Hart picture was
being shown), there rose the steadily increasing tromp of running feet. Persistent shouts rose above the tromping. An elderly man, sitting near my aunt,
mumbled something, got out of his seat, and went up the aisle at a dogtrot.
This started everybody. In an instant the audience was jamming the aisles.
'Fire!' shouted a woman who always expected to be burned up in a theatre;
but now the shouts outside were louder and coherent. 'The dam has broke!'
cried somebody. 'Go east!' screamed a small woman in front of my aunt. And
east they went, pushing and shoving and clawing, knocking women and
children down, emerging finally into the street, torn and sprawling. Inside the
theatre, Bill Hart was calmly calling some desperado's bluff and the brave girl
at the piano played 'Row! Row! Row!' loudly and then 'In My Harem.' Outside, men were streaming across the Statehouse yard, others were climbing
trees, a woman managed to get up onto the 'These Are My Jewels' statue,
whose bronze figures of Sherman, Stanton, Grant, and Sheridan watched
with cold unconcern the going to pieces of the capital city.

'I ran south to State Street, east on State to Third, south on Third to Town,
and out east on Town,' my Aunt Edith has written me. 'A tall spare woman
with grim eyes and a determined chin ran past me down the middle of the
street. I was still uncertain as to what was the matter, in spite of all the shouting.
I drew up alongside the woman with some effort, for although she was in her
late fifties, she had a beautiful easy running form and seemed to be in excellent
condition. "What is it?" I puffed. She gave me a quick glance and then looked
ahead again, stepping up her pace a trifle. "Don't ask me, ask God!" she said.

'When I reached Grant Avenue, I was so spent that Dr H. R. Mallory – you
remember Dr Mallory, the man with the white beard who looks like Robert
Browning? – well, Dr Mallory, whom I had drawn away from at the corner of
Fifth and Town, passed me. "It's got us!" he shouted, and I felt sure that
whatever it was *did* have us, for you know what conviction Dr Mallory's statements always carried. I didn't know at the time what he meant, but I found
out later. There was a boy behind him on roller-skates, and Dr Mallory mis-
took the swishing of the skates for the sound of rushing water. He eventually
reached the Columbus School for Girls, at the corner of Parsons Avenue and

Town Street, where he collapsed, expecting the cold frothing waters of the
Scioto to sweep him into oblivion. The boy on the skates swirled past him and
Dr Mallory realized for the first time what he had been running from. Looking
back up the street, he could see no signs of water, but nevertheless, after resting
a few minutes, he jogged on east again. He caught up with me at Ohio Avenue,
where we rested together. I should say that about seven hundred people passed

'It's got us!' he shouted

us. A funny thing was that all of them were on foot. Nobody seemed to have
had the courage to stop and start his car; but as I remember it, all cars had to
be cranked in those days, which is probably the reason.'

The next day, the city went about its business as if nothing had happened,
but there was no joking. It was two years or more before you dared treat the
breaking of the dam lightly. And even now, twenty years after, there are a few
persons, like Dr Mallory, who will shut up like a clam if you mention the
Afternoon of the Great Run.

The Night the Ghost Got In

THE ghost that got into our house on the night of November 17, 1915, raised such a hullabaloo of misunderstandings that I am sorry I didn't just let it keep on walking, and go to bed. Its advent caused my mother to throw a shoe through a window of the house next door and ended up with my grandfather shooting a patrolman. I am sorry, therefore, as I have said, that I ever paid any attention to the footsteps.

They began about a quarter past one o'clock in the morning, a rhythmic, quick-cadenced walking around the dining-room table. My mother was asleep in one room upstairs, my brother Herman in another; grandfather was in the attic, in the old walnut bed which, as you will remember, once fell on my father. I had just stepped out of the bathtub and was busily rubbing myself with a towel when I heard the steps. They were the steps of a man walking rapidly around the dining-room table downstairs. The light from the bathroom shone down the back steps, which dropped directly into the dining-room; I could see the faint shine of plates on the plate-rail; I couldn't see the table. The steps kept going round and round the table; at regular intervals a board creaked, when it was trod upon. I supposed at first that it was my father or my brother Roy, who had gone to Indianapolis but were expected home at any time. I suspected next that it was a burglar. It did not enter my mind until later that it was a ghost.

After the walking had gone on for perhaps three minutes, I tiptoed to Herman's room. 'Psst!' I hissed, in the dark, shaking him. 'Awp,' he said, in the low, hopeless tone of a despondent beagle – he always half suspected that something would 'get him' in the night. I told him who I was. 'There's something downstairs!' I said. He got up and followed me to the head of the back staircase. We listened together. There was no sound. The steps had ceased. Herman looked at me in some alarm: I had only the bath towel around my waist. He wanted to go back to bed, but I gripped his arm. 'There's something down there!' I said. Instantly the steps began again, circled the dining-room table like a man running, and started up the stairs toward us, heavily, two at a time. The light still shone palely down the stairs; we saw nothing coming; we only heard the steps. Herman rushed to his room and slammed the door. I slammed shut the door at the stairs top and held my knee against it. After a long minute, I slowly opened it again. There was nothing there. There was no sound. None of us ever heard the ghost again.

The slamming of the doors had aroused mother: she peered out of her room. 'What on earth are you boys doing?' she demanded. Herman ventured out of his room. 'Nothing,' he said, gruffly, but he was, in colour, a light green. 'What was all that running around downstairs?' said mother. So she had heard the steps, too! We just looked at her. 'Burglars!' she shouted, intuitively. I tried to quiet her by starting lightly downstairs.

'Come on, Herman,' I said.

'I'll stay with mother,' he said. 'She's all excited.'

I stepped back onto the landing.

'Don't either of you go a step,' said mother. 'We'll call the police.' Since the phone was downstairs, I didn't see how we were going to call the police – nor

He always half suspected that something would get him

did I want the police – but mother made one of her quick, incomparable decisions. She flung up a window of her bedroom which faced the bedroom windows of the house of a neighbour, picked up a shoe, and whammed it through a pane of glass across the narrow space that separated the two houses. Glass tinkled into the bedroom occupied by a retired engraver named Bodwell and his wife. Bodwell had been for some years in rather a bad way and was subject to mild 'attacks.' Most everybody we knew or lived near had *some* kind of attacks.

It was now about two o'clock of a moonless night; clouds hung black and low. Bodwell was at the window in a minute, shouting, frothing a little, shaking his fist. 'We'll sell the house and go back to Peoria,' we could hear Mrs Bodwell saying. It was some time before Mother 'got through' to Bodwell. 'Burglars!' she shouted. 'Burglars in the house!' Herman and I hadn't dared to tell her that it was not burglars but ghosts, for she was even more afraid of ghosts than of burglars. Bodwell at first thought that she meant there were burglars in his house, but finally he quieted down and called the police for us over an extension phone by his bed. After he had disappeared from the window, mother suddenly made as if to throw another shoe, not because there was further need of it but, as she later explained, because the thrill of heaving a shoe through a window glass had enormously taken her fancy. I prevented her.

The police were on hand in a commendably short time: a Ford sedan full of them, two on motorcycles, and a patrol wagon with about eight in it and a few reporters. They began banging at our front door. Flashlights shot streaks of gleam up and down the walls, across the yard, down the walk between our house and Bodwell's. 'Open up!' cried a hoarse voice. 'We're men from Headquarters!' I wanted to go down and let them in, since there they were, but mother wouldn't hear of it. 'You haven't a stitch on,' she pointed out. 'You'd catch your death.' I wound the towel around me again. Finally the cops put their shoulders to our big heavy front door with its thick bevelled glass and broke it in: I could hear a rending of wood and a splash of glass on the floor of the hall. Their lights played all over the living-room and crisscrossed nervously in the dining-room, stabbed into hallways, shot up the front stairs and finally up the back. They caught me standing in my towel at the top. A heavy policeman bounded up the steps. 'Who are you?' he demanded. 'I live here,' I said. 'Well, whattsa matta, ya hot?' he asked. It was, as a matter of fact, cold; I went to my room and pulled on some trousers. On my way out, a cop stuck a gun into my ribs. 'Whatta you doin' here?' he demanded. 'I live here,' I said.

The officer in charge reported to mother. 'No sign of nobody, lady,' he said. 'Musta got away – whatt'd he look like?' 'There were two or three of them,' mother said, 'whooping and carrying on and slamming doors.' 'Funny,' said the cop. 'All ya windows and doors was locked on the inside tight as a tick.'

Downstairs, we could hear the tromping of the other police. Police were all over the place; doors were yanked open, drawers were yanked open, windows were shot up and pulled down, furniture fell with dull thumps. A half-dozen policemen emerged out of the darkness of the front hallway upstairs. They began to ransack the floor: pulled beds away from walls, tore clothes off hooks in the closets, pulled suitcases and boxes off shelves. One of them found an old zither that Roy had won in a pool tournament. 'Looky here, Joe,' he said, strumming it with a big paw. The cop named Joe took it and turned it over. 'What is it?' he asked me. 'It's an old zither our guinea pig used to sleep on,' I said. It was true that a pet guinea pig we once had would never sleep anywhere except on the zither, but I should never have said so. Joe and the other cop looked at me a long time. They put the zither back on a shelf.

'No sign o' nuthin',' said the cop who had first spoken to mother. 'This guy,' he explained to the others, jerking a thumb at me, 'was nekked. The lady seems historical.' They all nodded, but said nothing; just looked at me. In the small silence we all heard a creaking in the attic. Grandfather was turning over in bed. 'What's 'at?' snapped Joe. Five or six cops sprang for the attic door before I could intervene or explain. I realized that it would be bad if they burst in on grandfather unannounced, or even announced. He was going through a phase in which he believed that General Meade's men, under steady hammering by Stonewall Jackson, were beginning to retreat and even desert.

When I got to the attic, things were pretty confused. Grandfather had evidently jumped to the conclusion that the police were deserters from

Police were all over the place

Meade's army, trying to hide away in his attic. He bounded out of bed wearing a long flannel nightgown over long woollen underwear, a nightcap, and a leather jacket around his chest. The cops must have realized at once that the indignant white-haired old man belonged in the house, but they had no chance to say so. 'Back, ye cowardly dogs!' roared grandfather. 'Back t' the lines, ye goddam lily-livered cattle!' With that, he fetched the officer who found the zither a flat-handed smack alongside his head that sent him sprawling. The others beat a retreat, but not fast enough; grandfather grabbed Zither's gun from its holster and let fly. The report seemed to crack the rafters; smoke filled the attic. A cop cursed and shot his hand to his shoulder. Somehow, we all finally got downstairs again and locked the door against the old gentleman. He fired once or twice more in the darkness and then went back to bed. 'That was grandfather,' I explained to Joe, out of breath. 'He thinks you're deserters.' 'I'll say he does,' said Joe.

The cops were reluctant to leave without getting their hands on somebody besides grandfather; the night had been distinctly a defeat for them. Furthermore, they obviously didn't like the 'layout'; something looked – and I can see their viewpoint – phony. They began to poke into things again. A reporter, a thin-faced, wispy man, came up to me. I had put on one of mother's blouses, not being able to find anything else. The reporter looked at me with mingled suspicion and interest. 'Just what the hell is the real lowdown here, Bud?' he asked. I decided to be frank with him. 'We had ghosts,' I said. He gazed at me a long time as if I were a slot machine into which he had, without results, dropped a nickel. Then he walked away. The cops followed him, the one grandfather shot holding his now-bandaged arm, cursing and blaspheming. 'I'm gonna get my gun back from that old bird,' said the zither-cop. 'Yeh,' said Joe. 'You – and who else?' I told them I would bring it to the station house the next day.

'What was the matter with that one policeman?' mother asked, after they had gone. 'Grandfather shot him,' I said. 'What for?' she demanded. I told her he was a deserter. 'Of all things!' said mother. 'He was such a nice-looking young man.'

Grandfather was fresh as a daisy and full of jokes at breakfast next morning. We thought at first he had forgotten all about what had happened, but he hadn't. Over his third cup of coffee, he glared at Herman and me. 'What was the idee of all them cops tarryhootin' round the house last night?' he demanded. He had us there.

More Alarms at Night

O NE of the incidents that I always think of first when I cast back over my youth is what happened the night that my father 'threatened to get Buck.' This, as you will see, is not precisely a fair or accurate description of what actually occurred, but it is the way in which I and the other members of my family invariably allude to the occasion. We were living at the time in an old house at 77 Lexington Avenue, in Columbus, Ohio. In the early years of the nineteenth century, Columbus won out, as state capital, by only one vote over Lancaster, and ever since then has had the hallucination that it is being followed, a curious municipal state of mind which affects, in some way or other, all those who live there. Columbus is a town in which almost anything is likely to happen and in which almost everything has.

My father was sleeping in the front room on the second floor next to that of my brother Roy, who was then about sixteen. Father was usually in bed by nine-thirty and up again by ten-thirty to protest bitterly against a Victrola record we three boys were in the habit of playing over and over, namely, 'No News, or What Killed the Dog,' a recitation by Nat Wills. The record had been played so many times that its grooves were deeply cut and the needle often kept revolving in the same groove, repeating over and over the same words. Thus: 'ate some burnt hoss flesh, ate some burnt hoss flesh, ate some burnt hoss flesh.' It was this reiteration that generally got father out of bed.

On the night in question, however, we had all gone to bed at about the same time, without much fuss. Roy, as a matter of fact, had been in bed all day with a kind of mild fever. It wasn't severe enough to cause delirium and my brother was the last person in the world to give way to delirium. Nevertheless, he had warned father when father went to bed, that he *might* become delirious.

About three o'clock in the morning, Roy, who was wakeful, decided to pretend that delirium was on him, in order to have, as he later explained it, some 'fun.' He got out of bed and, going to my father's room, shook him and said, 'Buck, your time has come!' My father's name was not Buck but Charles, nor had he ever been called Buck. He was a tall, mildly nervous, peaceable gentleman, given to quiet pleasures, and eager that everything should run smoothly. 'Hmm?' he said, with drowsy bewilderment. 'Get up, Buck,' said my brother, coldly, but with a certain gleam in his eyes. My father leaped out of bed, on the side away from his son, rushed from the room, locked the door behind him, and shouted us all up.

We were naturally enough reluctant to believe that Roy, who was quiet and self-contained, had threatened his father with any such abracadabra as father said he had. My older brother, Herman, went back to bed without any comment. 'You've had a bad dream,' my mother said. This vexed my father. 'I tell you he called me Buck and told me my time had come,' he said. We went to the door of his room, unlocked it, and tiptoed through it to Roy's room. He lay in his bed, breathing easily, as if he were fast asleep. It was apparent at a glance that he did not have a high fever. My mother gave my father a look. 'I tell you he did,' whispered father.

Our presence in the room finally seemed to awaken Roy and he was (or rather, as we found out long afterward, pretended to be) astonished and bewildered. 'What's the matter?' he asked. 'Nothing,' said my mother. 'Just your father had a nightmare.' 'I did not have a nightmare,' said father, slowly and firmly. He wore an old-fashioned, 'side-slit' nightgown which looked rather odd on his tall, spare figure. The situation, before we let it drop and everybody went back to bed again, became, as such situations in our family usually did, rather more complicated than ironed out. Roy demanded to know what had happened, and my mother told him, in considerably garbled fashion, what father had told her. At this a light dawned in Roy's eyes. 'Dad's got it backward,' he said. He then explained that he had heard father get out of bed and had called to him. 'I'll handle this,' his father had answered. 'Buck is downstairs.' 'Who is this Buck?' my mother demanded of father. 'I don't know any Buck and I never said that,' father contended, irritably. None of us (except Roy, of course) believed him. 'You had a dream,' said mother. 'People have these dreams.' 'I did not have a dream,' father said. He was pretty well nettled by this time, and he stood in front of a bureau mirror, brushing his hair with a pair of military brushes; it always seemed to calm father to brush his hair. My mother declared that it was 'a sin and a shame' for a grown man to wake up a sick boy simply because he (the grown man: father) had got on his back and had a bad dream. My father, as a matter of fact, *had* been known to have nightmares, usually about Lillian Russell and President Cleveland, who chased him.

We argued the thing for perhaps another half-hour, after which mother made father sleep in her room. 'You're all safe now, boys,' she said, firmly, as she shut her door. I could hear father grumbling for a long time, with an occasional monosyllable of doubt from mother.

It was some six months after this that father went through a similar experience with me. He was at that time sleeping in the room next to mine. I had been trying all afternoon, in vain, to think of the name Perth Amboy. It seems now like a very simple name to recall and yet on the day in question I thought of every other town in the country, as well as such words and names and phrases as terra cotta, Walla-Walla, bill of lading, vice versa, hoity-toity, Pall Mall, Bodley Head, Schumann-Heink, etc., without even coming close to Perth Amboy. I suppose terra cotta was the closest I came, although it was not very close.

Long after I had gone to bed, I was struggling with the problem. I began to indulge in the wildest fancies as I lay there in the dark, such as that there was no such town, and even that there was no such state as New Jersey. I fell to repeating the word 'Jersey' over and over again, until it became idiotic and meaningless. If you have ever lain awake at night and repeated one word over and over, thousands and millions and hundreds of thousands of millions of times, you know the disturbing mental state you can get into. I got to thinking that there was nobody else in the world but me, and various other wild imaginings of that nature. Eventually, lying there thinking these outlandish thoughts, I grew slightly alarmed. I began to suspect that one might lose one's mind over some such trivial mental tic as a futile search for terra firma Piggly Wiggly Gorgonzola Prester John Arc de Triomphe Holy Moses Lares and Penates. I began to feel the imperative necessity of human contact. This silly and alarming tangle of thought and fancy had gone far enough. I might get into some kind of mental aberrancy unless I found out the name of that Jersey town and could go to sleep. Therefore, I got out of bed, walked into the room where father was sleeping, and shook him. 'Um?' he mumbled. I shook him more fiercely and he finally woke up, with a glaze of dream and apprehension in his eyes. 'What's matter?' he asked, thickly. I must, indeed, have been rather wild of eye, and my hair, which is unruly, becomes monstrously tousled and snarled at night. 'Wha's it?' said my father, sitting up, in readiness to spring out of bed on the far side. The thought must have been going through his mind that all his sons were crazy, or on the verge of going crazy. I see that now, but I didn't then, for I had forgotten the Buck incident and did not realize how similar my appearance must have been to Roy's the night he called father Buck and told him his time had come. 'Listen,' I said. 'Name some towns in New Jersey quick!' It must have been around three in the morning. Father got up, keeping the bed between him and me, and started to pull his trousers on. 'Don't bother about dressing,' I said. 'Just name some towns in New Jersey.' While he hastily pulled on his clothes – I remember he left his socks off and put his shoes on his bare feet – father began to name, in a shaky voice, various New Jersey cities. I can still see him reaching for his coat without taking his eyes off me. 'Newark,' he said, 'Jersey City, Atlantic City, Elizabeth, Paterson, Passaic, Trenton, Jersey City, Trenton, Paterson –' 'It has two names,' I snapped. 'Elizabeth and Paterson,' he said. 'No, no!' I told him, irritably. 'This is one town with one name, but there are two words in it, like helter-skelter.' 'Helter-skelter,' said my father, moving slowly toward the bedroom door and smiling in a faint, strained way which I understand now – but didn't then – was meant to humour me. When he was within a few paces of the door, he fairly leaped for it and ran out into the hall, his coat-tails and shoe-laces flying. The exit stunned me. I had no notion that he thought I had gone out of my senses; I could only believe that he had gone out of *his* or that, only partially awake, he was engaged in some form of running in his sleep. I ran after him and I caught him at the door of mother's room and grabbed him, in order to reason with him. I shook him a little, thinking to wake him completely. 'Mary! Roy! Herman!' he shouted. I, too, began to shout for my brothers and my mother. My mother opened her door instantly, and there we were at 3.30 in the morning grappling and shouting, father partly dressed, but without socks or shirt, and I in pyjamas.

'*Now*, what?' demanded my mother, grimly, pulling us apart. She was capable, fortunately, of handling any two of us and she never in her life was alarmed by the words or actions of any one of us.

'Look out for Jamie!' said father. (He always called me Jamie when excited.) My mother looked at me.

'What's the matter with your father?' she demanded. I said I didn't know; I said he had got up suddenly and dressed and ran out of the room.

'Where did you think you were going?' mother asked him, coolly. He looked at me. We looked at each other, breathing hard, but somewhat calmer.

'He was babbling about New Jersey at this infernal hour of the night,' said father. 'He came to my room and asked me to name towns in New Jersey.' Mother looked at me.

'I just asked him,' I said. 'I was trying to think of one and couldn't sleep.'

'You see?' said father, triumphantly. Mother didn't look at him.

'Get to bed, both of you,' she said. 'I don't want to hear any more out of you tonight. Dressing and tearing up and down the hall at this hour in the morning!' She went back into the room and shut her door. Father and I went back to bed. 'Are you all right?' he called to me. 'Are you?' I asked. 'Well, good night,' he said. 'Good night,' I said.

Mother would not let the rest of us discuss the affair next morning at breakfast. Herman asked what the hell had been the matter. 'We'll go on to something more elevating,' said mother.

A Sequence of Servants

WHEN I look back on the long line of servants my mother hired during the years I lived at home, I remember clearly ten or twelve of them (we had about a hundred and sixty-two, all told, but few of them were memorable). There was, among the immortals, Dora Gedd, a quiet, mousy girl of thirty-two who one night shot at a man in her room, throwing our household into an uproar that was equalled perhaps only by the goings-on the night the ghost got in. Nobody knew how her lover, a morose garage man, got into the house, but everybody for two blocks knew how he got out. Dora had dressed up in a lavender evening gown for the occasion and she wore a mass of jewellery, some of which was my mother's. She kept shouting something from Shakespeare after the shooting – I forget just what – and pursued the gentleman downstairs from her attic room. When he got to the second floor he rushed into my father's room. It was this entrance, and not the shot or the shouting, that aroused father, a deep sleeper always. 'Get me out of here!' shouted the victim. This situation rapidly developed, from then on, into one of those bewildering involvements for which my family had, I am afraid, a kind of unhappy genius. When the cops arrived Dora was shooting out the Welsbach gas mantles in the living room, and her gentleman friend had fled. By dawn everything was quiet once more.

There were others. Gertie Straub: big, genial, and ruddy, a collector of pints of rye (we learned after she was gone), who came in after two o'clock one night from a dancing party at Buckeye Lake and awakened us by bumping into and knocking over furniture. 'Who's down there?' called mother from upstairs. 'It's me, dearie,' said Gertie, 'Gertie Straub.' 'What are you *doing*?' demanded mother. 'Dusting,' said Gertie.

Juanemma Kramer was one of my favourites. Her mother loved the name Juanita so dearly that she had worked the first part of it into the names of all her daughters – they were (in addition to a Juanita) Juanemma, Juanhelen, and Juangrace. Juanemma was a thin, nervous maid who lived in constant dread of being hypnotized. Nor were her fears unfounded, for she was so extremely susceptible to hypnotic suggestion that one evening at B. F. Keith's theatre when a man on the stage was hypnotized, Juanemma, in the audience, was hypnotized too and floundered out into the aisle making the same cheeping sound that the subject on the stage, who had been told he was a chicken, was making. The act was abandoned and some xylophone players were brought on to restore order. One night, when our house was deep in quiet slumber, Juanemma became hypnotized in her sleep. She dreamed that a man 'put her under' and then disappeared without 'bringing her out.' This was explained when, at last, a police surgeon whom we called in – he was the only doctor we could persuade to come out at three in the morning – slapped her into consciousness. It got so finally that any buzzing or whirring sound or any flashing

'Dusting,' said Gertie

object would put Juanemma under, and we had to let her go. I was reminded of her recently when, at a performance of the movie 'Rasputin and the Empress,' there came the scene in which Lionel Barrymore as the unholy priest hypnotizes the Czarevitch by spinning before his eyes a glittering watch. If Juanemma sat in any theatre and witnessed that scene she must, I am sure, have gone under instantly. Happily, she seems to have missed the picture, for otherwise Mr Barrymore might have had to dress up again as Rasputin (which God forbid) and journey across the country to get her out of it – excellent publicity but a great bother.

Before I go on to Vashti, whose last name I forget, I will look in passing at another of our white maids (Vashti was coloured). Belle Giddin distinguished herself by one gesture which fortunately did not result in the bedlam occasioned by Juanemma's hypnotic states or Dora Gedd's shooting spree. Belle burned her finger grievously, and purposely, one afternoon in the steam of a boiling kettle so that she could find out whether the pain-killer she had bought one night at a tent-show for fifty cents was any good. It was only fair.

Vashti turned out, in the end, to be partly legendary. She was a comely and sombre negress who was always able to find things my mother lost. 'I don't know what's become of my garnet brooch,' my mother said one day. 'Yassum,' said Vashti. In half an hour she had found it. 'Where in the world was it?' asked mother. 'In de yahd,' said Vashti. 'De dog mussa drug it out.'

Vashti was in love with a young coloured chauffeur named Charley, but she was also desired by her stepfather, whom none of us had ever seen but who was, she said, a handsome but messin' round gentleman from Georgia who had come north and married Vashti's mother just so he could be near Vashti. Charley, her fiancé, was for killing the stepfather but we counselled flight to another city. Vashti, however, would burst into tears and hymns and vow she'd never leave us; she got a certain pleasure out of bearing her cross. Thus we all lived in jeopardy, for the possibility that Vashti, Charley, and her stepfather might fight it out some night in our kitchen did not, at times, seem remote. Once I went into the kitchen at midnight to make some coffee. Charley was standing at a window looking out into the backyard; Vashti was rolling her eyes. 'Heah he come! Heah he come!' she moaned. The stepfather didn't show up, however.

Charley finally saved up twenty-seven dollars toward taking Vashti away but one day he impulsively bought a .22 revolver with a mother-of-pearl handle and demanded that Vashti tell him where her mother and stepfather lived. 'Doan go up dere, doan go *up* dere!' said Vashti. 'Mah mothah is just as rarin' as he is!' Charley, however, insisted. It came out then that Vashti didn't have any stepfather; there was no such person. Charley threw her over for a yellow gal named Nancy: he never forgave Vashti for the vanishing from his life of a menace that had come to mean more to him than Vashti herself. Afterwards, if you asked Vashti about her stepfather or about Charley she would say, proudly, and with a woman-of-the-world air, 'Neither one ob 'em is messin' round *me* any mo'.'

Mrs Doody, a huge, middle-aged woman with a religious taint, came into and went out of our house like a comet. The second night she was there she went berserk while doing the dishes and, under the impression that father was the Antichrist, pursued him several times up the backstairs and down the front. He had been sitting quietly over his coffee in the living room when she burst in from the kitchen waving a bread knife. My brother Herman finally felled her with a piece of Libby's cut-glass that had been a wedding present of mother's. Mother, I remember, was in the attic at the time, trying to find some old things, and, appearing on the scene in the midst of it all, got the quick and mistaken impression that father was chasing Mrs Doody.

'One night while doing the dishes . . .'

Mrs Robertson, a fat and mumbly old coloured woman, who might have been sixty and who might have been a hundred, gave us more than one turn during the many years that she did our washing. She had been a slave down South and she remembered having seen the troops marching – 'a mess o' blue, den a mess o' grey.' 'What,' my mother asked her once, 'were they fighting about?' 'Dat,' said Mrs Robertson, 'Ah don't know.' She had a feeling, at all times, that something was going to happen. I can see her now, staggering up from the basement with a basketful of clothes and coming abruptly to a halt in the middle of the kitchen. 'Hahk!' she would say, in a deep, guttural voice. We would all hark; there was never anything to be heard. Neither, when she shouted 'Look yondah!' and pointed a trembling hand at a window, was there ever anything to be seen. Father protested time and again that he couldn't stand Mrs Robertson around, but mother always refused to let her go. It seems that she was a jewel. Once she walked unbidden, a dishpan full of wrung-out clothes under her arm, into father's study, where he was engrossed in some figures. Father looked up. She regarded him for a moment in silence. Then – 'Look out!' she said, and withdrew. Another time, a murky winter afternoon, she came flubbering up the cellar stairs and bounced, out of breath, into the kitchen. Father was in the kitchen sipping some black coffee; he was in a jittery state of nerves from the effects of having had a tooth out, and had been in bed most of the day. 'Dey is a death watch downstaihs!' rumbled the old coloured lady. It developed that she had heard a strange 'chipping' noise back of the furnace. 'That was a cricket,' said father. 'Um-*hm*,' said Mrs Robertson. 'Dat was uh death watch!' With that she put on her hat and went home, poising just long enough at the back door to observe darkly to father, '*Dey ain't no way!*' It upset him for days.

Mrs Robertson had only one great hour that I can think of – Jack Johnson's victory over Mistah Jeffries on the Fourth of July, 1910. She took a prominent part in the coloured parade through the South End that night, playing a Spanish fandango on a banjo. The procession was led by the pastor of her church who, Mrs Robertson later told us, had 'splained that the victory of Jack over Mistah Jeffries proved 'de 'speriority ob de race.' 'What,' asked my mother, 'did he mean by that?' 'Dat,' said Mrs Robertson, 'Ah don't know.'

Our other servants I don't remember so clearly, except the one who set the house on fire (her name eludes me), and Edda Millmoss. Edda was always slightly morose but she had gone along for months, all the time she was with us, quietly and efficiently attending to her work, until the night we had Carson Blair and F. R. Gardiner to dinner – both men of importance to my father's ambitions. Then suddenly, while serving the entrée, Edda dropped everything and, pointing a quivering finger at father, accused him in a long rigmarole of having done her out of her rights to the land on which Trinity Church in New York stands. Mr Gardiner had one of his 'attacks' and the whole evening turned out miserably.

The Dog That Bit People

PROBABLY no one man should have as many dogs in his life as I have had, but there was more pleasure than distress in them for me except in the case of an Airedale named Muggs. He gave me more trouble than all the other fifty-four or five put together, although my moment of keenest embarrassment was the time a Scotch terrier named Jeannie, who had just had six puppies in the clothes closet of a fourth floor apartment in New York, had the unexpected seventh and last at the corner of Eleventh Street and Fifth Avenue during a walk she had insisted on taking. Then, too, there was the prize-winning French poodle, a great big black poodle – none of your little, untroublesome white miniatures – who got sick riding in the rumble seat of a car with me on her way to the Greenwich Dog Show. She had a red rubber bib tucked around her throat and, since a rain storm came up when we were half way through the Bronx, I had to hold over her a small green umbrella, really more of a parasol. The rain beat down fearfully and suddenly the driver of the car drove into a big garage, filled with mechanics. It happened so quickly that I forgot to put the umbrella down and I will always remember, with sickening distress, the look of incredulity mixed with hatred that came over the face of the particular hardened garage man that came over to see what we wanted, when he took a look at me and the poodle. All garage men, and people of that intolerant stripe, hate poodles with their curious hair cut, especially the pompoms that you got to leave on their hips if you expect the dogs to win a prize.

But the Airedale, as I have said, was the worst of all my dogs. He really wasn't my dog, as a matter of fact: I came home from a vacation one summer to find that my brother Roy had bought him while I was away. A big, burly, choleric dog, he always acted as if he thought I wasn't one of the family. There was a slight advantage in being one of the family, for he didn't bite the family as often as he bit strangers. Still, in the years that we had him he bit everybody but mother, and he made a pass at her once but missed. That was during the month when we suddenly had mice, and Muggs refused to do anything about them. Nobody ever had mice exactly like the mice we had that month. They acted like pet mice, almost like mice somebody had trained. They were so friendly that one night when mother entertained at dinner the Friraliras, a club she and my father had belonged to for twenty years, she put down a lot of little dishes with food in them on the pantry floor so that the mice would be satisfied with that and wouldn't come into the dining room. Muggs stayed out in the pantry with the mice, lying on the floor, growling to himself – not at the mice, but about all the people in the next room that he would have liked to get

at. Mother slipped out into the pantry once to see how everything was going.
Everything was going fine. It made her so mad to see Muggs lying there,
oblivious of the mice – they came running up to her – that she slapped him
and he slashed at her, but didn't make it. He was sorry immediately, mother
said. He was always sorry, she said, after he bit someone, but we could not
understand how she figured this out. He didn't act sorry.

Mother used to send a box of candy every Christmas to the people the
Airedale bit. The list finally contained forty or more names. Nobody could
understand why we didn't get rid of the dog. I didn't understand it very well
myself, but we didn't get rid of him. I think that one or two people tried to
poison Muggs – he acted poisoned once in a while – and old Major Moberly

Nobody knew exactly what was the matter with him

fired at him once with his service revolver near the Seneca Hotel in East Broad
Street – but Muggs lived to be almost eleven years old and even when he could
hardly get around he bit a Congressman who had called to see my father on
business. My mother had never liked the Congressman – she said the signs of
his horoscope showed he couldn't be trusted (he was Saturn with the moon in
Virgo) – but she sent him a box of candy that Christmas. He sent it right back,
probably because he suspected it was trick candy. Mother persuaded herself
it was all for the best that the dog had bitten him, even though father lost an
important business association because of it. 'I wouldn't be associated with
such a man,' mother said, 'Muggs could read him like a book.'

We used to take turns feeding Muggs to be on his good side, but that didn't always work. He was never in a very good humour, even after a meal. Nobody knew exactly what was the matter with him, but whatever it was it made him irascible, especially in the mornings. Roy never felt very well in the morning, either, especially before breakfast, and once when he came downstairs and found that Muggs had moodily chewed up the morning paper he hit him in the face with a grapefruit and then jumped up on the dining room table, scattering dishes and silverware and spilling the coffee. Muggs' first free leap carried him all the way across the table and into a brass fire screen in front of the gas grate but he was back on his feet in a moment and in the end he got Roy and gave him a pretty vicious bite in the leg. Then he was all over it; he never bit anyone more than once at a time. Mother always mentioned that as an argument in his favour; she said he had a quick temper but that he didn't hold a grudge. She was forever defending him. I think she liked him because he wasn't well. 'He's not strong,' she would say, pityingly, but that was inaccurate; he may not have been well but he was terribly strong.

One time my mother went to the Chittenden Hotel to call on a woman mental healer who was lecturing in Columbus on the subject of 'Harmonious Vibrations.' She wanted to find out if it was possible to get harmonious vibrations into a dog. 'He's a large tan-coloured Airedale,' mother explained. The woman said that she had never treated a dog but she advised my mother to hold the thought that he did not bite and would not bite. Mother was holding the thought the very next morning when Muggs got the iceman but she blamed that slip-up on the iceman. 'If you didn't think he would bite you, he wouldn't,' mother told him. He stomped out of the house in a terrible jangle of vibrations.

One morning when Muggs bit me slightly, more or less in passing, I reached down and grabbed his short stumpy tail and hoisted him into the air. It was a foolhardy thing to do and the last time I saw my mother, about six months ago, she said she didn't know what possessed me. I don't either, except that I was pretty mad. As long as I held the dog off the floor by his tail he couldn't get at me, but he twisted and jerked so, snarling all the time, that I realized I couldn't hold him that way very long. I carried him to the kitchen and flung him onto the floor and shut the door on him just as he crashed against it. But I forgot about the backstairs. Muggs went up the backstairs and down the frontstairs and had me cornered in the living room. I managed to get up onto the mantelpiece above the fireplace, but it gave way and came down with a tremendous crash throwing a large marble clock, several vases, and myself heavily to the floor. Muggs was so alarmed by the racket that when I picked myself up he had disappeared. We couldn't find him anywhere, although we whistled and shouted, until old Mrs Detweiler called after dinner that night. Muggs had bitten her once, in the leg, and she came into the living room only after we assured her that Muggs had run away. She had just seated herself when, with a great growling and scratching of claws, Muggs emerged from under a davenport where he had been quietly hiding all the time, and bit her again. Mother examined the bite and put arnica on it and told Mrs Detweiler that it was only a bruise. 'He just bumped you,' she said. But Mrs Detweiler left the house in a nasty state of mind.

Lots of people reported our Airedale to the police but my father held a municipal office at the time and was on friendly terms with the police. Even so, the cops had been out a couple of times – once when Muggs bit Mrs Rufus Sturtevant and again when he bit Lieutenant-Governor Malloy – but mother told them that it hadn't been Muggs' fault but the fault of the people who were bitten. 'When he starts for them, they scream,' she explained, 'and

Lots of people reported our dog to the police

that excites him.' The cops suggested that it might be a good idea to tie the dog up, but mother said that it mortified him to be tied up and that he wouldn't eat when he was tied up.

Muggs at his meals was an unusual sight. Because of the fact that if you reached toward the floor he would bite you, we usually put his food plate on top of an old kitchen table with a bench alongside the table. Muggs would stand on the bench and eat. I remember that my mother's Uncle Horatio, who boasted that he was the third man up Missionary Ridge, was splutteringly indignant when he found out that we fed the dog on a table because we were afraid to put his plate on the floor. He said he wasn't afraid of any dog that ever lived and that he would put the dog's plate on the floor if we would give it to him. Roy said that if Uncle Horatio had fed Muggs on the ground just before the battle he would have been the first man up Missionary Ridge. Uncle Horatio was furious. 'Bring him in! Bring him in now!' he shouted. 'I'll feed the – – on the floor!' Roy was all for giving him a chance, but my father wouldn't hear of it. He said that Muggs had already been fed. 'I'll feed him again!' bawled Uncle Horatio. We had quite a time quieting him.

Muggs at his meals was an unusual sight

In his last year Muggs used to spend practically all of his time outdoors. He didn't like to stay in the house for some reason or other – perhaps it held too many unpleasant memories for him. Anyway, it was hard to get him to come in and as a result the garbage man, the iceman, and the laundryman wouldn't come near the house. We had to haul the garbage down to the corner, take the laundry out and bring it back, and meet the iceman a block from home. After this had gone on for some time we hit on an ingenious arrangement for getting the dog in the house so that we could lock him up while the gas meter was read, and so on. Muggs was afraid of only one thing, an electrical storm. Thunder and lightning frightened him out of his senses (I think he thought a storm had broken the day the mantelpiece fell). He would rush into the house and hide under a bed or in a clothes closet. So we fixed up a thunder machine out of a long narrow piece of sheet iron with a wooden handle on one end. Mother would shake this vigorously when she wanted to get Muggs into the house. It made an excellent imitation of thunder, but I suppose it was the most round-about system for running a household that was ever devised. It took a lot out of mother.

A few months before Muggs died, he got to 'seeing things.' He would rise slowly from the floor, growling low, and stalk stiff-legged and menacing to-ward nothing at all. Sometimes the Thing would be just a little to the right or left of a visitor. Once a Fuller Brush salesman got hysterics. Muggs came wandering into the room like Hamlet following his father's ghost. His eyes were fixed on a spot just to the left of the Fuller Brush man, who stood it until Muggs was about three slow, creeping paces from him. Then he shouted. Muggs wavered on past him into the hallway grumbling to himself but the Fuller man went on shouting. I think mother had to throw a pan of cold water on him before he stopped. That was the way she used to stop us boys when we got into fights.

Muggs died quite suddenly one night. Mother wanted to bury him in the family lot under a marble stone with some such inscription as 'Flights of angels sing thee to thy rest' but we persuaded her it was against the law. In the end we just put up a smooth board above his grave along a lonely road. On the board I wrote with an indelible pencil 'Cave Canem.' Mother was quite pleased with the simple classic dignity of the old Latin epitaph.

University Days

I PASSED all the other courses that I took at my University, but I could never pass botany. This was because all botany students had to spend several hours a week in a laboratory looking through a microscope at plant cells, and I could never see through a microscope. I never once saw a cell through a microscope. This used to enrage my instructor. He would wander around the laboratory pleased with the progress all the students were making in drawing the involved and, so I am told, interesting structure of flower cells, until he came to me. I would just be standing there. 'I can't see anything,' I would say. He would begin patiently enough, explaining how anybody can see through a microscope, but he would always end up in a fury, claiming that I could *too* see through a microscope but just pretended that I couldn't. 'It takes away from the beauty of flowers anyway,' I used to tell him. 'We are not concerned with beauty in this course,' he would say. 'We are concerned solely with what I may call the *mechanics* of flars.' 'Well,' I'd say, 'I can't see anything.' 'Try it just once again,' he'd say, and I would put my eye to the microscope and see nothing at all, except now and again a nebulous milky substance – a phenomenon of maladjustment. You were supposed to see a vivid, restless clockwork of sharply defined plant cells. 'I see what looks like a lot of milk,' I would tell him. This, he claimed, was the result of my not having adjusted the microscope properly, so he would readjust it for me, or rather, for himself. And I would look again and see milk.

I finally took a deferred pass, as they called it, and waited a year and tried again. (You had to pass one of the biological sciences or you couldn't graduate.) The professor had come back from vacation brown as a berry, bright-eyed, and eager to explain cell-structure again to his classes. 'Well,' he said to me, cheerily, when we met in the first laboratory hour of the semester, 'we're going to see cells this time, aren't we?' 'Yes, sir,' I said. Students to right of me and to left of me and in front of me were seeing cells; what's more, they were quietly drawing pictures of them in their notebooks. Of course, I didn't see anything.

'We'll try it,' the professor said to me, grimly, 'with every adjustment of the microscope known to man. As God is my witness, I'll arrange this glass so that you see cells through it or I'll give up teaching. In twenty-two years of botany, I—' He cut off abruptly for he was beginning to quiver all over, like Lionel Barrymore, and he genuinely wished to hold onto his temper; his scenes with me had taken a great deal out of him.

So we tried it with every adjustment of the microscope known to man.

With only one of them did I see anything but blackness or the familiar lacteal opacity, and that time I saw, to my pleasure and amazement, a variegated constellation of flecks, specks, and dots. These I hastily drew. The instructor, noting my activity, came back from an adjoining desk, a smile on his lips and his eyebrows high in hope. He looked at my cell drawing. 'What's that?' he demanded, with a hint of a squeal in his voice. 'That's what I saw,' I said. 'You didn't, you didn't, you *did*n't!' he screamed, losing control of his temper instantly, and he bent over and squinted into the microscope. His head snapped up. 'That's your eye!' he shouted. 'You've fixed the lens so that it reflects! You've drawn your eye!'

Another course that I didn't like, but somehow managed to pass, was economics. I went to that class straight from the botany class, which didn't help me any in understanding either subject. I used to get them mixed up. But not as mixed up as another student in my economics class who came there direct from a physics laboratory. He was a tackle on the football team, named Bolenciecwcz. At that time Ohio State University had one of the best football teams in the country, and Bolenciecwcz was one of its outstanding stars. In order to be eligible to play it was necessary for him to keep up in his studies, a very difficult matter, for while he was not dumber than an ox he was not any smarter. Most of his professors were lenient and helped him along. None gave him more hints, in answering questions, or asked him simpler ones than the economics professor, a thin, timid man named Bassum. One day when we were on the subject of transportation and distribution, it came Bolenciecwcz's turn to answer a question. 'Name one means of transportation,' the professor said to him. No light came into the big tackle's eyes. 'Just any means of transportation,' said the professor. Bolenciecwcz sat staring at him. 'That is,' pursued the professor, 'any medium, agency, or method of going from one place to another.' Bolenciecwcz had the look of a man who is being led into a trap. 'You may choose among steam, horse-drawn, or electrically propelled vehicles,' said the instructor. 'I might suggest the one which we commonly take in making long journeys across land.' There was a profound silence in which everybody stirred uneasily, including Bolenciecwcz and Mr Bassum. Mr Bassum abruptly broke this silence in an amazing manner. 'Choo-choo-choo,' he said, in a low voice, and turned instantly scarlet. He glanced appealingly around the room. All of us, of course, shared Mr Bassum's desire that Bolenciecwcz should stay abreast of the class in economics, for the Illinois game, one of the hardest and most important of the season, was only a week off. 'Toot, toot, too-toooooooot!' some student with a deep voice moaned, and we all looked encouragingly at Bolenciecwcz. Somebody else gave a fine imitation of a locomotive letting off steam. Mr Bassum himself rounded off the little show. 'Ding, dong, ding, dong,' he said, hopefully. Bolenciecwcz was staring at the floor now, trying to think, his great brow furrowed, his huge hands rubbing together, his face red.

'How did you come to college this year, Mr Bolenciecwcz?' asked the professor. '*Chuf*fa chuffa, *chuf*fa chuffa.'

He was beginning to quiver all over like Lionel Barrymore

'M'father sent me,' said the football player.

'What on?' asked Bassum.

'I git an 'lowance,' said the tackle, in a low, husky voice, obviously embarrassed.

'No, no,' said Bassum. 'Name a means of transportation. What did you *ride* here on?'

'Train,' said Bolenciecwcz.

'Quite right,' said the professor. 'Now, Mr Nugent, will you tell us –'

If I went through anguish in botany and economics – for different reasons – gymnasium work was even worse. I don't even like to think about it. They wouldn't let you play games or join in the exercises with your glasses on and I couldn't see with mine off. I bumped into professors, horizontal bars, agricultural students, and swinging iron rings. Not being able to see, I could take it but I couldn't dish it out. Also, in order to pass gymnasium (and you had to pass it to graduate) you had to learn to swim if you didn't know how. I didn't like the swimming pool, I didn't like swimming, and I didn't like the swimming instructor, and after all these years I still don't. I never swam but I passed my gym work anyway, by having another student give my gymnasium number (978) and swim across the pool in my place. He was a quiet, amiable blonde youth, number 473, and he would have seen through a microscope for me if we could have got away with it, but we couldn't get away with it. Another thing I didn't like about gymnasium work was that they made you strip the day you registered. It is impossible for me to be happy when I am stripped and being asked a lot of questions. Still, I did better than a lanky agricultural student who was cross-examined just before I was. They asked each student what college he was in – that is, whether Arts, Engineering, Commerce, or Agriculture. 'What college are you in?' the instructor snapped at the youth in front of me. 'Ohio State University,' he said promptly.

It wasn't that agricultural student but it was another a whole lot like him who decided to take up journalism, possibly on the ground that when farming went to hell he could fall back on newspaper work. He didn't realize, of course, that that would be very much like falling back full-length on a kit of carpenter's tools. Haskins didn't seem cut out for journalism, being too embarrassed to talk to anybody and unable to use a typewriter, but the editor of the college paper assigned him to the cow barns, the sheep house, the horse pavilion, and the animal husbandry department generally. This was a genuinely big 'beat,' for it took up five times as much ground and got ten times as great a legislative appropriation as the College of Liberal Arts. The agricultural student knew animals, but nevertheless his stories were dull and colourlessly written. He took all afternoon on each of them, on account of having to hunt for each letter on the typewriter. Once in a while he had to ask somebody to help him hunt. 'C' and 'L,' in particular, were hard letters for him to find. His editor finally got pretty much annoyed at the farmer-journalist because his pieces were so uninteresting. 'See here, Haskins,' he snapped at him one day, 'Why is it we never have anything hot from you on the horse pavilion? Here we have two hundred head of horses on this campus – more than any other university in the Western Conference except Purdue – and yet you never get any real low down on them. Now shoot over to the horse barns and dig up something lively.' Haskins shambled out and came back in about an hour; he said he had something. 'Well, start it off snappily,' said the editor.

Bolenciecwcz was trying to think

'Something people will read.' Haskins set to work and in a couple of hours brought a sheet of typewritten paper to the desk; it was a two-hundred-word story about some disease that had broken out among the horses. Its opening sentence was simple but arresting. It read: 'Who has noticed the sores on the tops of the horses in the animal husbandry building?'

Ohio State was a land grant university and therefore two years of military drill was compulsory. We drilled with old Springfield rifles and studied the tactics of the Civil War even though the World War was going on at the time. At 11 o'clock each morning thousands of freshmen and sophomores used to deploy over the campus, moodily creeping up on the old chemistry building. It was good training for the kind of warfare that was waged at Shiloh but it had no connection with what was going on in Europe. Some people used to think there was German money behind it, but they didn't dare say so or they would have been thrown in jail as German spies. It was a period of muddy thought and marked, I believe, the decline of higher education in the Middle West.

As a soldier I was never any good at all. Most of the cadets were glumly indifferent soldiers, but I was no good at all. Once General Littlefield, who was commandant of the cadet corps, popped up in front of me during regimental drill and snapped, 'You are the main trouble with this university!' I think he meant that my type was the main trouble with the university but he may have meant me individually. I was mediocre at drill, certainly – that is, until my senior year. By that time I had drilled longer than anybody else in the Western Conference, having failed at military at the end of each preceding year so that I had to do it all over again. I was the only senior still in uniform. The uniform which, when new, had made me look like an interurban railway conductor, now that it had become faded and too tight made me look like Bert Williams in his bellboy act. This had a definitely bad effect on my morale. Even so, I had become by sheer practice little short of wonderful at squad manœuvres.

One day General Littlefield picked our company out of the whole regiment and tried to get it mixed up by putting it through one movement after another as fast as we could execute them: squads right, squads left, squads on right into line, squads right about, squads left front into line, etc. In about three minutes one hundred and nine men were marching in one direction and I was marching away from them at an angle of forty degrees, all alone. 'Company, halt!' shouted General Littlefield, 'That man is the only man who has it right!' I was made a corporal for my achievement.

The next day General Littlefield summoned me to his office. He was swatting flies when I went in. I was silent and he was silent too, for a long time. I don't think he remembered me or why he had sent for me, but he didn't want to admit it. He swatted some more flies, keeping his eyes on them narrowly before he let go with the swatter. 'Button up your coat!' he snapped. Looking back on it now I can see that he meant me although he was looking at a fly, but I just stood there. Another fly came to rest on a paper in front of the general and began rubbing its hind legs together. The general lifted the swatter cautiously. I moved restlessly and the fly flew away. 'You startled him!' barked General Littlefield, looking at me severely. I said I was sorry. 'That won't help the situation!' snapped the General, with cold military logic. I didn't see what I could do except offer to chase some more flies toward his desk, but I didn't say anything. He stared out the window at the faraway figures of co-eds crossing the campus toward the library. Finally, he told me I could go. So I went. He either didn't know which cadet I was or else he forgot what he wanted to see me about. It may have been that he wished to apologize for having called me the main trouble with the university; or maybe he had decided to compliment me on my brilliant drilling of the day before and then at the last minute decided not to. I don't know. I don't think about it much any more.

Draft Board Nights

I LEFT the University in June, 1918, but I couldn't get into the army on account of my sight, just as grandfather couldn't get in on account of his age. He applied several times and each time he took off his coat and threatened to whip the men who said he was too old. The disappointment of not getting to Germany (he saw no sense in everybody going to France) and the strain of running around town seeing influential officials finally got him down in bed. He had wanted to lead a division and his chagrin at not even being able to enlist as a private was too much for him. His brother Jake, some fifteen years younger than he was, sat up at night with him after he took to bed, because we were afraid he might leave the house without even putting on his clothes. Grandfather was against the idea of Jake watching over him – he thought it was a lot of tomfoolery – but Jake hadn't been able to sleep at night for twenty-eight years, so he was the perfect person for such a vigil.

On the third night, grandfather was wakeful. He would open his eyes, look at Jake, and close them again, frowning. He never answered any question Jake asked him. About four o'clock that morning, he caught his brother sound asleep in the big leather chair beside the bed. When once Jake did fall asleep he slept deeply, so that grandfather was able to get up, dress himself, undress Jake, and put him in bed without waking him. When my Aunt Florence came into the room at seven o'clock, grandfather was sitting in the chair reading the *Memoirs of U.S. Grant* and Jake was sleeping in the bed. 'He watched while I slept,' said grandfather, 'so now I'm watchin' while he sleeps.' It seemed fair enough.

One reason we didn't want grandfather to roam around at night was that he had said something once or twice about going over to Lancaster, his old home town, and putting his problem up to 'Cump' – that is, General William Tecumseh Sherman, also an old Lancaster boy. We knew that his inability to find Sherman would be bad for him and we were afraid that he might try to get there in the little electric runabout that had been bought for my grandmother. She had become, surprisingly enough, quite skilful at getting around town in it. Grandfather was astonished and a little indignant when he saw her get into the contraption and drive off smoothly and easily. It was her first vehicular triumph over him in almost fifty years of married life and he determined to learn to drive the thing himself. A famous old horseman, he approached it as he might have approached a wild colt. His brow would darken and he would begin to curse. He always leaped into it quickly, as if it might pull out from under him if he didn't get into the seat fast enough. The first few times he tried to run the electric, he went swiftly around in a small circle, drove over the curb, across the sidewalk, and up onto the lawn. We all tried to persuade him to give up, but his spirit was aroused. 'Git that goddam buggy back in the road!' he would say, imperiously. So we would manœuvre it back into the street and he would try again. Pulling too savagely on the guiding-bar – to teach the electric a lesson – was what took him around in a circle, and it was difficult to make him understand that it was best to relax and not get mad. He

About four o'clock he caught his brother asleep

had the notion that if you didn't hold her, she would throw you. And a man who (or so he often told us) had driven a four-horse McCormick reaper when he was five years old did not intend to be thrown by an electric runabout.

Since there was no way of getting him to give up learning to operate the electric, we would take him out to Franklin Park, where the roadways were wide and unfrequented, and spend an hour or so trying to explain the differences between driving a horse and carriage and driving an electric. He would keep muttering all the time; he never got it out of his head that when he took the driver's seat the machine flattened its ears on him, so to speak. After a few weeks, nevertheless, he got so he could run the electric for a hundred yards or so along a fairly straight line. But whenever he took a curve, he invariably pulled or pushed the bar too quickly and too hard and headed for a tree or a flower bed. Someone was always with him and we would never let him take the car out of the park.

One morning when grandmother was all ready to go to market, she called the garage and told them to send the electric around. They said that grandfather had already been there and taken it out. There was a tremendous to-do. We telephoned Uncle Will and he got out his Lozier and we started off to hunt for grandfather. It was not yet seven o'clock and there was fortunately little traffic. We headed for Franklin Park, figuring that he might have gone out there to try to break the car's spirit. One or two early pedestrians had seen a tall old gentleman with a white beard driving a little electric and cussing as he drove. We followed a tortuous trail and found them finally on Nelson Road, about four miles from the town of Shepard. Grandfather was standing in the road shouting, and the back wheels of the electric were deeply entangled in a barbed-wire fence. Two workmen and a farmhand were trying to get the thing loose. Grandfather was in a state of high wrath about the electric. 'The — – – — backed up on me!' he told us.

But to get back to the war. The Columbus draft board never called grandfather for service, which was a lucky thing for them because they would have had to take him. There were stories that several old men of eighty or ninety had been summoned in the confusion, but somehow or other grandfather was missed. He waited every day for the call, but it never came. My own experience was quite different. I was called almost every week, even though I had been exempted from service the first time I went before the medical examiners. Either they were never convinced that it was me or else there was some clerical error in the records which was never cleared up. Anyway, there was usually a letter for me on Monday ordering me to report for examination on the second floor of Memorial Hall the following Wednesday at 9 p.m. The second time I went up, I tried to explain to one of the doctors that I had already been exempted. 'You're just a blur to me,' I said, taking off my glasses. 'You're absolutely nothing to me,' he snapped, sharply.

I had to take off all my clothes each time and jog around the hall with a lot of porters and bank presidents' sons and clerks and poets. Our hearts and lungs would be examined, and then our feet; and finally our eyes. That always came last. When the eye specialist got around to me, he would always say, 'Why, you couldn't get into the service with sight like that!' 'I know,' I would say. Then a week or two later I would be summoned again and go through the same rigmarole. The ninth or tenth time I was called, I happened to pick up one of several stethoscopes that were lying on a table and suddenly, instead of finding myself in the line of draft men, I found myself in the line of examiners. 'Hello, doctor,' said one of them, nodding. 'Hello,' I said. That, of course, was before I took my clothes off; I might have managed it naked, but I doubt it. I was assigned, or rather drifted, to the chest-and-lung section, where I began to examine every other man, thus cutting old Dr Ridgeway's work in two. 'I'm glad to have you here, doctor,' he said.

I passed most of the men that came to me, but now and then I would exempt one just to be on the safe side. I began by making each of them hold his breath and then say 'mi, mi, mi, mi,' until I noticed Ridgeway looking at me curiously. He, I discovered, simply made them say 'ah,' and sometimes he didn't make them say anything. Once I got hold of a man who, it came out later, had swallowed a watch – to make the doctors believe there was something wrong with him inside (it was a common subterfuge: men swallowed nails,

There was a tremendous to-do

hairpins, ink, etc., in an effort to be let out). Since I didn't know what you were supposed to hear through a stethoscope, the ticking of the watch at first didn't surprise me, but I decided to call Dr Ridgeway into consultation, because nobody else had ticked. 'This man seems to tick,' I said to him. He looked at me in surprise but didn't say anything. Then he thumped the man, laid his ear to his chest, and finally tried the stethoscope. 'Sound as a dollar,' he said. 'Listen lower down,' I told him. The man indicated his stomach. Ridgeway gave him a haughty, indignant look. 'That is for the abdominal men to worry about,' he said, and moved off. A few minutes later, Dr Blythe Ballomy got around to the man and listened, but he didn't blink an eye; his grim expression never changed. 'You have swallowed a watch, my man,' he said, crisply. The draftee reddened in embarrassment and uncertainty. 'On *purpose*?' he asked. 'That I can't say,' the doctor told him, and went on.

I served with the draft board for about four months. Until the summonses ceased, I couldn't leave town and as long as I stayed and appeared promptly

An abdominal man worrying

for examination, even though I did the examining, I felt that technically I could not be convicted of evasion. During the daytime, I worked as publicity agent for an amusement park, the manager of which was a tall, unexpected young man named Byron Landis. Some years before, he had dynamited the men's lounge in the statehouse annexe for a prank; he enjoyed pouring buckets of water on sleeping persons, and once he had barely escaped arrest for jumping off the top of the old Columbus Transfer Company building with a home-made parachute.

He asked me one morning if I would like to take a ride in the new Scarlet Tornado, a steep and wavy roller-coaster. I didn't want to but I was afraid he would think I was afraid, so I went along. It was about ten o'clock and there was nobody at the park except workmen and attendants and concessionaires in their shirtsleeves. We climbed into one of the long gondolas of the roller-coaster and while I was looking around for the man who was going to run it, we began to move off. Landis, I discovered, was running it himself. But it was too late to get out; we had begun to climb, clickety-clockety, up the first steep incline, down the other side of which we careered at eighty miles an hour. 'I didn't know you could run this thing!' I bawled at my companion, as we catapulted up a sixty-degree arch and looped headlong into space. 'I didn't either!' he bawled back. The racket and the rush of air were terrific as we roared into

the pitch-black Cave of Darkness and came out and down Monohan's Leap, so called because a workman named Monohan had been forced to jump from it when caught between two approaching experimental cars while it was being completed. That trip, although it ended safely, made a lasting impression on me. It is not too much to say that it has flavoured my life. It is the reason I shout in my sleep, refuse to ride on the elevated, keep jerking the emergency brake in cars other people are driving, have the sensation of flying like a bird when I first lie down, and in certain months can't keep anything on my stomach.

During my last few trips to the draft board, I went again as a draft prospect, having grown tired of being an examiner. None of the doctors who had been my colleagues for so long recognized me, not even Dr Ridgeway. When he examined my chest for the last time, I asked him if there hadn't been another doctor helping him. He said there had been. 'Did he look anything like me?' I asked. Dr Ridgeway looked at me. 'I don't think so,' he said, 'he was taller.' (I had my shoes off while he was examining me.) 'A good pulmonary man,' added Ridgeway. 'Relative of yours?' I said yes. He sent me on to Dr Quimby, the specialist who had examined my eyes twelve or fifteen times before. He gave me some simple reading tests. 'You could never get into the army with eyes like that,' he said. 'I know,' I told him.

Late one morning, shortly after my last examination, I was awakened by the sound of bells ringing and whistles blowing. It grew louder and more insistent and wilder. It was the Armistice.

A Note at the End

THE hard times of my middle years I pass over, leaving the ringing bells of 1918, with all their false promise, to mark the end of a special sequence. The sharp edges of old reticences are softened in the autobiographer by the passing of time – a man does not pull the pillow over his head when he wakes in the morning because he suddenly remembers some awful thing that happened to him fifteen or twenty years ago, but the confusions and the panics of last year and the year before are too close for contentment. Until a man can quit talking loudly to himself in order to shout down the memories of blunderings and gropings, he is in no shape for the painstaking examination of distress and the careful ordering of events so necessary to a calm and balanced exposition of what, exactly, was the matter. The time I fell out of the gun room in Mr James Stanley's house in Green Lake, New York, is for instance, much too near for me to go into with any peace of mind, although it happened in 1925, the ill-fated year of 'Horses, Horses, Horses' and

A hotel room in Louisville

'Valencia.' There is now, I understand, a porch to walk out onto when you open the door I opened that night, but there wasn't then.

The mistaken exits and entrances of my thirties have moved me several times to some thought of spending the rest of my days wandering aimlessly around the South Seas, like a character out of Conrad, silent and inscrutable. But the necessity for frequent visits to my oculist and dentist has prevented this. You can't be running back from Singapore every few months to get your lenses changed and still retain the proper mood for wandering. Furthermore, my horn-rimmed glasses and my Ohio accent betray me, even when I sit on

They tried to sell me baskets

the terraces of little tropical cafés, wearing a pith helmet, staring straight ahead, and twitching a muscle in my jaw. I found this out when I tried wandering around the West Indies one summer. Instead of being followed by the whispers of men and the glances of women, I was followed by bead salesmen and native women with postcards. Nor did any dark girl, looking at all like Tondelaya in 'White Cargo,' come forward and offer to go to pieces with me. They tried to sell me baskets.

Under these circumstances it is impossible to be inscrutable and a wanderer who isn't inscrutable might just as well be back at Broad and High Streets in Columbus sitting in the Baltimore Dairy Lunch. Nobody from Columbus has ever made a first rate wanderer in the Conradean tradition. Some of them have been fairly good at disappearing for a few days to turn up in a hotel in Louisville with a bad headache and no recollection of how they got there, but they always scurry back to their wives with some cock-and-bull story of having lost their memory or having gone away to attend the annual convention of the Fraternal Order of Eagles.

There was, of course, even for Conrad's Lord Jim, no running away. The cloud of his special discomfiture followed him like a pup, no matter what ships he took or what wildernesses he entered. In the pathways between office and home and home and the houses of settled people there are always, ready to snap at you, the little perils of routine living, but there is no escape in the unplanned tangent, the sudden turn. In Martinique, when the whistle blew for the tourists to get back on the ship, I had a quick, wild, and lovely moment when I decided I wouldn't get back on the ship. I did, though. And I found that somebody had stolen the pants of my dinner jacket.

The Owl in the Attic

FOR ALTHEA

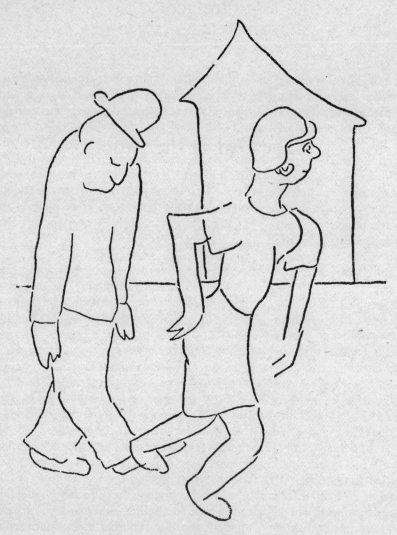

A gentleman and his wife going to call on friends

Preface

I SAW Thurber first in the summer of 1919. It was a steaming forenoon, when even the hot streets of Raritonga seemed deserted. The little packet-boat *Numidia* had slipped into the harbour during the night, to discharge copra, and when I saw a skiff being lowered I walked down toward the beach. The skiff had hardly grounded when Thurber stepped ashore, carrying a volume of Henry James and leading a honey bear by a small chain. As it happened, I was not to meet him again until years later, for my schooner left the island that afternoon to coast lazily eastward on the trade wind; but somehow his name kept bobbing up in the port gossip of those seas, and although the news was always fragmentary, the Thurber legend was, I later realized, steadily building in my mind.

There had been some talk in MacDonald's store about the *Numidia* – her doubtful tonnage and her unexplained visit to Penang the previous spring. Where Thurber had come aboard nobody seemed to know. I had drifted all the way to Manila before I again heard his name mentioned, this time in connection with a native ceremony on one of the islands when a young girl named Maia-Lo ('For-you-I-have-no-desire') had woven a special reed mat for the tall dark stranger to occupy alongside her own lovely self. Thurber, only faintly grasping the significance of the gesture, had hung about, trying to talk to the girl's uncle instead of lying down directly on the mat. The delay, so the story went, would have cost him his life if it hadn't been that they found a mechanical match-box trick in his pocket, and the uncle became so intrigued with its mysteries that he forgot the insult.

So the Thurber story ran – always fragmentary, vague. Once he had spent a night in a hotel room in Singapore with another man, trying to untangle a snarled fishing-line. After three hours of pulling the free end of the line through the loop of the snarl, he had abruptly got up and left the hotel. His companion never saw him again. Once, in a sailing-ship in which the cook had been put in irons for knifing a passenger, Thurber had volunteered to prepare breakfast. In the dim light he had made pancake batter out of ordinary stump powder, and had blown up the galley and part of the quarter-deck. It was in this affair that he lost the sight in his left eye, a circumstance that has since greatly influenced his character, because it carried with it the necessity always of sitting on the left side of a person. Once, in Kobe, sick of a fever and believed dying, he had taken the advice of an aunt who wrote him from Columbus, Ohio, directing him to drink tea made from sheep feet. Thurber recovered almost immediately, although the aunt, as I found out later, died.

It is impossible, as well as inadvisable, to sketch his life adequately. I am simply setting down these unconnected incidents, hoping to give some picture of the man, without which (or as Thurber would say 'without *whom*') it is difficult to understand the nature of his works. I finally met Thurber in New York, in the spring of 1926. He had come there for a week, to gather up a few soiled clothes which he had left once while passing through on his way to Paris, and had stayed on, taking up his abode in a poorly lighted room on West Thirteenth Street, now the site of a garage. In those days he had very little money and was in constant dread of something falling on his head from buildings – as he still is. I see him now, slinking around the streets, trailing a thin melancholy and leading a terrier bitch. He was a frequent visitor to the downtown restaurants and cafés, and was usually seen at a late breakfast, a morning newspaper on the table, his dog underneath. Sometimes, instead of the dog there was a girl. He began to write in those days, and later to draw. This talent for drawing simple objects with an unsharpened pencil he decided to leave undeveloped, on the advice of friends.

Also in these days he was forming the habits of living and thinking which later were to come out in his writings and drawings. He was early impressed by the seeming impossibility of completing a grammatical sentence. Forced to earn a living by his pen, he actually went through with many sentences that a more scholarly or a more pecunious person would have dropped half-way. It was his early struggle with pronouns and infinitives that we see reflected in his series of articles on modern English usage – a series which here for the first time is collected in book form, but the several chapters of which have worked their way separately into the curricula of many Eastern universities as models of English prose and imperfect communication.

Coincidental with Thurber's grammatical confusion came a renewed interest in and affection for small animals. Peculiarly sensible of a pet's predicament in a house occupied by people, he came to view with a wide sympathy the curious irrelevancies of man and beast, their gropings to come closer to each other, and the wall that divides them. From his boyhood in Columbus, Ohio, when an English bulldog had dominated the Thurber household without actually lending anything to it, he had sensed the dismal as well as the piquant aspects of pethood. Later, when his Scottish terrier gave birth to seven young ones in a two-room apartment in New York City, he enlarged his love for animals and deepened his experience.

In his New York existence, however, more than any other thing he was concerned with the relation between the sexes – that is, as between people rather than animals. Appalled at the grave thrumming of sex itself in the metropolis, he was at once amused and frightened by its manifestations among his friends, many of them married. This was the 'household' phase of the Thurber ordeal, the phase in which he vainly tried to rationalize the physical equipment of an ordinary apartment occupied by two people, and establish the position of kitchenware in relation to eroticism, children and dinner engagements. That he was afraid is obvious from the drawings in the book, the bent or 'stooped' postures of the males contrasting strongly with the erect and happy stance of the females. Into the real quandary of marriage he read a droll sadness. Above the still cool lake of marriage he saw rising the thin white mist of Man's disparity with Woman. In his drawings one finds not only the simple themes of love and misunderstanding, but also the rarer and tenderer insupportabilities. He is the one artist that I have ever known, capable of expressing, in a single drawing, physical embarrassment during emotional strain. That is, it is always apparent to Thurber that at the very moment one's heart is caught in an embrace, one's foot may be caught in a piano stool.

Thurber has now served his apprenticeship in life. He has learned to write simple English sentences, he has gone through with the worming of puppies, and he has practically given up trying to find out anything about sex. What he will go on to, no one can say, not knowing the man. At least, safe in these pages, are the records of his sorrows.

E.B.W.

Tea at Mrs Armsby's

'MY HUSBAND,' said little Mrs Monroe, 'is a collector.'
This statement surprised no one more than Mr Monroe, who was not a collector.

'And what do you collect, Mr Monroe?' asked Mrs Armsby, politely.

'Handkerchiefs,' said Mrs Monroe. 'He collects handkerchiefs.'

It was apparent to Mr Monroe that his wife's remarkable statements were the unfortunate result of their having attended a cocktail party before dropping in, late, at Mrs Armsby's. The teas which Mrs Armsby gave on Sundays were the sort at which tea is served. The people who attended them did not attend cocktail parties, which indeed were events almost as alien to their experience as the murders in the Rue Morgue. The Monroes did not like to go to Mrs Armsby's, but in nearly everyone's life there is a Mrs Armsby, at whose Sunday teas one feels obliged, at long intervals, to drop in – she was a schoolgirl chum of one's mother, or her husband is an influential man who might help one's own husband to advance. The Monroes were quite young. The others were quite middle-aged and, up to this point, had been discussing the stock market.

'My husband also collects pencils,' said Mrs Monroe. It was warm in the room. The closeness of the air had, as it were, 'got to' Mrs Monroe. One saw this. Fortunately, not more than one – Mr Monroe himself – saw this, for to the others there was no relationship between the atmosphere and the odd direction the small talk had thus suddenly taken.

'Indeed?' said Mrs Penwarden.

'My husband has eight hundred and seventy-four thousand pencils,' said Mrs Monroe.

'You collect pencils?' said Mrs Armsby, with polite interest.

Mr Monroe was aware that his wife was alluding in a fanciful and distressingly untimely manner to a habit of his, which was to bring home from the office several pencils each day and to leave them on his desk, or failing that, on her dressing table. She frequently spoke to him disapprovingly about such things. For example, he had an unfortunate predilection for leaving towels on her dressing table, too.

'Yes – I – have got a few pencils together – nothing much,' said Mr Monroe, with becoming modesty.

'He has seventy hundred and eighty-nine hundred thousand,' said Mrs Monroe.

'Really?' said Mrs Penwarden, with evident interest.

'I became interested in pencils in the Sudan,' said Mr Monroe. 'The heat is so intense there that it melts the lead in the average Venus or Faber –'

'Or Flaber,' said his wife.

'Or Flaber, as the natives call it,' continued Mr Monroe. 'The native Sudanese pencil, or vledt, will resist even the most terrific heat – even oxy-acetylene. My vledt formed the basis for my collection, which is now of a certain minor importance, perhaps.' At this point Mr Monroe was forced to pause, for his invention had run thin, largely owing to the fact that he knew very little about pencils and nothing at all about the Sudan.

'It must be interesting to collect pencils,' said Mr Penwarden.

'My husband collects towels, too,' said Mrs Monroe.

'It must be interesting to collect pencils,' said Mr Penwarden

'But perhaps my most amusing collection,' said Mr Monroe, 'as long as we seem, ha ha, to be discussing my collections . . . is my match folders.'

'Those little, ah – match folders?' asked Mr Gribbing.

'Yes. I see them as having a certain value – I mean as forming a record of a trend and as a sort of, well – a sort of chronicle of the present – trend.' He had chosen to risk a discussion of match folders rather than towels, but again found it difficult to pretend an easy familiarity with a collection which he did not possess. 'I presume, though,' said Mr Monroe, 'that match folders are a problem to every woman – if her husband brings as many home as I do.' He glanced hopefully from one lady to another and was rewarded by a desultory symposium of viewpoints on paper matches. In this momentary shift of the interest from himself and his wife, he stepped to her side and gripped her shoulder.

'Pull yourself together for the god's sake,' Mr Monroe.

'I want to lie down,' said Mrs Monroe.

'I'll get your things,' said her husband. 'Try not to lie down till I get your things.'

Hurriedly Mr Monroe left the room and brought back his wife's coat and handbag.

'My things,' said Mrs Monroe, with bewildering dignity. Her husband deftly assisted her to rise, a process which was more successful than he had dared hope it would be. Their adieux were finally made without anyone falling,

'Those little, ah – matchfolders?' asked Mr Gribbing

or being thrown, Mrs Monroe abruptly, as is often so happily the case, substituting a charming if rather odd little smile for further statements or observations.

'I should love sometime to see your Sudan pencils,' said Mrs Armsby, at the door.

'You must see them sometime,' said Mr Monroe.

'I had a most enjoyable time,' said Mrs Monroe. It was cooler in the hall. 'Goodbye, Mrs Armsby,' she added.

'So glad,' said Mrs Armsby. 'Goodbye, dear child.' Mr Monroe opened the door.

'Goodbye, Mrs Armsby,' said Mrs Monroe, with just a suspicion of tears. 'Good –'

'Taxi!' shouted Mr Monroe, pulling Mrs Monroe after him, into the street.

The Imperturbable Spirit

MR MONROE stood fingering some canes in a shop in the Fifties. Canes, it occurred to him, were imperturbable. He liked that adjective, which he had been encountering in a book he was reading on God, ethics, morals, humanism, and so on. The word stood staunch, like a bulwark, rumbled, like a caisson. Mr Monroe was pleased to find himself dealing in similes.

He finally decided not to buy a cane. Mrs Monroe was arriving that afternoon on the *Leviathan* and he would need both hands to wave porters around on the dock. His wife had to be looked after. She was such a child. When imperturbability was at the flood in Mr Monroe, his wife's nature took on for him a curiously dependent and childlike quality, not at all annoying, considerably endearing, and wholly mythical.

From the cane shop Mr Monroe wandered to a bookstore. On his imperturbable days it was almost impossible for him to work. He liked to brood and reflect and occasionally to catch glimpses of himself in store windows, slot-machine mirrors, etc., brooding and reflecting. He bought a paper-back novel, in the original French, by André Maurois. The gesture – it was purely that for the simple reason that he did not read French – added a vague fillip to his day. Then he walked part way up Fifth Avenue, in the brisk air, and finally hailed a cab.

When he got home he took a bath, put on clean linen and another suit, and sank into a great chair to read some more in the book on God, morals, and so on. In the course of this he looked up three words in a dictionary, 'eschatological,' 'maleficent,' and 'teleology.' He read the definition of the last word twice, frowned, and let it go. Despite the fact that the outlook for mankind was far from bright in the particular chapter he was reading, Mr Monroe began to feel pretty much the master of his fate. Non-fiction, of a philosophical nature, always affected him that way, regardless of its content.

Mr Monroe wandered leisurely about the pier, complimenting himself on having remembered to get a customs pass, and on the way his mind kept dealing in interesting ideas. With an imperturbable frown, he watched the big liner nosing in. Did fog at sea imply a malign aspect of the cosmos? If it came and went, without incident, did that connote luck, or what? Suppose it shielded an iceberg which sank the ship – did that prove the existence of an antic Malice? Mr Monroe liked the word antic. 'Antic,' he said, half aloud. He wondered vaguely if he, too, should not write a book about morals, malice, menace, and so on, showing how they could be handled by the imperturbable spirit. . . .

Little Mrs Monroe, burdened with coats and bundles, rosy, lovely, at length appeared. Mr Monroe's heart leapt up, but at the same time he set himself as if to receive a service in tennis. He remembered (oh, keenly) as he stepped toward her, how she was wont to regard him as a person likely to 'go to pieces' over trifles. Well, she would find him a changed man. He kissed her warmly, but withal in such a strangely masterful manner, that she was at first a little surprised – a tennis player taken aback by a sudden change in the tactics of an old, old opponent. In three minutes of backcourt rallying she figured out that he had been reading something, but she said nothing. She let his lobs go unkilled.

When Mrs Monroe stood in line at the desk where they assign inspectors, he offered to take her place. 'No, no,' she whispered. 'Just pretend you're not with me. It'll be easier.' A slow pallor came upon Mr Monroe's face.

'Whatta y' got?' he croaked.

'A dozen bottles of Benedictine,' she breathed.

'Oh my God!' said Mr Monroe, dropping, figuratively, his racquet.

An inspector stepped forward and stood waiting.

'So glad,' murmured Mrs Monroe to her husband, collectedly, as to a casual acquaintance. Mr Monroe fumbled at his hat, and wandered away, tugging at the left sleeve of his coat, a nervous gesture of his. She'd never get away with it. Twelve bottles! Quarts, probably, or magnums – no, it didn't come that way. Well, it came in big, bulky bottles anyway. Let's see, hadn't a new conspiracy law come in? Couldn't they send you to jail now? He could see himself in court, being flayed by a state's attorney. Mr Monroe had a phobia about law-breaking, even about ordinance-breaking. . . . 'Now, gentlemen of the jury . . .' The state's attorney put on his nose glasses, brought out a letter

They were really porters, but Mr Monroe thought they were guards

and read it in nasty, slow accents, a horrible, damning letter, which Mr Monroe had never seen before, but which, fiendishly enough, *was in his own handwriting*. The jury stirred.

'Now wait a minute –' began Mr Monroe, aloud.

'What *are* you talking about?' demanded his wife.

The courtroom mercifully faded. Mr Monroe turned and stared at his wife. 'Ah – ha, dear!' he said, thickly. 'I'm all through!' she said, brightly. 'Let's go home.'

By the time they reached their house, Mr Monroe was his old self, or rather his new self, again. He had even pretty well persuaded himself that his iron nerve had got the Benedictine through the customs. His strange, masterful manner came back. No sooner had he got into his slippers, however, and reached for his book, than Mrs Monroe, in the next room, emitted a small squeal. 'My hatbox!' she cried. 'We left it at the dock!'

'Oh, damn! damn!' said Mr Monroe. 'Well, I'll have to go back after it, that's all. What was in it?'

'Some cute hats I got for almost nothing and – well, that's about all.'

'*About* all?'

'Well, three of the bottles.'

Mr Monroe squealed, in turn. 'Ah, God,' he said, bitterly.

'There's nothing to be afraid of now, silly,' his wife said. 'They were passed through!'

'I'm not afraid; I'll handle this,' murmured her husband.

In a sort of stupor he went out, hailed a cab, and climbed in. Life got you. A scheme of morals? A shield against menace? What good did that do? Impertur – ha! Menace got you – no bigger than a man's hand at first, no bigger than a hatbox. . . . 'Now, gentlemen of the jury . . . conspiracy . . . defraud the government . . . seditious . . .'

Mr Monroe crept whitely through the wide street entrance to the docks. The last stragglers were piling baggage into taxis in the noisy channel beyond. A few suitcases and boxes were still coming down the travelling platform from the dock level above. At the bottom, where they tumbled in a heap, two guards stood to receive them. They were really porters, but Mr Monroe thought they were guards. They had big jaws. One of them gradually turned into a state's attorney before Mr Monroe's very eyes! The stricken husband wandered idly over to the other side of the moving platform. There stood a lonely, sinister hatbox, a trap, a pitfall, Exhibit A. 'Now, gentlemen . . .'

'That your box, brother?' asked the state's attorney.

'Oh, no,' said Mr Monroe, 'nope.' The porter seemed disappointed. Mr Monroe walked out into the channel where the taxis were. Then he walked back again; out again; and back again. The guards had turned away and were fussing with a trunk. Mr Monroe trembled. He walked stiffly to the hatbox, picked it up, and walked stiffly through the doorway, out into the street.

'Hey!' cried a loud voice. Mr Monroe broke into a run. 'Taxi!' continued the loud voice. But Mr Monroe was a hundred yards away. He ran three blocks

without stopping, walked half a block, and ran again. He came home by a
devious route, rested for a while outside his door, and went in. . . .

   That night Mr Monroe read to his wife from the morals, ethics, and imperturbability book. He read in a deep, impressive voice, and slowly, for there
was a lot his wife wouldn't grasp at once.

Mr Monroe Outwits a Bat

THE Monroes opened their summer place a little late, for carking cares had kept them long in town. The grass was greening and tangled when they arrived, and the house had a woodsy smell. Mr Monroe took a deep breath. 'I'll get a great sleep tonight,' he said. He put on some old clothes, pottered around, inspecting doors and windows, whistling. After dinner he went out under the stars and smelled the clear fine air. Abruptly there came to his ears a little scream from inside the house – the scream his wife gave when she dropped a cup or when some other trivial tragedy of the kitchen occurred. Mr Monroe hurried inside.

'Spider!' cried Mrs Monroe. 'Oh, kill it, kill it!' She always held that a spider, encountered but not slain, turned up in one's bed at night. Mr Monroe loved to kill spiders for his wife. He whacked this one off a tea towel with a newspaper, and scooped it outside the door into the petunia bed. It gave him a feeling of power, and enhanced the sweetness of his little wife's dependence on him. He was still glowing with his triumph, in a small, warm way, when he went to bed.

'Goodnight, dear,' he called, deeply. His voice was always a little deeper than usual, after a triumph.

'Goodnight, dear,' she called back from her room.

The night was sweet and clear. Nice old creaking sounds ran down the steps and back up again. Some of them sounded like the steps of a person.

'Afraid, dear?' he called out.

'Not with you here,' she answered, sleepily. There was a long, pleasant silence. Mr Monroe began to drowse. A very ominous sound brought him out of it, a distinct flut, a firm, insistent, rhythmic flut.

'Bat!' muttered Mr Monroe to himself.

At first he took the advent of the bat calmly. It seemed to be flying high, near the ceiling. He even boldly raised up on his elbows and peered through the dark. As he did so the bat, apparently out of sheer malice, almost clipped the top of his head. Mr Monroe scrambled under the covers, but instantly recovered his composure and put his head out again – just as the bat, returning in its orbit, skimmed across the bed once more. Mr Monroe pulled the covers over his head. It was the bat's round.

'Restless, dear?' called his wife, through her open door.

'What?' he said.

'Why, what's the matter?' she asked, slightly alarmed at his muffled tone.

'I'm all right, it's okay,' responded Mr Monroe, from under the covers.

'You sound funny,' said his wife. There was a pause.

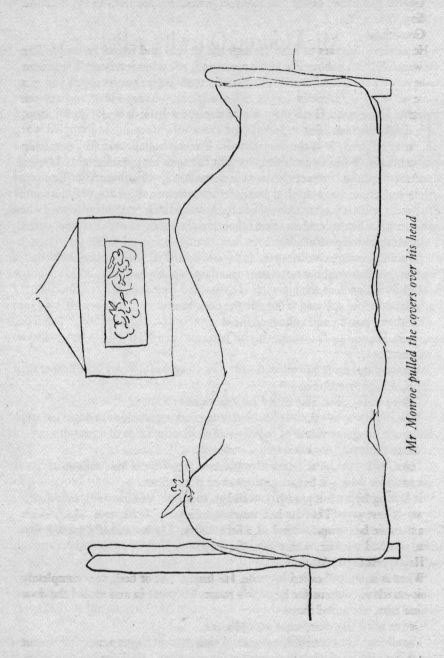

Mr Monroe pulled the covers over his head

'Goodnight, dear,' called Mr Monroe, poking his head out to say this, and pulling it in again.

'Goodnight.'

He strained his ears to hear through the covers, and found he could. The bat was still flitting above the bed in measured, relentless intervals. The notion came to the warm and stuffy Mr Monroe that the incessant repetition of a noise at regular intervals might drive a person crazy. He dismissed the thought, or tried to. If the dripping of water on a man's head, slowly, drip, drip, drip – flut, flut, flut . . .

'Damn it,' said Mr Monroe to himself. The bat was apparently just getting into its swing. It was flying faster. The first had just been practice. Mr Monroe suddenly bethought himself of a great spread of mosquito netting lying in a closet across the room. If he could get that and put it over the bed, he could sleep in peace. He poked his nose out from under a sheet, reached out a hand, and stealthily felt around for a match on a table by the bed – the light switch was yards away. Gradually his head and shoulders emerged. The bat seemed to be waiting for just this move. It zipped past his cheek. He flung himself back under the covers, with a great squeaking of springs.

'John?' called his wife.

'What's the matter now?' he asked, querulously.

'What *are* you doing?' she demanded.

'There's a bat in the room, if you want to know,' he said. 'And it keeps scraping the covers.'

'Scraping the covers?'

'Yes, scraping the covers.'

'It'll go away,' said his wife. 'They go away.'

'I'll drive it away!' shouted John Monroe, for his wife's tone was that of a mother addressing a child. 'How the devil the damn bat ever –' his voice grew dim because he was now pretty far under the bed clothes.

'I can't hear you, dear,' said Mrs Monroe. He popped his head out.

'I say how long is it before they go away?' he asked.

'It'll hang by its feet pretty soon and go to sleep,' said his wife, soothingly. 'It won't hurt you.' This last had a curious effect on Mr Monroe. Much to his own surprise he sat upright in bed, a little angry. The bat actually got him this time, brushed his hair, with a little 'Squeep!'

'Hey!' yelled Mr Monroe.

'What *is* it, dear?' called his wife. He leaped out of bed, now completely panic-stricken, and ran for his wife's room. He went in and closed the door behind him, and stood there.

'Get in with me, dear,' said Mrs Monroe.

'I'm all right,' he retorted, irritably. 'I simply want to get something to rout that thing with. I couldn't find anything in my room.' He flicked on the lights.

'There's no sense in your getting all worn out fighting a bat,' said his wife. 'They're terribly quick.' There seemed to him to be an amused sparkle in her eyes.

'Well, I'm terribly quick too,' grumbled Mr Monroe, trying to keep from shivering, and he slowly folded a newspaper into a sort of club. With this in his hand he stepped to the door. 'I'll shut your door after me,' he said, 'so the bat won't get in your room.' He went out, firmly closing the door behind him. He crept slowly along the hall till he came to his own room. He waited a while and listened. The bat was still going strong. Mr Monroe lifted the paper club and struck the jamb of the door, from the outside, a terrific blow. 'Wham!' went the blow. He hit again. 'Wham!'

'Did you get it, dear?' called his wife, her voice coming dimly through her door.

'Okay,' cried her husband, 'I got it.' He waited a long while. Then he slipped, on tiptoe, to a couch in the corridor halfway between his room and his wife's and gently, ever so gently, let himself down upon it. He slept lightly, because he was pretty chilly, until dawn, got up and tiptoed to his room. He peered in. The bat was gone. Mr Monroe got into bed and went to sleep.

The 'Wooing' of Mr Monroe

LITTLE Mrs Monroe met the challenge of the very blonde lady with all of her charming directness. She went to Miss Lurell's apartment and said to her, quite simply, 'I am Mrs John Monroe. I have come to tell you some things about John I think you should know.' The other woman met her simplicity with icy reticence. 'Please understand,' pursued Mrs Monroe, 'that I do not wish to interfere. John has told me of the strange beauty of it all. I just wanted to warn you that John is simply terrible with machinery.'

'There is no machinery in our association that I can think of,' said the lovely Miss Lurell, coldly.

'Oh,' said Mrs Monroe, 'there will be. May I smoke?' She lighted a cigarette, her first in months. 'Machinery is always bobbing up in John's life. He knows nothing at all about it, but I will say for him that he never runs from it. I might almost say that he attacks it. He attacks machinery.'

'I don't believe I understand,' said the other, as if to imply that she did not wish to understand. Mrs Monroe was about to inhale some smoke, thought better of it – she always choked – and smiled amicably.

'Not long ago,' she began, 'we went for a motor trip to John's university; he hadn't been back there for years. We stayed at a charming place on the campus, called the Union. It was very peaceful. We could see apple trees in blossom, from our window. It was early May –'

'Pray spare yourself memories which can only hurt,' murmured the other woman.

'Oh, it was really quite funny.' Mrs Monroe permitted herself what she had intended to be a gay, rippling laugh. 'We had been in our room only ten minutes, when John went across the hall to take a shower in a great tiled shower-room for alumni guests. I remember it was twilight, soft and dreamy –' Miss Lurell made a sound as of one who dreads sentimental tears. 'Well,' continued Mrs Monroe, 'John had forgotten to bring his bathrobe, of course, so he wore his raincoat. He always forgets his bathrobe – and theatre tickets.'

'I don't see what you can possibly hope to establish – by all this,' interrupted the blonde lady.

'I am telling you such an intimate story, because this was so typical of John,' said his wife. 'You see he has never really taken a successful shower in his life. He always gets the water to running too cold or too hot. This time it ran too cold. He kept twisting the handle and swearing until a man in an adjoining shower told him to turn it farther to the right. John shot it all the way to the right. Instantly a stream of boiling water flooded the bath. John didn't get

scalded, because he has learned not to get fully into a shower: he stands outside and sticks his feet in and then his shoulders. You see, I knew you wouldn't
have had any experience of John's showers –'

'You were quite right,' said the other, frigidly.

'Well, in a few seconds the whole place was a fog of steam and the heat was
frightful. John couldn't reach into the compartment again and turn the handle
back, so he began to go "Woo! Woo!" – like a child. He always goes "Woo!

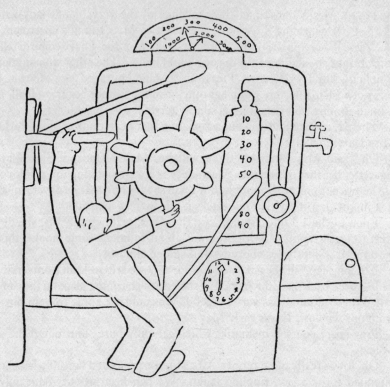

*The university engineer had to shut off the water in the whole
institution*

Woo!" when things go wrong with machinery. Of course he writes beautiful
sonnets, which I am sure you appreciate perhaps more deeply than I do, and
of course mechanical things are of no importance, but one must know what
to do with him in a case like this.'

'And what did *you* do?' asked Miss Lurell.

'Well, my dear, first the other man in the boiler-room – as it had now
become – climbed up on the wall of his shower and tried to reach over and get
at the handle from above, but the intense heat made that impossible. Then he
yelled at John to get a window-stick or something with which he could reach
down and knock the handle back onto "Cold." Of course John was too excited

to be of any use himself. Finally, in a panic, he rushed across the hall into my room, stark, raving –'

'Please!' said Miss Lurell.

'Stark, raving naked,' continued Mrs Monroe. 'He's so funny that way, really I just *screamed*. He was still making that "Woo! Woo!" noise and I knew instantly he had been fooling with the works of something. It was just the way he acted the time he short-circuited all the lights in a theatre one night between acts – we never found out how he did that – he got to wandering around and stumbled into a switch or something, probably thinking it was a water-cooler.'

'Fully dressed, I presume?'

'Oh, it's only when he's driven from a shower or something like that that he hasn't anything on,' said Mrs Monroe, simply. 'Well, he began yelling at me to get him a window-stick or something and finally pulled down a curtain rod, curtain and all, and would have rushed back across the hall with it the way he was, but I threw my negligée over him. When he got back the other man had had to leave, for the heat was unbearable. In the end, the university engineer had to shut off the water in the whole institution – all the campus buildings – they phoned him to do that because there was nobody in the Union who knew where the local water-switch was – I mean the one for that building. It was terrible, but that's the way John is – when he fools with machinery, he always disconnects the whole works. Once in a hotel in Nice, he –'

'May I ask,' cut in the other woman, 'how long you have endured this?'

'Eight years in June,' said Mrs Monroe. 'Naturally, I feel that the – next lady – should know what to expect.'

'Eight years,' murmured Miss Lurell. She rose. Mrs Monroe rose too.

'*Now* you will know what to do,' said Mrs Monroe. 'Don't argue with him when he begins to "Woo!" – just let him have his own way, but summon somebody instantly.'

'I know exactly what to do,' said Miss Lurell, with an odd smile. She accompanied little Mrs Monroe to the door, where she impulsively held out her hand. 'Apropos of nothing,' drawled the very blonde lady, 'may I ask if you play bridge?'

'Oh, very badly,' said Mrs Monroe. 'Unless –' she waved a gloved hand at a passing taxi, 'unless I hold a perfect grand slam.' She smiled back, over her shoulder, and went away.

Mr Monroe and the Moving Men

M R MONROE had never really had any experience in moving household goods before he did it, single-handed, on the eighth of August, 1930. The date will always be fixed in his mind that way, formally, formidably. It was rather an unusual time to move, but it couldn't be helped because on the ninth of August wreckers were going to start tearing down the house. Little Mrs Monroe was away, unavoidably away, terrifyingly away. We have here, then, the makings of a character study – or would have except for the fact that Mr Monroe didn't really have any character. He had a certain charm, yes; but not character. He evaded difficult situations; he had no talent for firm resolution; he immolated badly; and he wasn't even very good at renunciation, except when he was tired or a little sick. Not, you will see, the man to move household goods into storage when his wife is away.

The packers and movers were to come at two o'clock. Mrs Monroe could have told her husband that they wouldn't arrive until four-thirty; or he would have known it himself if always before, when they moved, he had not sneaked away from the house. Always before, Mr Monroe had been just as surprised to find himself in a new place as a mother dog is when she is lifted out from among the shoes in the clothes closet, where she has decided to have her puppies, and put into a lovely airy box with a pink coverlet.

Before she went away, little Mrs Monroe had led her husband from room to room, pointing out what was to go into storage and what was to be sent to the summer place in Connecticut. It was all quite simple, she told him. Apparently John Monroe hadn't been listening, however, for now, as he walked restlessly from room to room, picking up vases and putting them down again, he found he wasn't sure about anything. He wasn't sure about the china and glassware, for one thing. He stood and stared at them, trying to remember what it was his wife had said. All that he could recall was that she had spoken in the slow, precise way in which she always spoke to him in a crisis, as if he were a little deaf or feeble-minded. He decided, finally, that the glassware and china went into storage. Then he decided that they didn't. He tried to remember whether they already had plates and glasses at the summer place and realized, of course, that they must have. They ate there; they lived there. But he also realized that the ways of women are beyond the simple understanding of the masculine mind, and that the fact that a wife already has one set of dishes and glasses is no reason she can't – nay, mustn't, maybe – have another set. Mr Monroe sighed, and went in and turned on the bath water; then he turned it off again, for there were no towels. By this time it was getting on toward three o'clock. He took to wandering aimlessly around, wondering if he should wrap something up, or what.

After a time he came to a halt in front of a large chair – a large, flowered chair, he would have described it to his wife over the phone – which, in her tour around the place with him, little Mrs Monroe, he felt positive, had said something very definite about. He wondered what it had been. It now occurred to him, after deep thought, that his wife must have spoken only about the

They set to work so fast that three tables and a bed were down the stairs before Mr Monroe could say anything

things which were to be saved out of storage – it would have been silly for her to point out the things that were to go to the warehouse because nine-tenths of the things were to go to the warehouse. Obviously, then, reasoned Mr Monroe – and he was a bit proud of his brilliance in this matter – obviously she had pointed out only the things that were to be kept out. Now if he could only remember which things she had pointed out, he would be safe. He decided to move away from the flowered chair, to let it go, for the longer he looked at it the stronger became his conviction that he had never seen it before in his life.

This took him back to the chinaware and glasses. She must have said: 'And this, John. Remember – all this goes to the summer place.' Certainly. Or maybe she had said: 'And watch them when they pack this for storage, John; don't let them break anything.' Hmm. Mr Monroe lighted a cigarette and sat down. It was now almost four o'clock. Suppose the moving men didn't come? Well, if they didn't, the wreckers would tear the place down next day, with the furniture in it. Maybe he could prevail on the wreckers, for some enormous sum, to pack and move the stuff out, before they started wrecking. Of course wreckers wouldn't want to do that, but he saw himself dominating them, when they demurred. 'See here, my men,' he heard himself saying, coldly, '*I'm* in charge here – get that!' He loved himself in that rôle, and was often in it, in his day dreams, which, on this occasion, were abruptly interrupted by the arrival of the packers and movers.

They set to work so fast that three tables and a bed were down the stairs and onto the sidewalk before Mr Monroe could say anything. Well, he was pretty sure about the great big pieces of furniture, anyway – they must go to storage. Great big pieces of furniture were always stored – that's why storage ware-houses were so big. Mr Monroe began to feel that he was getting a grip on the situation. 'What about the china, chief?' one of the men asked him. Mr Monroe hesitated. 'Pack it and let it stand a while,' he said, at last. 'I want to think about it.' From downstairs later he could hear the voices of the men, huge, sweating, rough fellows, joking about him: 'This guy wants to think it over – ja get that, Joe?' Mr Monroe's indecision and evident nervousness began to show up in the movers' attitude toward him. The 'chief' and 'mister' with which they had first addressed him changed to 'buddy' and 'pardner' and finally, as Mr Monroe strove desperately for an air of dignity and authority, to 'sonny.'

In the end, most of the decisions were made by the men themselves. Joe stood with one of his hairy paws on a small writing desk. 'How about this, scout?' he asked. It was a favourite piece of Mrs Monroe's; John couldn't remember whether she had said anything about it; 'Okay,' said Joe, and he moved it out. John hadn't said anything. So it went. Meanwhile two packers had got the chinaware and glasses into two barrels. 'What about it, buddy?' they finally asked the head of the house. 'Well, here's the way it is,' he began. 'You see, it's quite a problem. I –' 'Better store it, sonny,' said one of the men. 'You don't need all this china.' 'Does it look like summer china to you?' asked Mr Monroe, rather meekly. 'Naw, dat's winter china,' said a man named Mike. 'Take it away, Bill.' Bill took it away, out to the storage van. Mr Monroe was now certain that his wife had wanted it saved out for the summer house. 'Oh God, God,' he said to himself, walking around and smoking rapidly.

By the time the movers reached the kitchen utensils, and called them to Mr Monroe's attention, he was becoming overwhelmed by the idiotic conviction that he was in the wrong house. What the hell were kitchen utensils doing here? They were up at the summer place, weren't they? It was only after an agonizing few moments that he realized they had rented the summer house

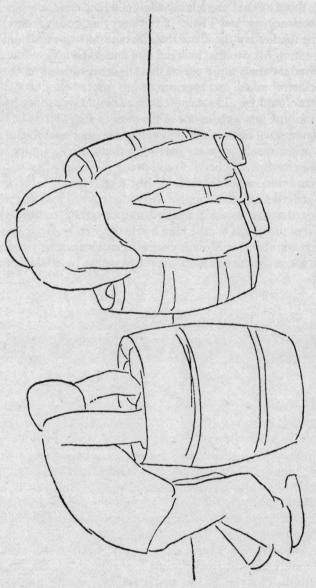

The packers got the chinaware and the glassware into two barrels

furnished. The men, tired of waiting for directions, picked the kitchenware up and carted it out to the van. 'Okay,' murmured Mr Monroe.

At length, there was nothing left but a few odds and ends, one of which was a large tin receptacle marked 'Flour.' 'Can't store this, buddy,' one of the men said, showing the head of the house that the can was two-thirds full of flour, with a spoon in it. Mr Monroe took the can, and when none of the men was looking, shoved the thing into a closet, shut the door, and sighed. 'Everything out of dat closet?' asked Joe, appearing from somewhere. 'Okay,' said Mr Monroe. 'Okay,' said Joe. The men went away as quickly as they had come.

Mr Monroe sank into a chair, one of the three or four objects he had saved out for the summer house. He slowly began to convince himself that all of his decisions – or the men's, anyway – had been right. After all, they were men experienced in moving. He began to feel pretty good about the whole thing; it was over and done with, thank God. Just then, into the edge of his consciousness, stalked a tall, thin thought. Mrs Monroe had told him what to do about getting the stuff to the summer house: a certain transfer man, who delivered out of town, was to call; John had been given his name, his address, and his phone number. Mr Monroe crushed a cigarette in his hand. Then he cried aloud. He couldn't remember the man's name. He couldn't remember anything.

The Monroes Find a Terminal

SHORTLY after nine o'clock little Mrs Monroe began quietly to put on her things. Mr Monroe, who was comfortably fixed in a deep chair, under a lamp, looked up apprehensively over his book.

'Where are we going?' he demanded, suspiciously.

'The French poodle gets in from Chicago tonight at nine-thirty,' said his wife. 'I didn't tell you before because I knew it would spoil your dinner, but it won't be anything, dear. We simply go over and pick up the puppy at the terminal so it won't have to stay all night in the crate. The shipper's letter gives all the directions.' She took a letter from her handbag and gave it to her husband. Mr Monroe, after a profound study, read one sentence aloud, slowly, 'Go to the West Terminal on Sixteenth Street and ask for Messenger Car of New York Central train 608, which gets in about nine-thirty.'

'It's only a step . . .' began Mrs Monroe, soothingly. (The Monroes lived, at the time, in the East Sixties.)

'It's just one of those letters that never work out,' said John Monroe, wisely. 'We'll get way over on Sixteenth Street and we'll see a lot of big, dark, locked buildings lighted by dismal street lamps. I'll ask a man where the West Terminal is and he won't know. You can't go directly to a terminal and get a dog. I've lived long enough to know that.'

'You're just trying to be ironical,' said his wife. 'You always make everything so hard.'

'All right, all right,' said Mr Monroe, 'but you'll see.' He dragged out of his chair, with a hard smile, got his hat and coat, and they went out and hailed a taxi.

'West Terminal,' said Mrs Monroe to the driver.

'What west terminal?' asked the driver. It came out after a long talk in which Mr Monroe, with a triumphant grin, took no part, that the taxi-man did not know of any west terminal where there might be a dog. Mrs Monroe ordered him to go to Sixteenth Street and proceed slowly west which, in the end, he did, sharing Mr Monroe's high scepticism. The street was ill-lighted, noisy with children. The farther west the Monroes went, the bigger, darker, and more firmly locked the buildings were. They passed the M. M. Cohen Co., Paper & Twine, the Ajax Examining and Shrinking Corporation, Ozaman Club No. 2, and a copper riveting works. Nothing looked like a freight terminal. At the corner of Tenth Avenue, Mrs Monroe commanded the driver to stop near the biggest and darkest building.

'I think this is it,' she said, cheerily. Her husband roused himself and peered out.

'National Biscuit Company,' he said, and relaxed back into his seat. He began to hum slightly. The driver looked around.

'You might get out and ask somebody,' said Mrs Monroe to her husband. This Mr Monroe, with strange mutterings, did. He stopped a man, conversed briefly, and returned to the taxi.

'He says a fellow named Joe has an express office on this street and does piano hauling,' said Mr Monroe, grimly. The chauffeur drove on. Just around the corner in Eleventh Avenue, a hopeful-looking structure loomed up. Mr Monroe looked out.

'The Economy Wiping Materials Company,' he said.

'I can read,' said his wife, shortly. After a moment she gave a little cry. 'Look, John,' she said, 'there it is!' She pointed at some freight cars in a small yard across the avenue. A light glowed in a shack marked 'N.Y.C.R.R.' They got out of the cab and stumbled across the street. A short, grey, deaf man with silver-rimmed spectacles answered their knock at the door of the shack. He failed from the first to get it quite clear in his mind what was wanted, but he got enough to affirm definitely that there was no poodle in the yards there.

'Where do you think the dog would be?' Mrs Monroe asked him.

'Lady,' he said, 'I don't know,' and disappeared. Mrs Monroe was for going into the yards and knocking on freight cars. 'He might bark,' she explained. Mr Monroe led her back to the taxi. 'You can't get a dog from a terminal by force,' he said, sternly. 'We'll go back home and think this thing out. First of all, is it coming freight or express – do you know that?' He had assumed his protective, man-of-the-world attitude.

'The express company is shipping it by freight,' said his wife, somewhat subdued by the experiences of the evening.

'They don't do that,' said Mr Monroe. 'The two things are separate.' His tone, however, carried little conviction. 'Probably express,' he added. 'I think it's only furniture that comes freighted.'

'I don't suppose,' said Mrs Monroe, 'they've given the poor doggy any water.'

'The dog has water; we'll get the dog,' said her husband, with his best executive air. He held her hand and they drove home in silence.

Back at the apartment, he asked for the phone book, and Mrs Monroe finally found it on Mr Monroe's bed. 'Now,' he said, 'look up under New York Central.' She did and began to read off, ' "General and Exec –" '

A short, grey, deaf man with silver-rimmed spectacles

'Go on,' said Mr Monroe.

' "Freight stations," ' continued his wife, ' "Pier 34 ER ft Rutgers slip, St Johns Pk Laight & Varick –" '

'Give me the book,' said Mr Monroe, importantly. He took it, flipped over a few pages, frowned, and began to look around nervously.

'Under your chair,' said his wife. He reached under his chair and found his tobacco pouch. 'Now look under American Railway Express,' pursued his wife. Mr Monroe did this, after filling his pipe.

'Here we are,' he said, ' "American Railway Express: Tracing department, Claim department, On Hand department" – ah, that's probably it – "438 West 55." When things are received they are considered on hand and –'

'It couldn't be that,' interrupted his wife. 'That's where they have dogs for a week or more. Let me have the book.' She went over and took it. Carefully and calmly she studied the listings. 'Here!' she said, ' "Terminals: Tenth Avenue and Thirty-third, Lexington and Forty-ninth." Now Lexington is east and the other west – it must be Tenth Avenue and Thirty-third. I'll call that number.'

'No use,' said her husband, pityingly. He yawned and began to remove his shoes. 'The shipper couldn't have been that far off – from Sixteenth to Thirty-third Street. If you phone there a guy will answer in a German accent and deny everything. Wait till morning and I'll call up a –' But Mrs Monroe was already on the phone. Suddenly she was talking, animatedly. 'Yes, 608. A little black dog. Is it? Oh, you did? Well, that's fine! We'll be right up!' She hung up the receiver. 'It's there!' she cried. 'The man said he had seen the puppy – the car was just brought in up there. Hurry, let's go right up and get it!'

Mr Monroe did not hurry. He put his shoes back on slowly, smiling strangely, like a diplomat at a conference.

'You see, my dear,' he began, as they started out again, 'you have to go at these things carefully and calmly and figure out logically where a dog, shipped from Chicago, would most naturally –' His wife smiled, even more strangely than he had, and kissed him.

'My great big wonderful husband,' she said, gently.

Mr Monroe Holds the Fort

THE country house, on this particular wintry afternoon, was most enjoyable. Night was trudging up the hill and the air was sharp. Mr Monroe had already called attention several times to the stark beauty of the black tree branches limned, as he put it, against the sky. The wood fire had settled down to sleepy glowing in the grate.

'It *is* a little lonely, though,' said Mrs Monroe. (The nearest house was far away.)

'I love it,' said her husband, darkly. At moments and in places like this, he enjoyed giving the impression of a strong, silent man wrapped in meditation. He stared, brooding, into the fire. Mrs Monroe, looking quite tiny and helpless, sat on the floor at his feet and leaned against him. He gave her shoulder two slow, reflective pats.

'I really don't mind staying here when Germaine is here – just we two,' said Mrs Monroe, 'but I think I would be terrified if I were alone.' Germaine, the maid, a buxom, fearless woman, was in town on shopping leave. The Monroes had thought it would be fun to spend the weekend alone and get their own meals, the way they used to.

'There's nothing in the world to be afraid of,' said Mr Monroe.

'Oh, it gets so terribly black outside, and you hear all kinds of funny noises at night that you don't hear during the day.' Mr Monroe explained to her why that was – expansion (said he) of woodwork in the cold night air, and so on. From there he somehow went into a discussion of firearms, which would have betrayed to practically anyone that his knowledge of guns was limited to a few impressive names like Colt and Luger. They were one of those things he was always going to read up on but never did. He mentioned quietly, however, that he was an excellent shot.

'Mr Farrington left his pistol here, you know,' said Mrs Monroe, 'but I've never touched it – ugh!'

'He did?' cried her husband. 'Where is it? I'd like to take a look at it.' Mr Farrington was the man from whom they had taken, on long lease, the Connecticut place.

'It's upstairs in the chest of drawers in the back room,' said Mrs Monroe. Her husband, despite her protests, went up and got it and brought it down. 'Please put it away!' said his wife. 'Is it loaded? Oh, don't do that! Please!' Mr Monroe, looking grim and competent, was aiming the thing, turning it over, scowling at it.

'It's loaded all right,' he said, 'all five barrels.'

'Chambers,' said his wife.

'Yes,' he said. 'Let me show you how to use it – after all, you can never tell when you're going to need a gun.'

'Oh, I'd never use it – even if one of those convicts that escaped yesterday came right up the stairs and I could shoot him, I'd just stand there. I'd be *paralyzed*!'

'Nonsense!' said Mr Monroe. 'You don't have to shoot a man. Get the drop on him, stand him up with his face against a wall, and phone the police. Look here –' he covered an imaginary figure, backed him against the wall, and sat down at the phone table. 'Always keep your eye on him; don't look into the transmitter.' Mr Monroe glared at his man, lifted up the receiver, holding the hook down with his finger, and spoke quietly to the phone. In the midst of this the phone rang. Mr Monroe started sharply.

'It's for you, dear,' he said presently. His wife took the receiver.

How curiously things happen! That is what Mr Monroe thought, an hour later, as he drove back from the station after taking his wife there to catch the 7.10. Imagine her mother getting one of those fool spells at this time! Imagine expecting a grown daughter to come running every time you felt a little dizzy! Imagine – well, the ways of women were beyond him. He turned into the drive of the country house. Judas, but it was dark! Dark and silent. Mr Monroe didn't put the machine in the garage. He got out and stood still, listening. Off toward the woods somewhere he heard a thumping noise. Partridge drumming, thought Mr Monroe. But partridge didn't thump, they whirred – didn't they? Oh, well, they probably thumped at this time of year.

It was good to get inside the house. He built up the fire, and turned on the overhead lights – his wife never allowed them turned on. Then he went into a couple of other rooms and turned on more lights. He wished he had gone in town with her. Of course she'd be back in the morning on the 10.10 and they'd have the rest of that day – Sunday – together. Still . . . he went to the drawer where he had put the revolver and got it out. He fell to wondering whether the thing would work. Long-unused guns often jammed, or exploded. He went out into the kitchen, carrying the pistol. His wife had told him to be sure and get himself a snack. He opened the refrigerator door, looked in, decided he wasn't hungry, and closed it again. He went back to the living-room and began to pace up and down. He decided to put the pistol on the mantel, butt toward him. Then he practised making quick grabs for it. Presently he sat down in a chair, picked up a *Nation* and began to read, at random: 'Two men are intimately connected with the killing of striking workers at Marion, North Carolina. . . .' Where had those convicts his wife mentioned escaped from? Dannemora? Matteawan? How far were those places from this house? Maybe having all the lights on was a bad idea. He got up and turned the upper lights off; and then turned them on again. . . . There was a step outside. Crunch! crunch! . . . Mr Monroe hurried to the mantel, knocked the gun on to the floor, fumbled for it, and stuck it in a hip pocket just as a knock sounded at the door.

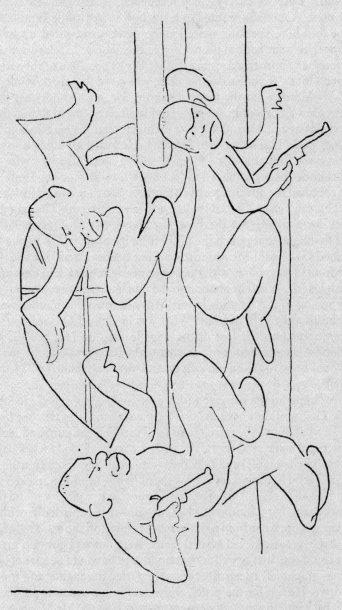

Burglars flitting about in the attic of a house in which the master is home alone

'Wha-' began Mr Monroe, and was surprised to find he couldn't say anything else. The knocking continued. He stepped to the door, stood far to one side, and said, 'Yeh?' A cheery voice responded. Reassured, Mr Monroe opened the door. A motorist wanted to know how to get to the Wilton road. Mr Monroe told him, speaking quite loudly. Afterwards, lifted up by this human contact, he went back to his reading in the *Nation*: 'Around 1.30 a.m. one of the foremen approached young Luther Bryson, 22, one of the victims, and harangued him: 'If you strike this time, you –, we will shoot it out with you.'' . . .' Mr Monroe put the magazine down. He got up and went to the victrola, selected a jazz record, and began to play it. It occurred to him that if there were steps outside, he couldn't hear them. He shut the machine off. The abrupt silence made him stand still, listening. He heard all kinds of noises. One of them came from upstairs – a quick, sliding noise, like a convict slipping into a clothes closet . . . the fellow had a beard and a blue-steel gun . . . a man in the dark had the advantage. Mr Monroe's mouth began to feel stuffy. 'Damn it! This can't go on!' he said aloud, and felt bucked up. Then someone put his heel down sharply on the floor just above. Mr Monroe tentatively picked up a flashlight, and pulled the pistol from his pocket. The phone rang sharply. 'Good God!' said Mr Monroe, backing against a wall. He slid on to the chair in front of the phone, with the gun in his right hand, and took up the receiver with his left. When he spoke into the transmitter his eyes kept roving around the room. 'H'lo,' he said. It was Mrs Monroe. Her mother was all right. Was he all right? He was fine. What was he doing? Oh, reading. (He kept the gun trained on the foot of the steps leading upstairs.) Well, what would he think if she came back out on that midnight train? Her mother was all right. Would he be too sleepy to wait up and meet her? Hell, no! That was fine! Do that! . . .

Mr Monroe hung up the receiver with a profound sigh of relief. He looked at his watch. Hm, wouldn't have to leave for the station for nearly two hours. Whistling, he went out to the refrigerator (still carrying the gun) and fetched out the butter and some cold meat. He made a couple of sandwiches (laying the gun on the kitchen table) and took them into the living-room (putting the gun in his pocket). He turned off the overhead lights, sat down, picked up a *Harper's* and began to read. Abruptly, that flitting, clothes-closety sound came from upstairs again. Mr Monroe finished his sandwiches hurriedly, with the gun on his lap, got up, went from room to room turning off the extra lights, put on his hat and overcoat, locked several doors, went out and got into his car. After all, he could read just as well at the station, and he would be sure of being there on time – might fall asleep otherwise. He started the engine, and whirled out of the drive. He felt for the pistol, which was in his overcoat pocket. He would slip it back into the chest of drawers upstairs later on. Mr Monroe came to a crossroads and a light. He began to whistle.

The Middle Years

WHEN, as John Monroe was helping the lovely lady on with her coat, she leaned ever so slightly – and unnecessarily – backwards, he was conscious of a quick warm glow. He was even more conscious of a vague perplexity, the reason for which – or one of the reasons, anyway – finally came washing up to him on the stream of memory. This had all happened before, almost precisely as now, but with another girl, and years before. *That* girl, he was painfully reminded, had not meant it. He had afterwards walked feverishly and miserably around in the rain for hours, smoking dozens of cigarettes. He hadn't slept that night.

He was proud of himself that now, going on thirty-six, he took such things more calmly. His heart didn't throb in his throat like a dollar watch. He didn't change colour or stammer. He didn't even meet this present lady's eyes at first. He did manage at last, as became a man of the world, to give her a subtle (as he felt) recognition of the dizzy little moment. It was nothing that he said, no extra pressure that he gave her hand. He merely favoured her with an intense and wonderful glance (or so he believed it to be), paving the way for a charming sequel without spoiling it all by seeming too youthfully impetuous. Of course if it came to impetuosity, he would show 'em who was impetuous. But, at thirty-five, to make the right effect, one had to go slow. Besides, he was a little tired, the party having lasted infernally late. He was glad that someone else was seeing the lady home this particular night. It was devilishly cold.

He had quite a sneezing spell when he got home, which somehow marred his admiration of himself in a glass. He noted that his hair, greying at the temples, was becoming more attractive every day. He tried a couple of brooding frowns, with his chin resting in his hand, and approved of them. Then he went to bed, resolved to think about the lovely lady quite a while, before falling asleep. He fell asleep in thirty-two seconds.

The next morning he awoke feeling much better than he usually did after being out late. He sprang out of bed quickly – without any of that dizziness which in recent years he had begun to experience if he arose too suddenly. He began whistling as he put a new blade in his razor. It was quite a while before he got at the source of the vague gaiety that lifted him up. Then he remembered the lovely lady, and the incident of the coat. Oddly enough, his spirits dropped just a trifle. He was surprised, but they did. His old, or as a matter of actual fact, his fairly recent, sense of perplexity came back. Things got complicated so easily, became weighty. Complications were a damned nuisance. Kept a man up late, kept him figuring. He fought off the sudden apparition of his wife's face, which leaped up to laugh at him, a little mockingly. She was, as luck would have it (he wasn't sure of his own definition of luck here), out of town, and wouldn't be back for a week. Of course, she wouldn't *mind*. He was, after all, old enough not to make a fool of himself. That, in her charmingly humorous way, was all little Mrs Monroe had ever required of him in the event of an – ah – of a communion, with anyone. Just so he selected a lady that a wife need not be ashamed of. Well, he had. Furthermore, she was probably waiting for him to give her a ring. Well, he would. After breakfast. The laughing face of his wife bobbed up again. He cut himself slightly with a razor, and swore. He couldn't find a clean shirt, and swore again. Damn it, she was *always* out of town!

She would be reading, stretched out, filmily, on a divan, soft, alluring

The knowledge that the lovely lady's husband was in Bermuda had been a part of Mr Monroe's first fine elation, when he was helping her on with her coat. Since this was the case, he wondered at himself for feeling a definite let-down in his ardour when, in looking up the lady's telephone number at his office, he met her husband's name in the book. The type seemed like a cold, black barrier. He remembered how, in the years behind him, the presence of competition, even of menace, had only spurred him on. In wending his way back among old memories, Mr Monroe recalled a cold, glittery night of a long-gone December, when he had stood for hours under a girl's window, throwing pebbles up at it until, for the sake of her reputation, she consented to go to the Christmas dance his fraternity was giving, instead of to another fellow's. She had been reported engaged to the other fellow, too. . . . Judas, it had been cold standing under that window! It *must* have been. He rose and closed the window of his office. The day was bitter and gloomy. He decided not to call the lady until after dinner.

A hot bath and a good dinner at a quiet place put Mr Monroe in pretty fine fettle. He decided to call the lady up at once. When he got back to his apartment, however, he decided, on further reflection, that this would not be very

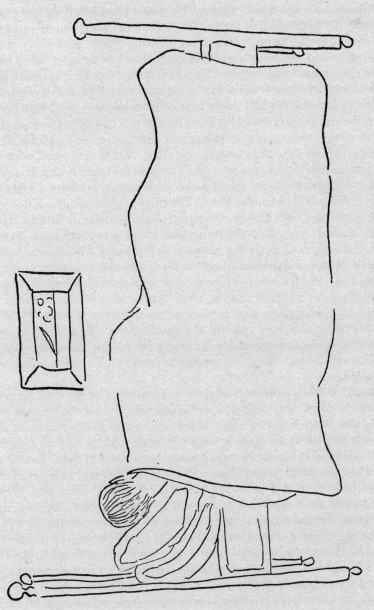

He crept back under the covers

subtle. No, the way to do it was to drop in on her around midnight. She was one of those people who were invariably up, long after midnight. He wondered how they did it, night in and night out. She would be reading, stretched out, filmily, on a divan, soft, alluring. He would make a striking and graceful entrance. To fortify himself for this adventure – the word 'ordeal' just grazed his consciousness – he got out a volume of Henry James. He would begin the communion on a mature, a 'wonderful' plane. It might become – who knew? – one of those pleasurable, comfortable, and just slightly aching episodes, which mean so much. He was reduced to a momentary confusion, at this point, when it came to him that the lady might have other patterns in mind than those of Henry James. It also crossed his mind that he was lapsing into a basis singularly devoid, somehow, of that impetuosity which, over his cocktail at dinner, he had told himself he had to get into the affair. *Had* to get? – hell, wanted to!

It was just ten o'clock, and he mustn't drop around until midnight, anyway. That would give any other callers a chance to depart. He lighted a cigar and began reading in 'The Golden Bowl.' The effect of three minutes of this was to make him undeniably drowsy. 'Here, here!' he muttered to himself. He got up and dashed some cold water on his face, before going back to his book and cigar. Even so, his lids shortly began to droop again. Mr Monroe met this situation grimly. He decided to put on his dinner jacket, and he went to the clothes closet and got it out – or the parts of it he could find. He had no notion where his studs might be, but he knew that he ought to know. Little Mrs Monroe's mocking face kept preceding him wherever he went. Finally he got everything together, and laid the array out on a bed. Then he began leisurely to undress. It struck him, as he glimpsed himself in a long glass, that a tall thin man looks like an ass in socks and garters. The thought depressed him terribly.

Instead of changing into his smoking jacket at once, he placed all his clothes over the backs of chairs, put on a pair of pyjamas, and lay down on the bed to smoke a cigarette. Cigars were too heavy; they got to you if you needed sleep. He looked at his watch again. It wasn't quite eleven. Mr Monroe considered the whole situation again. Perhaps it would be better if he didn't go over until *one*. Then you could be pretty sure any other guests would have departed. Of course he knew that if he waited two hours he would fall asleep. Well, he would set the alarm clock for a quarter to one – give him plenty of time to spring up and get dressed. So he set the clock and crawled beneath the covers.

The loud ringing of the alarm bell woke him, after what seemed only a few minutes. He rose up slowly and shut it off, after which he rested on one elbow for a minute or so. He got, then, with fine resolution, about halfway out of bed, groped for a cigarette, found one, and put it down again without lighting it. Slowly, very slowly, he crept back under the covers, and switched off the light at the head of the bed. He sighed deeply.

The Pet Department

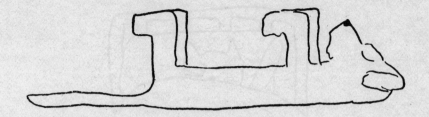

Q. I enclose a sketch of the way my dog, William, has been lying for two days now. I think there must be something wrong with him. Can you tell me how to get him out of this?

Mrs L. L. G.

A. I should judge from the drawing that William is in a trance. Trance states, however, are rare with dogs. It may just be ecstasy. If at the end of another twenty-four hours he doesn't seem to be getting anywhere, I should give him up. The position of the ears leads me to believe that he may be enjoying himself in a quiet way, but the tail is somewhat alarming.

Q. Our cat, who is thirty-five, spends all of her time in bed. She follows every move I make, and this is beginning to get to me. She never seems sleepy nor particularly happy. Is there anything I could give her?

Miss L. Mc.

A. There are no medicines which can safely be given to induce felicity in a cat, but you might try lettuce, which is a soporific, for the wakefulness. I would have to see the cat watching you to tell whether anything could be done to divert her attention.

Q. My husband, who is an amateur hypnotizer, keeps trying to get our bloodhound under his control. I contend that this is not doing the dog any good. So far he has not yielded to my husband's influence, but I am afraid that if he once got under, we couldn't get him out of it.

A. A. T.

A. Dogs are usually left cold by all phases of psychology, mental telepathy, and the like. Attempts to hypnotize this particular breed, however, are likely to be fraught with a definite menace. A bloodhound, if stared at fixedly, is liable to gain the impression that it is under suspicion, being followed, and so on. This upsets a bloodhound's life, by completely reversing its whole scheme of behaviour.

Q. My wife found this owl in the attic among a lot of ormolu clocks and old crystal chandeliers. We can't tell whether it's stuffed or only dead. It is sitting on a strange and almost indescribable sort of iron dingbat.

Mr Molleff

A. What your wife found is a museum piece – a stuffed cockatoo. It looks to me like a rather botchy example of taxidermy. This is the first stuffed bird I have ever seen with its eyes shut, but whoever had it stuffed probably wanted it stuffed that way. I couldn't say what the thing it is sitting on is supposed to represent. It looks broken.

Q. Our gull cannot get his head down any farther than this, and bumps into things.

H. L. F.

A. You have no ordinary gull to begin with. He looks to me a great deal like a rabbit backing up. If he *is* a gull, it is impossible to keep him in the house. Naturally he will bump into things. Give him his freedom.

Q. My police dog has taken to acting very strange, on account of my father coming home from work every night for the past two years and saying to him, 'If you're a police dog, where's your badge?', after which he laughs (my father).

ELLA R.

A. The constant reiteration of any piece of badinage sometimes has the same effect on present-day neurotic dogs that it has on people. It is dangerous and thoughtless to twit a police dog on his powers, authority, and the like. From the way your dog seems to hide behind tables, large vases, and whatever that thing is that looks like a suitcase, I should imagine that your father has carried this thing far enough – perhaps even too far.

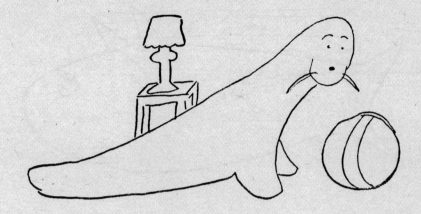

Q. My husband's seal will not juggle, although we have tried everything.
GRACE H.

A. Most seals will not juggle; I think I have never known one that juggled. Seals balance things, and sometimes toss objects (such as the large ball in your sketch) from one to another. This last will be difficult if your husband has but one seal. I'd try him in plain balancing, beginning with a billiard cue or something. It may be, of course, that he is a non-balancing seal.

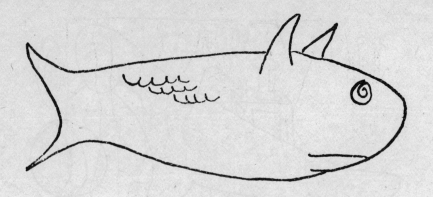

Q. We have a fish with ears and wonder if it is valuable.

JOE WRIGHT

A. I find no trace in the standard fish books of any fish with ears. Very likely the ears do not belong to the fish, but to some mammal. They look to me like a mammal's ears. It would be pretty hard to say what species of mammal, and almost impossible to determine what particular member of that species. They may merely be hysterical ears, in which case they will go away if you can get the fish's mind on something else.

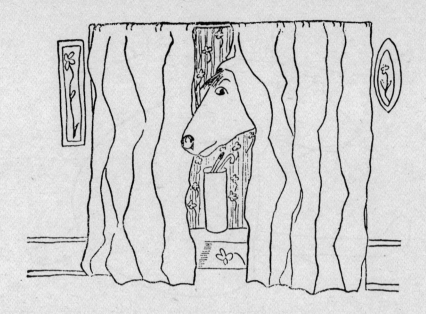

Q. How would you feel if every time you looked up from your work or anything, there was a horse peering at you from behind something? He prowls about the house at all hours of the day and night. Doesn't seem worried about anything, merely wakeful. What should I do to discourage him?

MRS GRACE VOYNTON

A. The horse is probably sad. Changing the flowered decorations of your home to something less like open meadows might discourage him, but then I doubt whether it is a good idea to discourage a sad horse. In any case speak to him quietly when he turns up from behind things. Leaping at a horse in a house and crying 'Roogie, roogie!' or 'Whoosh!' would only result in breakage and bedlam. Of course you might finally get used to having him around, if the house is big enough for both of you.

Q. The fact that my dog sits this way so often leads me to believe that something is preying on his mind. He seems always to be studying. Would there be any way of finding out what this is?

ARTHUR

A. Owing to the artificially complex life led by city dogs of the present day, they tend to lose the simpler systems of intuition which once guided all breeds, and frequently lapse into what comes very close to mental perplexity. I myself have known some very profoundly thoughtful dogs. Usually, however, their problems are not serious and I should judge that your dog has merely mislaid something and wonders where he put it.

Q. We have cats the way most people have mice.

Mrs C. L. Footloose

A. I see you have. I can't tell from your communication, however, whether you wish advice or are just boasting.

Q. No one has been able to tell us what kind of dog we have. I am enclosing a sketch of one of his two postures. He only has two. The other one is the same as this except he faces in the opposite direction.

Mrs Eugenja Black

A. I think that what you have is a cast-iron lawn dog. The expressionless eye and the rigid pose are characteristic of metal lawn animals. And that certainly is a cast-iron ear. You could, however, remove all doubt by means of a simple test with a hammer and a cold chisel, or an acetylene torch. If the animal chips, or melts, my diagnosis is correct.

Q. My oldest boy, Ford Maddox Ford Griswold, worked this wooden horse loose from a merry-go-round one night when he and some other young people were cutting up. Could you suggest any use for it in a family of five?

MRS R. L. S. GRISWOLD

A. I cannot try the patience of my public nor waste my own time dealing with the problems of insensate animals. Already I have gone perhaps too far afield in the case of stuffed birds and cast-iron lawn dogs. Pretty soon I should be giving advice on wire-haired fox terrier weather-vanes.

Q. Mr Jennings bought this beast when it was a pup in Montreal for a St Bernard, but I don't think it is. It's grown enormously and is stubborn about letting you have anything, like the bath towel it has its paws on, and the hat, both of which belong to Mr Jennings. He got it that bowling ball to play with but it doesn't seem to like it. Mr Jennings is greatly attached to the creature.

Mrs Fanny Edwards Jennings

A. What you have is a bear. While it isn't my bear, I should recommend that you dispose of it. As these animals grow older they get more and more adamant about letting you have anything, until finally there might not be anything in the house you could call your own – except possibly the bowling ball. Zoos use bears. Mr Jennings could visit it.

Q. Sometimes my dog does not seem to know me. I think he must be crazy. He will draw away, or show his fangs, when I approach him.

H. M. Morgan, Jr

A. So would I, and I'm not crazy. If you creep up on your dog the way you indicate in the drawing, I can understand his viewpoint. Put your shirt in and straighten up; you look as if you had never seen a dog before, and that is undoubtedly what bothers the animal. These maladjustments can often be worked out by the use of a little common sense.

Q. After a severe storm we found this old male raven in the study of my father, the Hon. George Morton Bodwell, for many years head of the Latin Department at Tufts, sitting on a bust of Livy which was a gift to him from the class of '92. All that the old bird will say is 'Grawk.' Can ravens be taught to talk or was Poe merely 'romancing'?

MRS H. BODWELL COLWETHER

A. I am handicapped by an uncertainty as to who says 'Grawk,' the raven or your father. It just happens that 'Arrk' is what ravens say. I have never known a raven that said anything but 'Arrk.'

Q. I have three Scotch terriers which take things out of closets and down from shelves, etc. My veterinarian advised me to gather together all the wreckage, set them down in the midst of it, and say 'ba-ad Scotties!' This, however, merely seems to give them a kind of pleasure. If I spank one, the other two jump me – playfully, but they jump me.

MRS O. S. PROCTOR

A. To begin with, I question the advisability of having three Scotch terriers. They are bound to get you down. However, it seems to me that you are needlessly complicating your own problem. The Scotties probably think that you are trying to enter into the spirit of their play. Their inability to comprehend what you are trying to get at will in the end make them melancholy, and you and the dogs will begin to drift farther and farther apart. I'd deal with each terrier, and each object, separately, beginning with the telephone, the disconnection of which must inconvenience you sorely.

Q. My husband paid a hundred and seventy-five dollars for this moose to a man in Dorset, Ontario, who said he had trapped it in the woods. Something is wrong with his antlers, for we have to keep twisting them back into place all the time. They're loose.

MRS OLIPHANT BEATTY

A. You people are living in a fool's paradise. The animal is obviously a horse with a span of antlers strapped onto his head. If you really want a moose, dispose of the horse; if you want to keep the horse, take the antlers off. Their constant pressure on his ears isn't a good idea.

The Seal in the Bedroom

Preface

O NCE a friend of a friend of mine was on a London bus. At her stop she came down the stair just behind two ladies who, even during descent, were deep in conversation; surely only the discussion of the short-comings of a common acquaintance could have held them so absorbed. She heeded their voices but none of their words, until the lady in advance stopped on a step, turned and declaimed in melodious British: 'Mad, I don't say. Queer, I grant you. Many's the time I've seen her nude at the piano.'

It has been, says this friend of my friend's, the regret of her days that she did not hear what led up to that strange fragment of biography.

But there I stray from her. It is infinitely provocative, I think, to be given only the climax; infinitely beguiling to wander back from it along the dappled paths of fancy. The words of that lady of the bus have all the challenge of a Thurber drawing – indeed, I am practically convinced that she herself *was* a Thurber drawing. No one but Mr. Thurber could have thought of her.

Mr James Thurber, our hero, deals solely in culminations. Beneath his pictures he sets only the final line. You may figure for yourself, and good luck to you, what under heaven could have gone before, that his sombre citizens find themselves in such remarkable situations. It is yours to ponder how penguins get into drawing-rooms and seals into bedchambers, for Mr. Thurber will only show them to you some little time after they have arrived there. Superbly he slaps aside preliminaries. He gives you a glimpse of the startling present and leaves you to construct the astounding past. And if, somewhere in that process, you part with a certain amount of sanity, doubtless you are better off without it. There is too much sense in this world, anyway.

These are strange people that Mr. Thurber has turned loose upon us. They seem to fall into three classes – the playful, the defeated and the ferocious. All of them have the outer semblance of unbaked cookies; the women are of a dowdiness so overwhelming that it becomes tremendous style. Once a heckler, who should have been immediately put out, complained that the Thurber women have no sex appeal. The artist was no more than reproachful. 'They have for my men,' he said. And certainly the Thurber men, those deplorably *désoigné* Thurber men, would ask no better.

There is about all these characters, even the angry ones, a touching quality. They expect so little of life; they remember the old discouragements and await the new. They are not shrewd people, nor even bright, and we must all be very patient with them. Lambs in a world of wolves, they are, and there is on them a protracted innocence. One sees them daily, come alive from the pages of *The New Yorker* – sees them in trains and ferry-boats and station waiting-rooms and all the big, sad places where a face is once beheld, never to be seen again. It is curious, perhaps terrible, how Mr Thurber has influenced the American face and physique, and some day he will surely answer for it. People didn't go about looking like that before he started drawing. But now there are more and more of them doing it, all the time. Presently, it may be, we shall become a nation of Thurber drawings, and then the Japanese can come over and lick the tar out of us.

Of the birds and animals so bewilderingly woven into the lives of the Thurber people it is best to say but little. Those tender puppies, those faint-hearted hounds – I think they are hounds – that despondent penguin – one goes weak with sentiment. No man could have drawn, much less thought of, those creatures unless he felt really right about animals. One gathers that Mr Thurber does, his art aside; he has fourteen resident dogs and more are expected. Reason totters.

All of them, his birds and his beasts and his men and women, are actually dashed off by the artist. Ten minutes for a drawing he regards as drudgery. He draws with a pen, with no foundations of pencil, and so sure and great is his draughtsmanship that there is never a hesitating line, never a change. No one understands how he makes his boneless, loppy beings, with their shy kinship to the men and women of Picasso's later drawings, so truly and gratifyingly decorative. And no one, with the exception of God and possibly Mr Thurber, knows from-what dark breeding-ground come the artist's ideas. Analysis promptly curls up; how is one to shadow the mental processes of a man who is impelled to depict a seal looking over the headboard of a bed occupied by a broken-spirited husband and a virago of a wife, and then to write below the scene the one line 'All right, have it your way – you heard a seal bark'?[1] . . . Mad, I don't say. Genius I grant you.

It is none too soon that Mr Thurber's drawings have been assembled in one space. Always one wants to show an understanding friend a conceit that the artist published in *The New Yorker* – let's see, how many weeks ago was it? and always some other understanding friend has been there first and sneaked the back copies of the magazine home with him. And it is necessary really to show the picture. A Thurber must be seen to be believed – there is no use trying to tell the plot of it. Only one thing is more hopeless than attempting to describe a Thurber drawing, and that is trying not to tell about it. So everything is going to be much better, I know, now that all the pictures are here together. Perhaps the one constructive thing in this year of hell is the publication of this collection.

And it is my pleasure and privilege – though also, I am afraid, my presumption – to introduce to you, now, one you know well already; one I revere as an artist and cleave to as a friend. Ladies and gentlemen – Mr James Thurber.

DOROTHY PARKER

September, 1932

[1] See *Vintage Thurber*, Volume One, page 418.

'Have you people got any .38 Cartridges?'

'I'm helping Mr Gorley with his novel, darling'

'When I realize that I once actually loved you I go cold all over'

'Everybody noticed it. You gawked at her all evening'

'You're the only woman that ever let me alone'

'Mamma! Come quick! I think Grandpa is folding up'

'Perhaps a woman's intuition could solve your problem, Mr Barr'

'So I says to him, "Don't take that tone with me, Mr Gebholtz"'

'Mamma always gets sore and spoils the game for everybody'

'I wouldn't be uneasy – one of my husbands was gone for three weeks'

'Here's a study for you, Doctor – he faints'

'*Well, what's come over you suddenly?*'

'*She was crazy about him, but he interfered with her novel*'

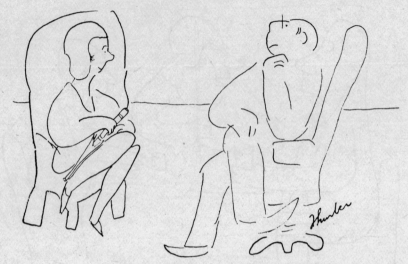

'*I keep toying with the idea of suicide, Doctor*'

'*Stop me!*'

'I understand she kills herself in the next act and he goes back to his wife'

'Will you be good enough to dance this outside?'

'Your wife seems terribly smart, Mr Bruce'

'He got Aphasia and forgot where I lived'

'Why don't you get dressed, then, and go to pieces like a man?'

'Your ailment is on the tip of my tongue, Mrs Cartright – let me think'

'I told the analyst everything except my experience with Mr Rinesfoos'

'Lookit, Herman – flars!'

'They're playing "Bolero," Mr Considine – It drives me mad!'

'I can tell you right now that isn't going to work'

'Here's to the old-time saloon, stranger!'

'I don't know. George got it somewhere'

'Have you fordotten our ittle suicide pact?'

'I yielded, yes – but I never led your husband on, Mrs Fisher!'

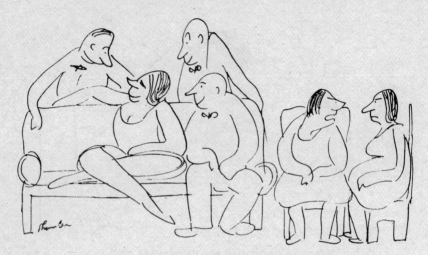

'What kind of a woman is it, I ask you, that goes gallivanting around in a foreign automobile?'

'No son of mine is going to stand there and tell me he's scared of the woods'

'Two best falls out of three – Okay, Mr Montague?'

'Hello, dear! – how's everything in the Marts of Trade?'

'Get a load of this sunset, babe!'

'They say he has no weakness'

'Then he wrote me from Detroit that he couldn't get married because there
was crazy people in his ancestors'

'Are you the young man that bit my daughter?'

'You keep your wife's name out of this, Ashby!'

'If I'm a fake, officer, how do you account for this?'

The Bloodhound and the Bug

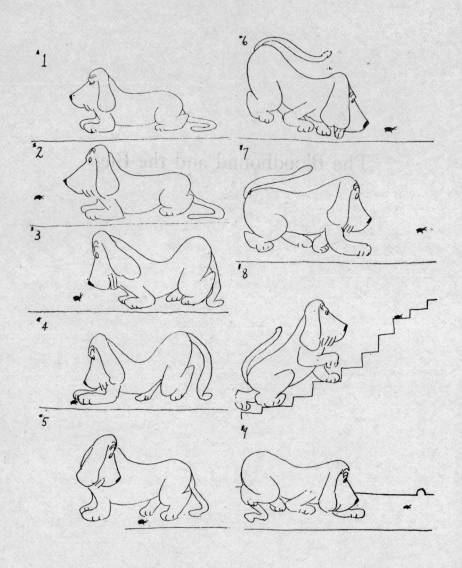

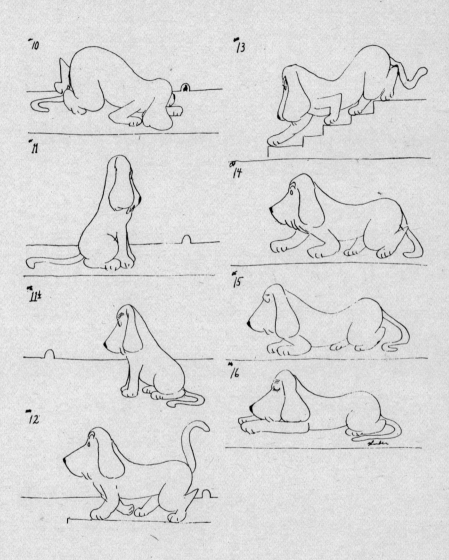

The Race of Life

A PARABLE

THIS sequence of thirty-five drawings represents the life story of a man and his wife; or several days, a month or a year in their life and in that of their child; or their alternately interflowing and diverging streams of consciousness over any given period. It seems to lend itself to a wide variety of interpretations. Anything may be read into it, or left out of it, without making a great deal of difference. Two or three previewers were brought up short by this picture or that – mainly the Enormous Rabbit – and went back and started over again from the beginning. This mars the flow of the sequence by interrupting the increasing tempo of the action. It is better to skip pictures, or tear them out, rather than to begin over again and try to fit them in with some preconceived idea of what is going on.

The Enormous Rabbit, which brought two engravers and a receptionist up short, perhaps calls for a few words of explanation. It can be an Uncrossed Bridge which seems, at first glance, to have been burned behind somebody, or it can be Chickens Counted Too Soon, or a ringing phone, or a thought in the night, or a faint hissing sound. More than likely it is an Unopened Telegram which when opened proves not to contain the dreadful news one had expected but merely some such innocuous query as: 'Did you find my silver-rimmed glasses in brown case after party Saturday?'

The snow in which the bloodhounds are caught may be either real snow or pieces of paper torn up.

The Start

Swinging Along

Neck and Neck

Accident

Water Jump

The Beautiful Stranger

The Quarrel

The Pacemaker

Spring Dance

Faster

The Enormous Rabbit

Escape

Top Speed

Winded

Quand Même

Breathing Spell

The Dive

Dog Trot

Down Hill

Menace

Up Hill

Dogs in the Blizzard

Out of the Storm

The Skull

The Water Hole

The Laggard

Indians!

War Dance

Gone!

The Bear

Sunset

On Guard

Dawn: Off Again

Final Sprint

The Goal

The Bloodhound and the Hare

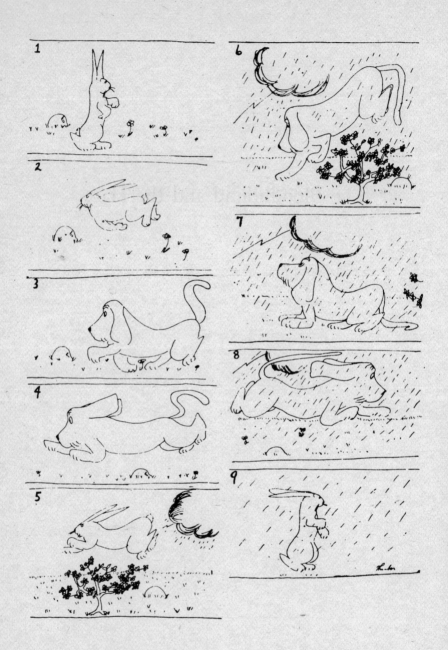

The Thurber Carnival

FOR

HAROLD ROSS

With increasing admiration,
wonder and affection

My Fifty Years with James Thurber

I HAVE not actually known Thurber for fifty years, since he was only forty-eight on his last birthday, but the publishers of this volume felt that 'fifty' would sound more effective than 'forty-eight' in the title of an introduction to so large a book, a point which I was too tired to argue about.

James Thurber was born on a night of wild portent and high wind in the year 1894, at 147 Parsons Avenue, Columbus, Ohio. The house, which is still standing, bears no tablet or plaque of any description, and is never pointed out to visitors. Once Thurber's mother, walking past the place with an old lady from Fostoria, Ohio, said to her, 'My son James was born in that house,' to which the old lady, who was extremely deaf, replied, 'Why, on the Tuesday morning train, unless my sister is worse.' Mrs Thurber let it go at that.

The infant Thurber was brought into the world by an old practical nurse named Margery Albright, who had delivered the babies of neighbour women before the Civil War. He was, of course, much too young at the time to have been affected by the quaint and homely circumstances of his birth, to which he once alluded, a little awkwardly, I think, as 'the Currier and Ives, or old steel engraving, touch, attendant upon my entry into this vale of tears.' Not a great deal is known about his earliest years, beyond the fact that he could walk when he was only two years old, and was able to speak whole sentences by the time he was four.

Thurber's boyhood (1900–1913) was pretty well devoid of significance. I see no reason why it should take up much of our time. There is no clearly traceable figure or pattern in this phase of his life. If he knew where he was going, it is not apparent from this distance. He fell down a great deal during this period, because of a trick he had of walking into himself. His gold-rimmed glasses forever needed straightening, which gave him the appearance of a person who hears somebody calling but can't make out where the sound is coming from. Because of his badly focused lenses, he saw, not two of everything, but one and a half. Thus, a four-wheeled wagon would not have eight wheels for him, but six. How he succeeded in preventing these two extra wheels from getting into his work, I have no way of knowing.

Thurber's life baffles and irritates the biographer because of its lack of design. One has the disturbing feeling that the man contrived to be some place without actually having gone there. His drawings, for example, sometimes seem to have reached completion by some other route than the common one of intent.

The writing, is, I think, different. In his prose pieces he appears always to have started from the beginning and to have reached the end by way of the middle. It is impossible to read any of the stories from the last line to the first without experiencing a definite sensation of going backward. This seems to me to prove that the stories were written and did not, like the drawings, just suddenly materialize.

Thurber's very first bit of writing was a so-called poem entitled 'My Aunt Mrs John T. Savage's Garden at 185 South Fifth Street, Columbus, Ohio.' It is of no value or importance except insofar as it demonstrates the man's appalling memory for names and numbers. He can tell you to this day the names of all the children who were in the fourth grade when he was. He remembers the phone numbers of several of his high school chums. He knows the birthdays of all his friends and can tell you the date on which any child of theirs was christened. He can rattle off the names of all the persons who attended the lawn fete of the First M.E. Church in Columbus in 1907. This ragbag of precise but worthless information may have helped him in his work, but I don't see how.

I find, a bit to my surprise, that there is not much else to say. Thurber goes on as he always has, walking now a little more slowly, answering fewer letters, jumping at slighter sounds. In the past ten years he has moved restlessly from one Connecticut town to another, hunting for the Great Good Place, which he conceives to be an old Colonial house, surrounded by elms and maples, equipped with all modern conveniences, and overlooking a valley. There he plans to spend his days reading 'Huckleberry Finn,' raising poodles, laying down a wine cellar, playing *boules*, and talking to the little group of friends which he has managed somehow to take with him into his crotchety middle age.

This book contains a selection of the stories and drawings the old boy did in his prime, a period which extended roughly from the year Lindbergh flew the Atlantic to the day coffee was rationed. He presents this to his readers with his sincere best wishes for a happy new world.

JAMES THURBER

The Lady on 142

THE train was twenty minutes late, we found out when we bought our tickets, so we sat down on a bench in the little waiting room of the Cornwall Bridge station. It was too hot outside in the sun. This midsummer Saturday had got off to a sulky start, and now, at three in the afternoon, it sat, sticky and restive, in our laps.

There were several others besides Sylvia and myself waiting for the train to get in from Pittsfield: a coloured woman who fanned herself with a *Daily News*, a young lady in her twenties reading a book, a slender, tanned man sucking dreamily on the stem of an unlighted pipe. In the centre of the room, leaning against a high iron radiator, a small girl stared at each of us in turn, her mouth open, as if she had never seen people before. The place had the familiar, pleasant smell of railroad stations in the country, of something compounded of wood and leather and smoke. In the cramped space behind the ticket window, a telegraph instrument clicked intermittently, and once or twice a phone rang and the stationmaster answered it briefly. I couldn't hear what he said.

I was glad, on such a day, that we were going only as far as Gaylordsville, the third stop down the line, twenty-two minutes away. The stationmaster had told us that our tickets were the first tickets to Gaylordsville he had ever sold. I was idly pondering this small distinction when a train whistle blew in the distance. We all got to our feet, but the stationmaster came out of his cubbyhole and told us it was not our train but the 12:45 from New York, northbound. Presently the train thundered in like a hurricane and sighed ponderously to a stop. The stationmaster went out onto the platform and came back after a minute or two. The train got heavily under way again, for Canaan.

I was opening a pack of cigarettes when I heard the stationmaster talking on the phone again. This time his words came out clearly. He kept repeating one sentence. He was saying, 'Conductor Reagan on 142 has the lady the office was asking about.' The person on the other end of the line did not appear to get the meaning of the sentence. The stationmaster repeated it and hung up. For some reason, I figured that he did not understand it either.

Sylvia's eyes had the lost, reflective look they wear when she is trying to remember in what box she packed the Christmas-tree ornaments. The expressions on the faces of the coloured woman, the young lady, and the man with the pipe had not changed. The little staring girl had gone away.

Our train was not due for another five minutes, and I sat back and began trying to reconstruct the lady on 142, the lady Conductor Reagan had, the lady the office was asking about. I moved nearer to Sylvia and whispered, 'See if the trains are numbered in your timetable.' She got the timetable out of her handbag and looked at it. 'One forty-two,' she said, 'is the 12:45 from New York.' This was the train that had gone by a few minutes before. 'The woman was taken sick,' said Sylvia. 'They are probably arranging to have a doctor or her family meet her.'

The coloured woman looked around at her briefly. The young woman, who had been chewing gum, stopped chewing. The man with the pipe seemed oblivious. I lighted a cigarette and sat thinking. 'The woman on 142,' I said to Sylvia, finally, 'might be almost anything, but she definitely is not sick.' The only person who did not stare at me was the man with the pipe. Sylvia gave me her temperature-taking look, a cross between anxiety and vexation. Just then our train whistled and we all stood up. I picked up our two bags and Sylvia took the sack of string beans we had picked for the Connells.

When the train came clanking in, I said in Sylvia's ear, 'He'll sit near us. You watch.' 'Who? Who will?' she said. 'The stranger,' I told her, 'the man with the pipe.'

Sylvia laughed. 'He's not a stranger,' she said. 'He works for the Breeds.' I was certain that he didn't. Women like to place people; every stranger reminds them of somebody.

The man with the pipe was sitting three seats in front of us, across the aisle, when we got settled. I indicated him with a nod of my head. Sylvia took a book out of the top of her overnight bag and opened it. 'What's the matter with you?' she demanded. I looked around before replying. A sleepy man and woman sat across from us. Two middle-aged women in the seat in front of us were discussing the severe griping pain one of them had experienced as the result of an inflamed diverticulum. A slim, dark-eyed young woman sat in the seat behind us. She was alone.

'The trouble with women,' I began, 'is that they explain everything by illness. I have a theory that we would be celebrating the twelfth of May or even the sixteenth of April as Independence Day if Mrs Jefferson hadn't got the idea her husband had a fever and put him to bed.'

Sylvia found her place in the book. 'We've been all through that before,' she said. 'Why couldn't the woman on 142 be sick?'

That was easy. I told her. 'Conductor Reagan,' I said, 'got off the train at Cornwall Bridge and spoke to the stationmaster. "I've got the woman the office was asking about," he said.'

Sylvia cut in. 'He said "lady." '

I gave the little laugh that annoys her. 'All conductors say "lady," ' I explained. 'Now, if a woman had got sick on the train, Reagan would have said, "A woman got sick on my train. Tell the office." What must have happened is that Reagan found, somewhere between Kent and Cornwall Bridge, a woman the office had been looking for.'

Sylvia didn't close her book, but she looked up. 'Maybe she got sick before she got on the train, and the office was worried,' said Sylvia. She was not giving the problem close attention.

'If the office knew she got on the train,' I said patiently, 'they wouldn't have asked Reagan to let them know if he found her. They would have told him about her when she got on.' Sylvia resumed her reading.

'Let's stay out of it,' she said. 'It isn't any of our business.'

I hunted for my Chiclets but couldn't find them. 'It might be everybody's business,' I said, 'every patriot's.'

'I know, I know,' said Sylvia. 'You think she's a spy. Well, I still think she's sick.'

I ignored that. 'Every conductor on the line has been asked to look out for her,' I said. 'Reagan found her. She won't be met by her family. She'll be met by the FBI.'

'Or the OPA,' said Sylvia. 'Alfred Hitchcock things don't happen on the New York, New Haven & Hartford.'

I saw the conductor coming from the other end of the coach. 'I'm going to tell the conductor,' I said, 'that Reagan on 142 has got the woman.'

'No, you're not,' said Sylvia. 'You're not going to get us mixed up in this. He probably knows anyway.'

The conductor, short, stocky, silvery-haired, and silent, took up our tickets. He looked like a kindly Ickes. Sylvia, who had stiffened, relaxed when I let him go by without a word about the woman on 142. 'He looks exactly as if he knew where the Maltese Falcon is hidden, doesn't he?' said Sylvia, with the laugh that annoys me.

'Nevertheless,' I pointed out, 'you said a little while ago that he probably knows about the woman on 142. If she's just sick, why should they tell the conductor on *this* train? I'll rest more easily when I know that they've actually got her.'

Sylvia kept on reading as if she hadn't heard me. I leaned my head against the back of the seat and closed my eyes.

The train was slowing down noisily and a brakeman was yelling 'Kent! Kent!' when I felt a small, cold pressure against my shoulder. 'Oh,' the voice of the woman in the seat behind me said, 'I've dropped my copy of *Coronet* under your seat.' She leaned closer and her voice became low and hard. 'Get off here, Mister,' she said.

'We're going to Gaylordsville,' I said.

'You and your wife are getting off here, Mister,' she said.

I reached for the suitcases on the rack. 'What do you want, for heaven's sake?' asked Sylvia.

'We're getting off here,' I told her.

'Are you *really* crazy?' she demanded. 'This is only Kent.'

'Come on, sister,' said the woman's voice. 'You take the overnight bag and the beans. You take the big bag, Mister.'

Sylvia was furious. 'I *knew* you'd get us into this,' she said to me, 'shouting about spies at the top of your voice.'

That made me angry. 'You're the one that mentioned spies,' I told her. 'I didn't.'

'You kept talking about it and talking about it,' said Sylvia.

'Come on, get off, the two of you,' said the cold, hard voice.

We got off. As I helped Sylvia down the steps, I said, 'We know too much.'

'Oh, shut up,' she said.

We didn't have far to go. A big black limousine waited a few steps away. Behind the wheel sat a heavy-set foreigner with cruel lips and small eyes. He scowled when he saw us. 'The boss don't want nobody up deh,' he said.

'It's all right, Karl,' said the woman. 'Get in,' she told us. We climbed into the back seat. She sat between us, with the gun in her hand. It was a handsome, jewelled derringer.

'Alice will be waiting for us at Gaylordsville,' said Sylvia, 'in all this heat.'

The house was a long, low, rambling building, reached at the end of a poplar-lined drive. 'Never mind the bags,' said the woman. Sylvia took the string beans and her book and we got out. Two huge mastiffs came bounding off the terrace, snarling. 'Down, Mata!' said the woman. 'Down, Pedro!' They slunk away, still snarling.

Sylvia and I sat side by side on a sofa in a large, handsomely appointed living room. Across from us, in a chair, lounged a tall man with heavily lidded black eyes and long, sensitive fingers. Against the door through which we had entered the room leaned a thin, undersized young man, with his hands in the pockets of his coat and a cigarette hanging from his lower lip. He had a drawn, sallow face and his small, half-closed eyes stared at us incuriously. In a corner of the room, a squat, swarthy man twiddled with the dials of a radio. The woman paced up and down, smoking a cigarette in a long holder.

'Well, Gail,' said the lounging man in a soft voice, 'to what do we owe thees unexpected visit?'

Gail kept pacing. 'They got Sandra,' she said finally.

The lounging man did not change expression. 'Who got Sandra, Gail?' he asked softly.

'Reagan, on 142,' said Gail.

The squat, swarthy man jumped to his feet. 'All da time Egypt say keel dees Reagan!' he shouted. 'All da time Egypt say bomp off dees Reagan!'

The lounging man did not look at him. 'Sit down, Egypt,' he said quietly. The swarthy man sat down. Gail went on talking.

'The punk here shot off his mouth,' she said. 'He was wise.' I looked at the man leaning against the door.

'She means you,' said Sylvia, and laughed.

'The dame was dumb,' Gail went on. 'She thought the lady on the train was sick.'

I laughed. 'She means you,' I said to Sylvia.

'The punk was blowing his top all over the train,' said Gail. 'I had to bring 'em along.'

Sylvia, who had the beans on her lap, began breaking and stringing them. 'Well, my dear lady,' said the lounging man, 'a mos' homely leetle tawtch.'

'Wozza totch?' demanded Egypt.

'Touch,' I told him.

Gail sat down in a chair. 'Who's going to rub 'em out?' she asked.

'Freddy,' said the lounging man. Egypt was on his feet again.

'Na! Na!' he shouted. 'Na da ponk! Da ponk bomp off da las' seex, seven peop'!'

The lounging man looked at him. Egypt paled and sat down.

'I thought *you* were the punk,' said Sylvia. I looked at her coldly.

'I know where I have seen you before,' I said to the lounging man. 'It was at Zagreb, in 1927. Tilden took you in straight sets, six-love, six-love, six-love.'

The man's eyes glittered. 'I theenk I bomp off thees man myself,' he said.

Freddy walked over and handed the lounging man an automatic. At this moment, the door Freddy had been leaning against burst open and in rushed the man with the pipe, shouting, 'Gail! Gail! Gail!' . . .

'Gaylordsville! Gaylordsville!' bawled the brakeman. Sylvia was shaking me by the arm. 'Quit moaning,' she said. 'Everybody is looking at you.' I rubbed my forehead with a handkerchief. 'Hurry up!' said Sylvia. 'They don't stop here long.' I pulled the bags down and we got off.

'Have you got the beans?' I asked Sylvia.

Alice Connell was waiting for us. On the way to their home in the car, Sylvia began to tell Alice about the woman on 142. I didn't say anything.

'He thought she was a spy,' said Sylvia.

They both laughed. 'She probably got sick on the train,' said Alice. 'They were probably arranging for a doctor to meet her at the station.'

'That's just what I told him,' said Sylvia.

I lighted a cigarette. 'The lady on 142,' I said firmly, 'was definitely not sick.'

'Oh, Lord,' said Sylvia, 'here we go again.'

The Catbird Seat

MR MARTIN bought the pack of Camels on Monday night in the most crowded cigar store on Broadway. It was theatre time and seven or eight men were buying cigarettes. The clerk didn't even glance at Mr Martin, who put the pack in his overcoat pocket and went out. If any of the staff at F & S had seen him buy the cigarettes, they would have been astonished, for it was generally known that Mr Martin did not smoke and never had. No one saw him.

It was just a week to the day since Mr Martin had decided to rub out Mrs Ulgine Barrows. The term 'rub out' pleased him because it suggested nothing more than the correction of an error – in this case an error of Mr Fitweiler. Mr Martin had spent each night of the past week working out his plan and examining it. As he walked home now he went over it again. For the hundredth time he resented the element of imprecision, the margin of guesswork that entered into the business. The project as he had worked it out was casual and bold, the risks were considerable. Something might go wrong anywhere along the line. And therein lay the cunning of his scheme. No one would ever see in it the cautious, painstaking hand of Erwin Martin, head of the filing department at F & S, of whom Mr Fitweiler had once said, 'Man is fallible but Martin isn't.' No one would see his hand, that is, unless it were caught in the act.

Sitting in his apartment, drinking a glass of milk, Mr Martin reviewed his case against Mrs Ulgine Barrows, as he had every night for seven nights. He began at the beginning. Her quacking voice and braying laugh had first profaned the halls of F & S on March 7, 1941 (Mr Martin had a head for dates). Old Roberts, the personnel chief, had introduced her as the newly appointed special adviser to the president of the firm, Mr Fitweiler. The woman had appalled Mr Martin instantly, but he hadn't shown it. He had given her his dry hand, a look of studious concentration, and a faint smile. 'Well,' she had said, looking at the papers on his desk, 'are you lifting the oxcart out of the ditch?' As Mr Martin recalled that moment, over his milk, he squirmed slightly. He must keep his mind on her crimes as a special adviser, not on her peccadilloes as a personality. This he found difficult to do, in spite of entering an objection and sustaining it. The faults of the woman as a woman kept chattering on in his mind like an unruly witness. She had, for almost two years now, baited him. In the halls, in the elevator, even in his own office, into which she romped now and then like a circus horse, she was constantly shouting these silly questions at him. 'Are you lifting the oxcart out of the ditch? Are you tearing up the pea patch? Are you hollering down the rain barrel? Are you scraping around the bottom of the pickle barrel? Are you sitting in the catbird seat?'

It was Joey Hart, one of Mr Martin's two assistants, who had explained what the gibberish meant. 'She must be a Dodger fan,' he had said. 'Red Barber announces the Dodger games over the radio and he uses those expressions – picked 'em up down South.' Joey had gone on to explain one or two. 'Tearing up the pea patch' meant going on a rampage; 'sitting in the catbird seat' meant sitting pretty, like a batter with three balls and no strikes on him. Mr Martin dismissed all this with an effort. It had been annoying, it had driven him near to distraction, but he was too solid a man to be moved to murder by anything so childish. It was fortunate, he reflected as he passed on to the important charges against Mrs Barrows, that he had stood up under it so well. He had maintained always an outward appearance of polite tolerance. 'Why, I even believe you like the woman,' Miss Paird, his other assistant, had once said to him. He had simply smiled.

A gavel rapped in Mr Martin's mind and the case proper was resumed. Mrs Ulgine Barrows stood charged with wilful, blatant, and persistent attempts to destroy the efficiency and system of F & S. It was competent, material, and relevant to review her advent and rise to power. Mr Martin had got the story from Miss Paird, who seemed always able to find things out. According to her, Mrs Barrows had met Mr Fitweiler at a party, where she had rescued him from the embraces of a powerfully built drunken man who had mistaken the president of F & S for a famous retired Middle Western football coach. She had led him to a sofa and somehow worked upon him a monstrous magic. The aging gentleman had jumped to the conclusion there and then that this was a woman of singular attainments, equipped to bring out the best in him and in the firm. A week later he had introduced her into F & S as his special adviser. On that day confusion got its foot in the door. After Miss Tyson, Mr Brundage, and Mr Bartlett had been fired and Mr Munson had taken his hat and stalked out, mailing in his resignation later, old Roberts had been emboldened to speak to Mr Fitweiler. He mentioned that Mr Munson's department had been 'a little disrupted' and hadn't they perhaps better resume the old system there? Mr Fitweiler had said certainly not. He had the greatest faith in Mrs Barrow's ideas. 'They require a little seasoning, a little seasoning, is all,' he had added. Mr Roberts had given it up. Mr Martin reviewed in detail all the changes wrought by Mrs Barrows. She had begun chipping at the cornices of the firm's edifice and now she was swinging at the foundation stones with a pickaxe.

Mr Martin came now, in his summing up, to the afternoon of Monday, November 2, 1942 – just one week ago. On that day, at 3 p.m., Mrs Barrows had bounced into his office. 'Boo!' she had yelled. 'Are you scraping around the bottom of the pickle barrel?' Mr Martin had looked at her from under his green eyeshade, saying nothing. She had begun to wander about the office, taking it in with her great, popping eyes. 'Do you really need *all* these filing cabinets?' she had demanded suddenly. Mr Martin's heart had jumped. 'Each of these files,' he had said, keeping his voice even, 'plays an indispensable part in the system of F & S.' She had brayed at him, 'Well, don't tear up the pea patch!' and gone to the door. From there she had bawled, 'But you sure have got a lot of fine scrap in here!' Mr Martin could no longer doubt that the finger was on his beloved department. Her pickaxe was on the upswing, poised for the first blow. It had not come yet; he had received no blue memo from the enchanted Mr Fitweiler bearing nonsensical instructions deriving from the obscene woman. But there was no doubt in Mr Martin's mind that one would be forthcoming. He must act quickly. Already a precious week had gone by. Mr Martin stood up in his living room, still holding his milk glass. 'Gentlemen of the jury,' he said to himself. 'I demand the death penalty for this horrible person.'

The next day Mr Martin followed his routine, as usual. He polished his glasses more often and once sharpened an already sharp pencil, but not even Miss Paird noticed. Only once did he catch sight of his victim; she swept past him in the hall with a patronizing 'Hi!' At five-thirty he walked home, as usual, and had a glass of milk, as usual. He had never drunk anything stronger in his life – unless you could count ginger ale. The late Sam Schlosser, the S of F & S, had praised Mr Martin at a staff meeting several years before for his temperate habits. 'Our most efficient worker neither drinks nor smokes,' he had said. 'The results speak for themselves.' Mr Fitweiler had sat by, nodding approval.

Mr Martin was still thinking about that red-letter day as he walked over to the Schrafft's on Fifth Avenue near Forty-sixth Street. He got there, as he always did, at eight o'clock. He finished his dinner and the financial page of the *Sun* at a quarter to nine, as he always did. It was his custom after dinner to take a walk. This time he walked down Fifth Avenue at a casual pace. His gloved hands felt moist and warm, his forehead cold. He transferred the Camels from his overcoat to a jacket pocket. He wondered, as he did so, if they did not represent an unnecessary note of strain. Mrs Barrows smoked only Luckies. It was his idea to puff a few puffs on a Camel (after the rubbing-out), stub it out in the ashtray holding her lipstick-stained Luckies, and thus drag a small red herring across the trail. Perhaps it was not a good idea. It would take time. He might even choke, too loudly.

Mr Martin had never seen the house on West Twelfth Street where Mrs Barrows lived, but he had a clear enough picture of it. Fortunately, she had bragged to everybody about her ducky first-floor apartment in the perfectly darling three-storey red-brick. There would be no doorman or other attendants; just the tenants of the second and third floors. As he walked along, Mr Martin realized that he would get there before nine-thirty. He had considered walking north on Fifth Avenue from Schrafft's to a point from which it would take him until ten o'clock to reach the house. At that hour people were less likely to be coming in or going out. But the procedure would have made an awkward loop in the straight thread of his casualness, and he had abandoned it.

It was impossible to figure when people would be entering or leaving the house, anyway. There was a great risk at any hour. If he ran into anybody, he would simply have to place the rubbing-out of Ulgine Barrows in the inactive file forever. The same thing would hold true if there were someone in her apartment. In that case he would just say that he had been passing by, recognized her charming house and thought to drop in.

It was eighteen minutes after nine when Mr Martin turned into Twelfth Street. A man passed him, and a man and a woman talking. There was no one within fifty paces when he came to the house, halfway down the block. He was up the steps and in the small vestibule in no time, pressing the bell under the card that said 'Mrs Ulgine Barrows.' When the clicking in the lock started, he jumped forward against the door. He got inside fast, closing the door behind him. A bulb in a lantern hung from the hall ceiling on a chain seemed to give a monstrously bright light. There was nobody on the stair, which went up ahead of him along the left wall. A door opened down the hall in the wall on the right. He went toward it swiftly, on tiptoe.

'Well, for God's sake, look who's here!' bawled Mrs Barrows, and her braying laugh rang out like the report of a shotgun. He rushed past her like a football tackle, bumping her. 'Hey, quit shoving!' she said, closing the door behind them. They were in her living room, which seemed to Mr Martin to be lighted by a hundred lamps. 'What's after you?' she said. 'You're as jumpy as a goat.' He found he was unable to speak. His heart was wheezing in his throat. 'I – yes,' he finally brought out. She was jabbering and laughing as she started to help him off with his coat. 'No, no,' he said. 'I'll put it here.' He took it off and put it on a chair near the door. 'Your hat and gloves, too,' she said. 'You're in a lady's house.' He put his hat on top of the coat. Mrs Barrows seemed larger than he had thought. He kept his gloves on. 'I was passing by,' he said. 'I recognized – is there anyone here?' She laughed louder than ever. 'No,' she said, 'we're all alone. You're as white as a sheet, you funny man. Whatever *has* come over you? I'll mix you a toddy.' She started toward a door across the room. 'Scotch-and-soda be all right? But say, you don't drink, do you?' She turned and gave him her amused look. Mr Martin pulled himself together. 'Scotch-and-soda will be all right,' he heard himself say. He could hear her laughing in the kitchen.

Mr Martin looked quickly around the living room for the weapon. He had counted on finding one there. There were andirons and a poker and something in a corner that looked like an Indian club. None of them would do. It couldn't be that way. He began to pace around. He came to a desk. On it lay a metal paper knife with an ornate handle. Would it be sharp enough? He reached for it and knocked over a small brass jar. Stamps spilled out of it and it fell to the floor with a clatter. 'Hey,' Mrs Barrows yelled from the kitchen, 'are you tearing up the pea patch?' Mr Martin gave a strange laugh. Picking up the knife, he tried its point against his left wrist. It was blunt. It wouldn't do.

When Mrs Barrows reappeared, carrying two highballs, Mr Martin, standing there with his gloves on, became acutely conscious of the fantasy he had wrought. Cigarettes in his pocket, a drink prepared for him – it was all too grossly improbable. It was more than that; it was impossible. Somewhere in the back of his mind a vague idea stirred, sprouted. 'For heaven's sake, take off those gloves,' said Mrs Barrows. 'I always wear them in the house,' said Mr Martin. The idea began to bloom, strange and wonderful. She put the glasses on a coffee table in front of a sofa and sat on the sofa. 'Come over here, you odd little man,' she said. Mr Martin went over and sat beside her. It was difficult getting a cigarette out of the pack of Camels, but he managed it. She held a match for him, laughing. 'Well,' she said, handing him his drink, 'this is perfectly marvellous. You with a drink and a cigarette.'

Mr Martin puffed, not too awkwardly, and took a gulp of the highball. 'I drink and smoke all the time,' he said. He clinked his glass against hers. 'Here's nuts to that old windbag, Fitweiler,' he said, and gulped again. The stuff tasted awful, but he made no grimace. 'Really, Mr Martin,' she said, her voice and posture changing, 'you are insulting our employer.' Mrs Barrows was now all special adviser to the president. 'I am preparing a bomb,' said Mr Martin, 'which will blow the old goat higher than hell.' He had only had a little of the drink, which was not strong. It couldn't be that. 'Do you take dope or something?' Mrs Barrows asked coldly. 'Heroin,' said Mr Martin. 'I'll be coked to the gills when I bump that old buzzard off.' 'Mr Martin!' she shouted, getting to her feet. 'That will be all of that. You must go at once.' Mr Martin took another swallow of his drink. He tapped his cigarette out in the ashtray and put the pack of Camels on the coffee table. Then he got up. She stood glaring at him. He walked over and put on his hat and coat. 'Not a word about this,' he said, and laid an index finger against his lips. All Mrs Barrows could bring out was 'Really!' Mr Martin put his hand on the door-knob. 'I'm sitting in the catbird seat,' he said. He stuck his tongue out at her and left. Nobody saw him go.

Mr Martin got to his apartment, walking, well before eleven. No one saw him go in. He had two glasses of milk after brushing his teeth, and he felt elated. It wasn't tipsiness, because he hadn't been tipsy. Anyway, the walk had worn off all effects of the whisky. He got in bed and read a magazine for a while. He was asleep before midnight.

Mr Martin got to the office at eight-thirty the next morning, as usual. At a quarter to nine, Ulgine Barrows, who had never before arrived at work before ten, swept into his office. 'I'm reporting to Mr Fitweiler now!' she shouted. 'If he turns you over to the police, it's no more than you deserve!' Mr Martin gave her a look of shocked surprise. 'I beg your pardon?' he said. Mrs Barrows snorted and bounced out of the room, leaving Miss Paird and Joey Hart staring after her. 'What's the matter with that old devil now?' asked Miss Paird. 'I have no idea,' said Mr Martin, resuming his work. The other two looked at him and then at each other. Miss Paird got up and went out. She walked slowly past the closed door of Mr Fitweiler's office. Mrs Barrows was yelling inside, but she was not braying. Miss Paird could not hear what the woman was saying. She went back to her desk.

Forty-five minutes later, Mrs Barrows left the president's office and went into her own, shutting the door. It wasn't until half an hour later that Mr Fitweiler sent for Mr Martin. The head of the filing department, neat, quiet, attentive, stood in front of the old man's desk. Mr Fitweiler was pale and nervous. He took his glasses off and twiddled them. He made a small, bruffing sound in his throat. 'Martin,' he said, 'you have been with us more than twenty years.' 'Twenty-two, sir,' said Mr Martin. 'In that time,' pursued the president, 'your work and your – uh – manner have been exemplary.' 'I trust so, sir,' said Mr Martin. 'I have understood, Martin,' said Mr Fitweiler, 'that you have never taken a drink or smoked.' 'That is correct, sir,' said Mr Martin. 'Ah, yes.' Mr Fitweiler polished his glasses. 'You may describe what you did after leaving the office yesterday, Martin,' he said. Mr Martin allowed less than a second for his bewildered pause. 'Certainly, sir,' he said. 'I walked home. Then I went to Schrafft's for dinner. Afterward I walked home again. I went to bed early, sir, and read a magazine for a while. I was asleep before eleven.' 'Ah, yes,' said Mr Fitweiler again. He was silent for a moment, searching for the proper words to say to the head of the filing department. 'Mrs Barrows,' he said finally, 'Mrs Barrows has worked hard, Martin, very hard. It grieves me to report that she has suffered a severe breakdown. It has taken the form of a persecution complex accompanied by distressing hallucinations.' 'I am very sorry, sir,' said Mr Martin. 'Mrs Barrows is under the delusion,' continued Mr Fitweiler, 'that you visited her last evening and behaved yourself in an – uh – unseemly manner.' He raised his hand to silence Mr Martin's little pained outcry. 'It is the nature of these psychological diseases,' Mr Fitweiler said, 'to fix upon the least likely and most innocent party as the – uh – source of persecution. These matters are not for the lay mind to grasp, Martin. I've just had my psychiatrist, Dr Fitch, on the phone. He would not, of course, commit himself, but he made enough generalizations to substantiate my suspicions. I suggested to Mrs Barrows when she had completed her – uh – story to me this morning, that she visit Dr Fitch, for I suspected a condition at once. She flew, I regret to say, into a rage, and demanded – uh – requested that I call you on the carpet. You may not know, Martin, but Mrs Barrows had planned a re-organization of your department – subject to my approval, of course, subject to my approval. This brought you, rather than anyone else, to her mind – but again that is a phenomenon for Dr Fitch and not for us. So, Martin, I am afraid Mrs Barrows' usefulness here is at an end.' 'I am dreadfully sorry, sir,' said Mr Martin.

It was at this point that the door to the office blew open with the suddenness of a gas-main explosion and Mrs Barrows catapulted through it. 'Is the little rat denying it?' she screamed. 'He can't get away with that!' Mr Martin got up and moved discreetly to a point beside Mr Fitweiler's chair. 'You drank and smoked at my apartment,' she bawled at Mr Martin, 'and you know it! You called Mr Fitweiler an old windbag and said you were going to blow him up

when you got coked to the gills on your heroin!' She stopped yelling to catch
her breath and a new glint came into her popping eyes. 'If you weren't such a
drab, ordinary little man,' she said, 'I'd think you'd planned it all. Sticking
your tongue out, saying you were sitting in the catbird seat, because you
thought no one would believe me when I told it! My God, it's really too perfect!' She brayed loudly and hysterically, and the fury was on her again. She
glared at Mr Fitweiler. 'Can't you see how he has tricked us, you old fool?
Can't you see his little game?' But Mr Fitweiler had been surreptitiously pressing all the buttons under the top of his desk and employees of F & S began
pouring into the room. 'Stockton,' said Mr Fitweiler, 'you and Fishbein will
take Mrs Barrows to her home. Mrs Powell, you will go with them.' Stockton,
who had played a little football in high school, blocked Mrs Barrows as she
made for Mr Martin. It took him and Fishbein together to force her out of the
door into the hall, crowded with stenographers and office boys. She was still
screaming imprecations at Mr Martin, tangled and contradictory imprecations. The hubbub finally died out down the corridor.

'I regret that this has happened,' said Mr Fitweiler. 'I shall ask you to dismiss it from your mind, Martin.' 'Yes, sir,' said Mr Martin, anticipating his
chief's 'That will be all' by moving to the door. 'I will dismiss it.' He went out
and shut the door, and his step was light and quick in the hall. When he entered
his department he had slowed down to his customary gait, and he walked
quietly across the room to the W20 file, wearing a look of studious concentration.

Memoirs of a Drudge

Mr Thurber . . . went to Ohio State University for his formal education. His informal education included . . . drudgery on several newspapers—in Columbus, in New York, and in Paris.—*From 'Horse Sense in American Humour,' by Walter Blair*.

I DON'T know about that. There is, of course, a certain amount of drudgery in newspaper work, just as there is in teaching classes, tunnelling into a bank, or being President of the United States. I suppose that even the most pleasurable of imaginable occupations, that of batting baseballs through the windows of the R.C.A. Building, would pall a little as the days ran on. Seldom, it is true, do I gather my grandchildren about my knees and tell them tall tales out of my colourful years as a leg man, but I often sit in the cane-seated rocker on the back porch, thinking of the old days and cackling with that glee known only to ageing journalists. Just the other evening, when the womenfolks were washing up the supper dishes and setting them to dreen, they could hear me rocking back and forth and laughing to myself. I was thinking about the Riviera edition of the *Chicago Tribune* in southern France during the winter of 1925–1926.

Seven or eight of us had been assigned to the task of getting out a little six-page newspaper, whose stories were set up in 10-point type, instead of the customary 8-point, to make life easier for everybody, including the readers. Most of our news came by wire from the Paris edition, and all we had to do was write headlines for it, a pleasurable occupation if you are not rushed, and we were never rushed. For the rest, we copied from the *Eclaireur de Nice et du Sud-Est*, a journal filled with droll and mystical stories, whose translation, far from being drudgery, was pure joy. Nice, in that indolent winter, was full of knaves and rascals, adventurers and impostors, *pochards* and *indiscrets*, whose ingenious exploits, sometimes in full masquerade costume, sometimes in the nude, were easy and pleasant to record.

We went to work after dinner and usually had the last chronicle of the diverting day written and ready for the linotypers well before midnight. It was then our custom to sit around for half an hour, making up items for the society editor's column. She was too pretty, we thought, to waste the soft southern days tracking down the arrival of prominent persons on the Azure Coast. So all she had to do was stop in at the Ruhl and the Negresco each day and pick up the list of guests who had just registered. The rest of us invented enough items to fill up the last half of her column, and a gay and romantic cavalcade, indeed, infested the littoral of our imagination. 'Lieutenant General and Mrs Pendleton Gray Winslow,' we would write, 'have arrived at their villa, Heart's Desire, on Cap d'Antibes, bringing with them their prize Burmese monkey,

Thibault.' Or 'The Hon. Mr Stephen H. L. Atterbury, Chargé-d'Affaires of
the American Legation in Peru, and Mrs Atterbury, the former Princess Ti
Ling of Thibet, are motoring to Monte Carlo from Aix-en-Provence, where
they have been visiting Mr Atterbury's father, Rear Admiral A. Watson
Atterbury, U.S.N., retired. Mr Stephen Atterbury is the breeder of the
famous Schnauzer-Pincer, Champion Adelbert von Weigengrosse of Tamer-
lane, said to be valued at $15,000.' In this manner we turned out, in no time at
all, and with the expenditure of very little mental energy, the most glittering
column of social notes in the history of the American newspaper, either here
or abroad.

As the hour of midnight struck twice, in accordance with the dreamy
custom of town and church clocks in southern France, and our four or five
hours of drudgery were ending, the late Frank Harris would often drop in at
the *Tribune* office, and we would listen to stories of Oscar Wilde, Walt Whitman, Bernard Shaw, Emma Goldman, and Frank Harris. Thus ran the harsh
and exacting tenor of those days of slavery.

It is true that the languorous somnolence of our life was occasionally
broken up. This would happen about one night a week, around ten o'clock,
when our French composing room went on strike. The printers and their fore-
man, a handsome, black-bearded giant of a man, whose rages resembled the
mistral, wanted to set up headlines in their own easygoing way, using whatever
size type was handiest and whatever space it would fit into most easily. That is
the effortless hit-or-miss system which has made a crazy quilt of French newspaper headlines for two hundred years, and André and his men could not
understand why we stubbornly refused to adopt so sane and simple a method.
So now and then, when he couldn't stand our stupid and inviolable headline
schedules any longer, André would roar into our little city room like a storm
from the Alps. Behind him in the doorway stood his linotypers, with their hats
and coats on. Since the Frenchmen could comprehend no English and spoke
only *Nicois*, an argot entirely meaningless to us, our arguments were carried
on in shouting and gesticulating and a great deal of waving of French and
American newspapers in each other's faces. After a while all the combatants
on both sides would adjourn to the bar next door, still yelling and gesturing,
but after four or five rounds of beer we would fall to singing old Provençal
songs and new American ones, and there would be a truce for another six or
seven days, everybody going back to work, still singing.

On one of those nights of battle, song, and compromise, several of us
defenders of the immutable American headline went back to the bar after we
had got the *Tribune* to press and sat up till dawn, drinking *grog américain*. Just
as the sun came up, we got on a train for Cannes, where the most talked-about
international struggle of the year was to take place that afternoon, the tennis
match between Suzanne Lenglen and Helen Wills. As we climbed aboard, one
of my colleagues, spoiling for an argument, declared that a French translation
he had read of Edgar Allan Poe's 'The Raven' was infinitely superior to the
poem in the original English. How we had got around to this curious subject I

have no idea, but it seemed natural enough at the time. I remember that a young reporter named Middleton visited all the compartments on the train, demanding of their sleepy and startled French occupants if they did not believe that a raven was more likely to say '*Jamais plus*' than 'Nevermore.' He returned with the claim that our fellow-passengers to a man were passionately on the side of '*Jamais plus*.' So passed a night of drudgery in the fond, far-away days of the Third Republic and the Riviera edition of the *Chicago Tribune*.

We had the long days of warm blue weather for our own, to climb the Corniche roads or wind up the mountain in a *char à bancs* to the magical streams and the million springtime flowers of St-Martin-Vésubie. Sometimes we sat the day out on the terrace of a restaurant overlooking the Bay of Angels and gave the tireless Albert suggestions as to where he might find Henry James. Albert was a young Englishman who did interviews for us with distinguished visitors to the Riviera, and he had got the curious idea that the celebrated novelist was hiding away in a *pension* somewhere between St Tropez and Mentone, rewriting 'The Golden Bowl.' We decided that Albert had got his tip about the whereabouts of the great dead man from some ageing aunt who lived in the parlours and the gardens of the past. It was one way to spend an afternoon, sitting over our glasses of vermouth-cassis, bringing back to life the poor, sensitive creator of Peter Quint and Mme de Vionnet, figuring him lost and wandering, ever so wonderfully, somewhere among the bougainvillaea and the passionflowers. Thus in fancy and in dream passed the long days of warm blue weather.

Before going to France, I worked on the Columbus *Evening Dispatch*, a fat and amiable newspaper, whose city editor seldom knew where I was and got so that he didn't care. He had a glimpse of me every day at 9 A.M., arriving at the office, and promptly at ten he saw me leave it, a sheaf of folded copy paper in my pocket and a look of enterprise in my eye. I was on my way to Marzetti's, a comfortable restaurant just down the street, where a group of us newspapermen met every morning. We would sit around for an hour, drinking coffee, telling stories, drawing pictures on the tablecloth, and giving imitations of the more eminent Ohio political figures of the day, many of whom fanned their soup with their hats but had enough good, old-fashioned horse sense to realize that a proposal to shift the clocks of the state from Central to Eastern standard time was directly contrary to the will of the Lord God Almighty and that the supporters of the project would burn in hell.

After this relaxing and often stimulating interlude I would stroll out to the Carnegie Library and read the New York *World* in the periodical room. It so happened that the city offices, which I was assigned to cover, were housed at that time in the library building, the old City Hall having burned down the first night I ever attended a council meeting in it. After I had put the *World* back on its rack, only a little fragment of forenoon remained in which to gather the news, but I somehow managed the aggravating chore.

Nor were the city offices dull and colourless places. Secretary Killam of the Civil Service Commission had a tuba, on which I learned to play a few notes, an exciting and satisfying experience, as anyone who has brought forth a blast from a tuba knows. The lady dance-hall inspector was full of stories of the goings on in the more dubious clubs about town, in one of which, she reported, the boys and girls contrived to two-step without moving their feet. And the Mayor's office was frequently besieged by diverting and passionate taxpayers: an elderly gentleman who could get KDKA on the steel rims of his spectacles, a woman who was warned of the approach of earthquakes by a sharp twinge in her left side, and a lady to whom it had been revealed in a vision that the new O'Shaughnessy storage dam had not been constructed of concrete but of Cream of Wheat.

So ran the mornings away in the years of my servitude on the Columbus *Dispatch*. The afternoons, after three o'clock, I had to myself. I used to spend a great many of them at home, lying down. That tuba took quite a little out of me.

Now we come to the six months of drudgery on the New York *Evening Post*, back in the days of Sacco and Vanzetti, the Hall-Mills case, and Daddy Browning. The city editor of the paper, a gentleman with a keen eye for the frailties of men and a heart overflowing with *misericordia*, apparently decided I did not look like a man capable of handling spot news – that is, events in the happening, such as warehouse fires and running gun fights. He therefore set me to writing what he called overnight feature stories. These were stories that could be printed anytime – tomorrow, or next week, or not at all, if the flow of important news was too heavy. They were designed to fit in between accounts of murder trials and train wrecks, to brighten the ominous page and lighten, if possible, the uneasy heart of the reader. So it came about that when other reporters were out wearing themselves down in quest of the clangorous and complicated fact, I could be observed wandering the quiet shore above the noisy torrent of contemporary history, examining the little miracles and grotesqueries of the time.

I wrote only one story a day, usually consisting of fewer than a thousand words. Most of the reporters, when they went out on assignments, first had to get their foot in the door, but the portals of the fantastic and the unique are always left open. If an astonished botanist produced a black evening primrose, or thought he had produced one, I spent the morning prowling his gardens. When a lady in the West Seventies sent in word that she was getting messages from the late Walter Savage Landor in heaven, I was sent up to see what the importunate poet had on his mind. On the occasion of the arrival in town of Major Monroe of Jacksonville, Florida, who claimed to be a hundred and seventeen years old, I walked up Broadway with him while he roundly cursed the Northern dogs who jostled him, bewailing the while the passing of Bob Lee and Tom Jackson and Joe Johnston. I studied gypsies in Canarsie and generals in the Waldorf, listened to a man talk backward and watched a blindfolded boy play ping-pong. Put it all together and I don't know what it comes to, but it wasn't drudgery.

It was not often, in the *Post* or no *Sturm-und-Drang* phase, that I wandered farther afield than the confines of Greater New York. On the occasion of the hundred-and-fiftieth anniversary of Washington's crossing the Delaware, however, I was sent over to Trenton to report the daylong celebration. (Once in a long while I got a spot news assignment like that.) At a little past ten in the morning I discovered the hotel room which a group of the more convivial newspapermen had set up as their headquarters, and at a little past twelve I was asleep in a chair there. When I woke up it was dark, and the celebration was over. I hadn't sent anything to my paper, and by that time it was too late. I went home. The *Post*, I found out, had used the Associated Press account of what went on in Trenton.

When I got to work the next morning, the city editor came over to my desk. 'Let's see,' he said, 'what did I send you out on yesterday?' 'It didn't pan out,' I told him. 'No story.' 'The hell with it, then,' he said. 'Here, get on this – lady says there are violets growing in the snow over in Red Bank.' 'Violets don't grow in the snow,' I reminded him. 'They might in Red Bank,' he said. 'Slide on over there.' I slid instead to a bar and put in a phone call to the Chief of Police in Red Bank. A desk sergeant answered and I asked him about the violets. 'Ain't no violence over here,' he told me, and hung up. It wasn't much to hang a story on, as we say, but I hung one on it. But first I had a few more drinks with a man I had met at the bar, very pleasant fellow, captain of a barge or something. Shortly after the strange case of the violets in the snow, I left the newspaper game and drifted into the magazine game.

And now, in closing, I wish to leave with my little readers, both boys and girls, this parting bit of advice: Stay out of the magazine game.

The Cane in the Corridor

'FUNNY thing about post-operative mental states,' said Joe Fletcher, rocking the big brandy glass between the palms of his hands and studying the brown tides reflectively. 'They take all kinds of curious turns.'

George Minturn moved restlessly in his chair, making a new pattern of his long legs. 'Let's go to Barney's,' he said. 'Let's go to Barney's now.'

Mrs Minturn walked over and emptied an ashtray into the fireplace as eloquently as if she were winding the clock. 'It's much too late,' she said. 'I'm sure everybody we'd want to see has left there and gone home to bed.'

Minturn finished his brandy and poured out some more.

'You remember Reginald Gardiner's imitation of wallpaper,' continued Fletcher, 'in which he presented a visual design as making a pattern of sound? Many post-operative cases make those interesting transferences. I know one man who kept drawing on a piece of paper what the ringing of a telephone *looks* like.'

'I don't want to hear about him,' said Minturn.

Fletcher drank the last of his brandy and held up his glass; after a moment his host walked over and poured in a little more.

Mrs Minturn found herself finishing her own drink and getting another one, although she seldom touched anything after dinner. 'Here's to the Washington Bridge,' she said. 'Here's to some big dam or other. Let's talk about some big dam. After all, you're an engineer, Joe.'

Fletcher lighted a cigarette, holding his brandy glass between his knees. 'Which brings up an interesting point,' he said. 'I mean, if occupational experience gives a special shape and colour to the patient's perceptions, then the theory that it is not really a hallucination but a deeper insight into reality probably falls down. For instance, if the number eighteen clangs for one patient and whistles for another – say for George here –'

Minturn spilled ashes on the lapel of his dinner coat and rubbed them into it. 'I don't want to hear any numbers,' he said thickly. 'I don't want to hear any more about it.'

His wife, who had been trying to get Fletcher's eye but couldn't, since he continued to study his brandy, spoke up sharply. 'George is just getting over a frightful cold,' she said, 'and he's prettily easily shaken. He would worry frightfully about people, but he doesn't dare think about them. They upset him so.' Fletcher did look at her now, and smiled. She realized she had not said what she had meant to say. Something oblique but cleverly phrased and nicely pointed had got lost on its way to her tongue. 'You think you're so darn smart,' she said.

Minturn got up and began to pace. The brandy had run out. He sat down and lighted a cigarette.

'Of course, the people that doctors refer to as squashes,' pursued Fletcher, 'the invertebrates, you might say, just lie there like vegetables. It is the high-strung cases that manifest the interesting – manifestations. As you just said, Nancy, you think you're so darn smart. I mean, hospitalization moves the mind toward a false simplification. A man gets the idea that he can hold pro-cesses in his hand, the way I'm holding this glass. He lies there, you might say, pulling the easy little meanings out of life as simply as if they were daisy petals.'

'Daisy petals,' said Minturn. 'Where's brandy? Why isn't there any more brandy?'

'He gets the idea,' Fletcher went on, 'that he knows as much about life as Alfred North Whitehead or Carson McCullers.'

Minturn said, 'Oh, God.'

'Carson McCullers makes George nervous,' said Mrs Minturn, 'and you know it.'

'I ask you to remember I have scarcely seen you people since Carson McCullers began to write,' said Fletcher stiffly. 'I know "Sanctuary" upset George so he had to go away to the mountains. I *do* know that.'

'He didn't go away to the mountains at all,' said Mrs Minturn. 'So you *don't* know that.'

'I want to go away to the mountains now,' said Minturn. He began pacing around again, picking up things.

'There's more brandy in the kitchen, darling,' said Mrs Minturn. 'In the kitchen,' she repeated as he started upstairs.

'Oh,' said Minturn. He went out to the kitchen.

Mrs Minturn went over to Fletcher and stood looking down at him. 'It's very sweet of you, Joe, to keep harping on hospitals and sick people and mental states,' she said. 'I know why you're doing it. You're doing it because George didn't come to see you when you were in the hospital. You know very well that George is too sensitive to visit people in the hospital.'

Fletcher stood up, too. 'Is that why *you* didn't come to see me?' he asked. She was taller than he was. He sat down again.

'Yes, it was, if you want to know so much,' she said. 'George would have sensed it and he would have worried about you all the time. As it was, he *did* worry about you all the time. But he can't stand things the way you can. You know how sensitive he's always been.'

Fletcher tried to drink out of his empty glass. 'He wasn't so goddam sensi-tive when we were both with the Cleveland Telephone Company. He wasn't so goddam sensitive then. No, he was practically a regular guy.'

Mrs Minturn drew herself up a little higher. 'It is just quite possible, per-haps,' she said, 'that you were just not quite perceptious at that time.' She went slowly back to her chair and sat down as Minturn came in with a bottle of brandy and a corkscrew.

'Here,' he said, handing them to Fletcher. Fletcher put down his glass, inserted the corkscrew accurately into the centre of the cork, twisted it competently, and pulled out the cork. 'Wonderful thing, technology,' said Minturn, 'wonderful thing, wonderful thing. I want a drink.' Fletcher poured a great splash of brandy into his host's glass and another into his own.

'He doesn't happen to mean he *believes* in it,' said Mrs Minturn. 'The trouble with you is you can't tell when a person is allusive even.'

'You're thinking of Technocracy,' Fletcher told her, taking her glass and pouring a small quantity of brandy into it with studious precision.

'Maybe,' said Mrs Minturn, darkly, 'and just maybe not.'

'Why can't we go home now? Why can't we go home now, Nancy?' said Minturn from deep down in his chair.

'We *are* home, dear,' said Mrs Minturn. She turned to Fletcher. 'Anybody that thinks I can't appreciate a game that two can play at is definitely,' said Mrs Minturn, hiccuping, 'crazy.' She held her breath and tried counting ten slowly.

'Why don't you try bending over and drinking out of the opposite side of your glass?' asked Fletcher.

Minturn sat up a little in his chair.

'Don't have to say things like that,' he said, severely.

To compensate for her hiccups, Mrs Minturn assumed a posture of strained dignity. Minturn slid farther down into his chair. They both watched Fletcher, who had set the brandy revolving in his glass and was studying it. He took a sip of his drink. 'It is a common misconception,' he said, 'that post-operative mental states disappear on the patient's advent from the hospital. Out of the hospital, they might recur at any time, and some pretty strange phenomena could happen – as in the case of the hospitalization of a friend.'

'If you're just trying to get George down, it's not going to be of the least consequence. I can assure you of that,' said Mrs Minturn. 'He's stronger than you are in lots of more important ways.'

'Phenomena,' said Minturn.

'I'm talking of what *I* might do, not of what George might do,' said Fletcher, 'in case you consider the manifestation what you choose to call weakness.'

'Well,' said Mrs Minturn, 'I certainly do – that and meanness.'

'I want to see Mrs Trimingham,' said Minturn. 'I want to go to Bermuda.'

'I suppose it would be too much to say that you can't very well disprove what I'm saying till I say it,' said Fletcher.

'No, it wouldn't,' said Mrs Minturn. 'I don't see why we can't talk about the Grand Coolidge Dam, or something.' She laughed. 'That's really frightfully funny. It really is.' She laughed again.

Minturn had closed his eyes, but he opened them again. 'Can't say I do,' he said. 'Can't say I do.'

Fletcher went over and splashed some more brandy into Minturn's glass.

'Let us say that George is lying in the hospital,' he said. 'Now, because of a recurring phenomena, I call on him every day.'

'That's cheap,' said Mrs Minturn, 'and that's pompous.'

'It's no more pompous than it is predictable,' said Fletcher, sharply. 'It's a condition. It just so happens that it might take the turn of me calling on George every day, from the time he goes in until he gets out.'

'You can't do that,' said George. 'There's such a thing as the law.'

'Of course he can't,' said Mrs Minturn. 'Besides, George is not going to the hospital.'

'I'm not going to the hospital,' said Minturn.

'Everybody goes to the hospital sooner or later,' said Fletcher. His voice was rising.

'Nine hundred million people don't,' said Mrs Minturn, 'all the time.'

'I'm stating a pathological case!' shouted Fletcher. 'Hypothetical. George has been lying there in that bed for six weeks!'

'No,' said Minturn.

'You ought to be ashamed of yourself,' said Mrs Minturn.

'Why?' asked Fletcher. 'I'm not saying there is anything the matter with him. He's convalescing, but he can't get up.'

'Why can't I get up?' asked Minturn.

'Because you're too weak. You have no more strength than a house mouse. You feel as if you were coming apart like a cheap croquet mallet. If you tried to stand, your knees would bend the wrong way, like a flamingo's.'

'I want to go home,' mumbled Minturn.

'You *are* home,' said his wife.

'He means from the hospital,' Fletcher told her, 'in the corridors of which, by the way, you hear my cane tapping practically all the time.'

'What are *you* doing there?' said Minturn thickly.

'I come to see you every day,' said Fletcher. 'I have been to see you every day since you got there.' He had been moving around the room, and now he went back and sat down.

'Can't stand you calling on me every day,' said Minturn. He finished his drink and poured a new one with some effort.

'Don't worry about it, George,' said Mrs Minturn. 'We'll take you to the Mayo brothers or someplace and he'll never find out about it.'

'I don't want to go to the Mayo brothers,' said Minturn.

Fletcher sat forward in his chair. 'And what's more,' he said, 'I bring you very strange things. That's part of it. That's part of the phenomena. I bring you puzzles that won't work, linked nails that won't come apart, pigs in clover in which the little balls are glued to the bottom of the box. I bring you mystery novels in Yiddish, and artificial flowers made of wire and beads, and horehound candy.'

'Terrible, terrible rat,' said Mrs Minturn, 'terrible rat Fletcher.'

'Police find something to do about that,' said Minturn. 'Such a thing as law and order. Such a thing as malpractice.'

'And liquorice whips,' continued Fletcher, 'and the complete files of *Physical Culture* for 1931; and matchboxes that go broo-oo-oo, broo-oo-oo.'

'Broo,' said Minturn. 'I want to go to Twenty-One.'

'Terrible, terrible, terrible rat,' said Mrs Minturn.

'I see,' said Fletcher. 'You don't even feel sorry for poor old tap-tap. Tap, tap, tap, tap, tap.'

'What's that?' said Minturn.

'That's my cane in the corridor,' said Fletcher. 'You are lying there, trying to unwrassle something I have brought you, when, tap, tap, tap, here I come again.'

'Terrible rat, go home,' said Mrs Minturn.

Fletcher bowed to her gravely. 'I'm going,' he said. 'It constitutes the first occasion on which I have ever been ejected from this or any other house, but that is as it should be, I presume.'

'Don't throw anybody out,' said Minturn. 'Tap, tap, tap,' he added.

Halfway to the hall door, Fletcher turned. 'That's right, laugh,' he said. 'Tap, tap, tap, tap, tap, then.'

'Tap, tap, tap,' said Minturn from far down near the floor. A new attack of hiccups kept Mrs Minturn speechless, but she stood up as her guest went out into the hall. Minturn was still saying 'Tap, tap,' and Mrs Minturn was hiccuping, as Fletcher found his hat and coat and went out the front door into the melting snow, looking for a taxi.

The Secret Life of James Thurber

I HAVE only dipped here and there into Salvador Dali's 'The Secret Life of Salvador Dali' (with paintings by Salvador Dali and photographs of Salvador Dali), because anyone afflicted with what my grandmother's sister Abigail called 'the permanent jumps' should do no more than skitter through such an autobiography, particularly in these melancholy times.

One does not have to skitter far before one comes upon some vignette which gives the full shape and flavour of the book: the youthful dreamer of dreams biting a sick bat or kissing a dead horse, the slender stripling going into man's estate with the high hope and fond desire of one day eating a live but roasted turkey, the sighing lover covering himself with goat dung and aspic that he might give off the true and noble odour of the ram. In my flying trip through Dali I caught other glimpses of the great man: Salvador adoring a seed ball fallen from a plane tree, Salvador kicking a tiny playmate off a bridge, Salvador caressing a crutch, Salvador breaking the old family doctor's glasses with a leather-thonged mattress-beater. There would appear to be only two things in the world that revolt him (and I don't mean a long-dead hedgehog). He is squeamish about skeletons and grasshoppers. Oh, well, we all have our idiosyncrasies.

Señor Dali's memoirs have set me to thinking. I find myself muttering as I shave, and on two occasions I have swung my crutch at a little neighbour girl on my way to the post office. Señor Dali's book sells for six dollars. My own published personal history (Harper & Brothers, 1933) sold for $1.75. At the time I complained briefly about this unusual figure, principally on the ground that it represented only fifty cents more than the price asked for a book called 'The Adventures of Horace the Hedgehog,' published the same month. The publishers explained that the price was a closely approximated vertical, prefigured on the basis of profitable ceiling, which in turn was arrived at by taking into consideration the effect on diminishing returns of the horizontal factor.

In those days all heads of business firms adopted a guarded kind of double talk, commonly expressed in low, muffled tones, because nobody knew what was going to happen and nobody understood what had. Big business had been frightened by a sequence of economic phenomena which had clearly demonstrated that our civilization was in greater danger of being turned off than of gradually crumbling away. The upshot of it all was that I accepted the price of $1.75. In so doing, I accepted the state of the world as a proper standard by which the price of books should be fixed. And now, with the world in ten times as serious a condition as it was in 1933, Dali's publishers set a price of six dollars on his life story. This brings me to the inescapable conclusion that the price-fixing principle, in the field of literature, is not global but personal. The trouble, quite simply, is that I told too much about what went on in the house I lived in and not enough about what went on inside myself.

Let me be the first to admit that the naked truth about me is to the naked truth about Salvador Dali as an old ukulele in the attic is to a piano in a tree, and I mean a piano with breasts. Señor Dali has the jump on me from the beginning. He remembers and describes in detail what it was like in the womb. My own earliest memory is of accompanying my father to a polling booth in Columbus, Ohio, where he voted for William McKinley.

It was a drab and somewhat battered tin shed set on wheels, and it was filled with guffawing men and cigar smoke; all in all, as far removed from the paradisiacal placenta of Salvador Dali's first recollection as could well be imagined. A fat, jolly man dandled me on his knee and said that I would soon be old enough to vote against William Jennings Bryan. I thought he meant that I could push a folded piece of paper into the slot of the padlocked box as soon as my father was finished. When this turned out not to be true, I had to be carried out of the place kicking and screaming. In my struggles I knocked my father's derby off several times. The derby was not a monstrously exciting love object to me, as practically everything Salvador encountered was to him, and I doubt, if I had that day to live over again, that I could bring myself, even in the light of exotic dedication as I now know it, to conceive an intense and perverse affection for the derby. It remains obstinately in my memory as a rather funny hat, a little too large in the crown, which gave my father the appearance of a tired, sensitive gentleman who had been persuaded against his will to take part in a game of charades.

We lived on Champion Avenue at the time, and the voting booth was on Mound Street. As I set down these names, I begin to perceive an essential and important difference between the infant Salvador and the infant me. This difference can be stated in terms of environment. Salvador was brought up in Spain, a country coloured by the legends of Hannibal, El Greco, and Cervantes. I was brought up in Ohio, a region steeped in the tradition of Coxey's Army, the Anti-Saloon League, and William Howard Taft. It is only natural that the weather in little Salvador's soul should have been stirred by stranger winds and enveloped in more fantastic mists than the weather in my own soul. But enough of mewling apology for my lacklustre early years. Let us get back to my secret life, such as it was, stopping just long enough to have another brief look at Señor Dali on our way.

Salvador Dali's mind goes back to a childhood half imagined and half real, in which the edges of actuality were sometimes less sharp than the edges of dream. He seems somehow to have got the idea that this sets him off from Harry Spencer, Charlie Doakes, I. Feinberg, J. J. McNaboe, Willie Faulkner, Herbie Hoover, and me. What Salvie had that the rest of us kids didn't was the perfect scenery, characters, and costumes for his desperate little rebellion against the clean, the conventional, and the comfortable. He put perfume on his hair (which would have cost him his life in, say, Bayonne, N. J., or Youngstown, Ohio), he owned a lizard with two tails, he wore silver buttons on his shoes, and he knew, or imagined he knew, little girls named Galuchka and Dullita. Thus he was born halfway along the road to paranoia, the soft Poictesme of his prayers, the melting Oz of his oblations, the capital, to put it so that you can see what I am trying to say, of his heart's desire. Or so, anyway, it must seem to a native of Columbus, Ohio, who, as a youngster, bought his twelve-dollar suits at the F. & R. Lazarus Co., had his hair washed out with Ivory soap, owned a bull terrier with only one tail, and played (nicely and a bit diffidently) with little girls named Irma and Betty and Ruby.

Another advantage that the young Dali had over me, from the standpoint of impetus toward paranoia, lay in the nature of the adults who peopled his real world. There was, in Dali's home town of Figueras, a family of artists named Pitchot (musicians, painters, and poets), all of whom adored the ground that the *enfant terrible* walked on. If one of them came upon him throwing himself from a high rock – a favourite relaxation of our hero – or hanging by his feet with his head immersed in a pail of water, the wild news was spread about the town that greatness and genius had come to Figueras. There was a woman who put on a look of maternal interest when Salvador threw rocks at her. The mayor of the town fell dead one day at the boy's feet. A doctor in the community (not the one he had horsewhipped) was seized of a fit and attempted to beat him up. (The contention that the doctor was out of his senses at the time of the assault is Dali's, not mine.)

The adults around me when I was in short pants were neither so glamorous nor so attentive. They consisted mainly of eleven maternal great-aunts, all Methodists, who were staunch believers in physic, mustard plasters, and Scripture, and it was part of their dogma that artistic tendencies should be treated in the same way as hiccups or hysterics. None of them was an artist, unless you can count Aunt Lou, who wrote sixteen-stress verse, with hit-and-miss rhymes, in celebration of people's birthdays or on the occasion of great national disaster. It never occurred to me to bite a bat in my aunts' presence or to throw stones at them. There was one escape, though: my secret world of idiom.

Two years ago my wife and I, looking for a house to buy, called on a firm of real-estate agents in New Milford. One of the members of the firm, scrabbling through a metal box containing many keys, looked up to say, 'The key to the Roxbury house isn't here.' His partner replied, 'It's a common lock. A skeleton will let you in.' I was suddenly once again five years old, with wide eyes and open mouth. I pictured the Roxbury house as I would have pictured it as a small boy, a house of such dark and nameless horrors as have never crossed the mind of our little bat-biter.

It was of sentences like that, nonchalantly tossed off by real-estate dealers, great-aunts, clergymen, and other such prosaic persons, that the enchanted private world of my early boyhood was made. In this world, businessmen who phoned their wives to say that they were tied up at the office sat roped to their swivel chairs, and probably gagged, unable to move or speak, except somehow, miraculously, to telephone; hundreds of thousands of businessmen tied to their chairs in hundreds of thousands of offices in every city of my fantastic cosmos. An especially fine note about the binding of all the businessmen in all the cities was that whoever did it always did it around five o'clock in the afternoon.

Then there was the man who left town under a cloud. Sometimes I saw him all wrapped up in the cloud, and invisible, like a cat in a burlap sack. At other times it floated, about the size of a sofa, three or four feet above his head, following him wherever he went. One could think about the man under the cloud before going to sleep; the image of him wandering around from town to town was a sure soporific.

Not so the mental picture of a certain Mrs Huston, who had been terribly cut up when her daughter died on the operating table. I could see the doctors too vividly, just before they set upon Mrs Huston with their knives, and I could hear them. 'Now, Mrs Huston, will we get up on the table like a good girl, or will we have to be put there?' I could usually fight off Mrs Huston before I went to sleep, but she frequently got into my dreams, and sometimes she still does.

I remember the grotesque creature that came to haunt my meditations when one evening my father said to my mother, 'What did Mrs Johnson say when you told her about Betty?' and my mother replied, 'Oh, she was all ears.' There were many other wonderful figures in the secret, surrealist landscapes of my youth: the old lady who was always up in the air, the husband who did not seem to be able to put his foot down, the man who lost his head during a fire but was still able to run out of the house yelling, the young lady who was, in reality, a soiled dove. It was a world that, of necessity, one had to keep to oneself and brood over in silence, because it would fall to pieces at the touch of words. If you brought it out into the light of actual day and put it to the test of questions, your parents would try to laugh the miracles away, or they would take your temperature and put you to bed. (Since I always ran a temperature, whenever it was taken, I was put to bed and left there all alone with Mrs Huston.)

Such a world as the world of my childhood is, alas, not year-proof. It is a ghost that, to use Henley's words, gleams, flickers, vanishes away. I think it must have been the time my little Cousin Frances came to visit us that it began surely and forever to dissolve. I came into the house one rainy dusk and asked where Frances was. 'She is,' said our cook, 'up in the front room crying her heart out.' The fact that a person could cry so hard that his heart would come out of his body, as perfectly shaped and glossy as a red velvet pincushion, was news to me. For some reason I had never heard the expression, so common in American families whose hopes and dreams run so often counter to attainment. I went upstairs and opened the door of the front room. Frances, who was three years older than I, jumped up off the bed and ran past me, sobbing, and down the stairs.

My search for her heart took some fifteen minutes. I tore the bed apart and kicked up the rugs and even looked in the bureau drawers. It was no good. I looked out the window at the rain and the darkening sky. My cherished mental image of the man under the cloud began to grow dim and fade away. I discovered that, all alone in a room, I could face the thought of Mrs Huston with cold equanimity. Downstairs, in the living room, Frances was still crying. I began to laugh.

Ah there, Salvador!

Recollections of the Gas Buggy

Footnotes to An Era for the Future Historian

Now that the humorous magazines have taken to printing drawings of horses rearing at the sight of an automobile, and of children exclaiming as a car goes by, 'What is that thing, Mamma? Mamma, what is that thing, huh, Mamma?,' it is perhaps not out of place to prepare some small memorial in advance of the passing of the motor car. It appears to have reached, on its way backward to oblivion, what corresponds roughly to the year 1903.

I think that no one has drawn a darker or more vivid picture of the approaching doom of the gas engine than Mrs Robertson, the aged coloured washerwoman whose prophecies and pronouncements I have the privilege of listening to every Monday morning. Mrs Robertson is, for my money, an extremely sound woman, although admittedly my judgment of soundness has sometimes been questioned.

Some of the opinions of Mrs Robertson which I recall offhand are these: 'If you don't pay no mind to diseases, they will go away.' 'The night was made partly for rest and partly as a punishment for the sinful.' And 'The government only allows you to keep furniture for two months.' This last conviction grows out of Mrs Robertson's habit of buying furniture on the instalment plan and failing to keep up her payments longer than six or seven weeks, with the result that the things are repossessed. She looks upon this recurring ritual in her domestic life as a form of federal taxation.

Mrs Robertson's beliefs and feelings about the future of the automobile (which I have been leading up to) go like this: the oil supplies of the world are being dried up in order to prevent future wars. This will also put an end forever to pleasure driving, but that is all right because, if people kept on riding in cars, they would soon lose the use of both legs, and the life of Man would pass from the earth.

If Mrs Robertson is right in her predictions, I should like to set down my own few unique experiences with gas-driven vehicles before I forget them. They may possibly serve as footnotes to the work of some future historian, lightening a little the dolorous annals of the automobile.

Let me admit, to begin with, that the automobile and I were never in tune with each other. There was a fundamental incompatibility between us that amounted at times almost to chemical repulsion. I have felt the headlights of an automobile following me the way the eyes of a cat follow the ominous activities of a neighbour's dog. Some of the machines I have owned have seemed to me to bridle slightly when I got under the wheel. Neither the motor car nor myself would greatly mourn if one of us were suddenly extinguished.

Years ago, an aunt of my father's came to visit us one winter in Columbus, Ohio. She enjoyed the hallucination, among others, that she was able to drive a car. I was riding with her one December day when I discovered to my horror, that she thought the red and green lights on the traffic signals had been put up by the municipality as a gay and expansive manifestation of the Yuletide spirit. Although we finally reached home safely, I never completely recovered from the adventure, and could not be induced, after that day, to ride in a car on holidays.

When I got an automobile of my own and began to drive it, I brought to the enterprise a magnificent ignorance of the workings of a gas engine, and a profound disinterest in its oily secrets. On several occasions, worried friends of an engineering turn of mind attempted to explain the nature of gas engines to me, but they succeeded only in losing me in a mechanical maze of terminology. I developed the notion that the gas engine was more soundly constructed than I was. I elaborate this point only to show you on what unequal terms the motor car and I were brought together.

Out of my long and dogged bouts with automobiles of various makes, there comes back to me now only one truly pleasurable experience. There may have been others, but I doubt it. I was driving in the British Isles in 1938, and came one day to a sudden, coughing stop in a far and lonely section of Scotland. The car had run out of gas in the wilderness. This car's gasoline gauge had a trick of mounting toward 'Full' instead of sinking toward 'Empty' when the tank was running low, one of many examples of pure cussedness of which it was capable. There I was, miles from any village, with not even a farmhouse in sight. On my left was a thick woods, out of which the figure of a man suddenly appeared. He asked me what was the matter, and I said I had run out of petrol. 'It just happens,' he told me, 'that I have a can of petrol.' With that, he went back into the woods, and came out again with a five-gallon can of gasoline. He put it in the tank for me, I thanked him, paid for it, and drove on.

Once when I was telling this true but admittedly remarkable story, at a party in New York, a bright-eyed young woman exclaimed, 'But when the man emerged from the lonely woods, miles away from any village, far from the nearest farmhouse, carrying a five-gallon can of gasoline, why didn't you ask him how he happened to be there with it?' I lighted a cigarette. 'Madam,' I said, 'I was afraid he would vanish.' She gave a small laugh and moved away from me. Everybody always does.

Another experience I had in England the same year helped to shake the faith of at least one Briton in the much-vaunted Yankee affinity for machinery. The battery of my car had run down in a village about twenty miles from York, my destination. I put in a call to a garage and a young mechanic showed up presently in a wrecking car. He said he would give me a tow for a few yards. I was to let the clutch in and out (or out and in, whichever it is) and start the engine that way. It is a device as old as the automobile itself, and years before I had managed it successfully. Any child or old lady can do it.

So he attached a rope to the back of his car and the front of mine, and we were off. I kept letting the clutch out and in (or in and out) madly, but nothing happened. The garage man kept stopping every 500 yards or so and coming back to consult with me. He was profoundly puzzled. It was farther than he had ever dragged a car in his life. We must have gone, in this disheartening manner, about a third of the way to York. Finally he got out for the seventh time and said to me, 'What gear have you got her in?' I didn't have her in any gear. I had her in neutral. She had been in neutral all the while.

Now, as any child or old lady knows, you have to have her in gear. If she is in neutral, it is like trying to turn on the electric lights when there are no bulbs in the sockets. The garage mechanic looked at me with the special look garage mechanics reserve for me. It is a mixture of incredulity, bewilderment, and distress. I put her in low gear, he gave me a short haul, and she started. I paid him and, as I drove off, I could see him in the rear-view mirror, standing in the road still staring after me with that look.

After I had got back to America (safe and sound, to the surprise of my friends), I produced this same expression on the face of a garage man in Connecticut one afternoon. I had driven the same car from Newtown to Litchfield on a crisp October day. It happened that I was just getting over an attack of grippe, and still running a temperature of a couple of degrees. The car, out of plain deviltry, began to run one, too. The red fluid in the engine gauge on the dashboard started to rise alarmingly. It got to the point marked 'Danger.' I drove into a garage in a pretty jumpy state of mind. A garage man looked at the gauge and said the thermostat was clogged – or something of the kind. I was standing outside the car, staring at the dashboard and its, to me, complicated dials, when I noticed to my horror that one of them registered 1650. I pointed a shaking finger at it and said to the mechanic, 'That dial shouldn't be registering as high as all that, should it?' He gave me the same look I had got from the man in England. 'That's your radio dial, Mac,' he said. 'You got her set at WQXR.'

I got into the car and drove home. The garage man stared after me until I was out of sight. He is probably still telling it around.

My temperature rose a degree that night, and I developed a theory about my automobile. The thing possessed, I decided, a certain antic intelligence, akin to that of a six-months-old poodle. It had run a temperature that afternoon out of mischief and mockery, because I was running one. It had deliberately betrayed me in the Scottish wilderness that other afternoon, by running its gasoline gauge toward 'Full' instead of 'Empty.' I began to wonder what I had done to the car to arouse its malice. Finally I put my finger on it. The car had probably never forgiven me for an incident that had occurred at the border between Belgium and France one day in 1937.

We had stopped at the Belgian customs on our way into France. A customs man leaned into the car, glanced at the mileage recorded on the speedometer, and said something in French. I thought he said I would have to pay one franc for every kilometre the car had travelled. I was loudly indignant in French and in English. The car had gone about 35,000 miles. I figured this out in kilo-metres, and it came roughly to 55,000. Changing that figure into francs and then into dollars, still loudly and angrily, I estimated I would have to pay around $1800 to the Belgian customs. The customs man kept trying to get a word in, and so did my wife, but I roared on to my peroration. I shouted that the car had not cost one half of $1800 when it was new, and even then it hadn't been worth a third of that. I announced that I would not pay as much as fifty dollars to drive the car into Oz or Never-Never Land (*Jamais-Jamais Pays*).

The engine, which had been running, stopped. The customs man finally got in a word. Dismissing me as obviously insane, he spoke to my wife. He shouted that he had said nothing about $1800 or even eight dollars. He had simply made some small comment on the distance the car had gone. As far as he was concerned, we could drive it to *Jamais-Jamais Pays* and stay there. He turned on his heel and stalked away, and I started the motor. It took quite a while. The car was acting up. The night my fever rose, I thought I knew why. It had resented the slighting remarks I made about its value and had determined to get even with me.

It got even with me in more ways than I have described.

Whenever I tried to put chains on a tyre, the car would maliciously wrap them around a rear axle. If I parked it ten feet from a fire plug and went into a store, it would be only five feet from the plug when I came out. If it saw a nail in the road, the car would swerve and pick the nail up. Once, driving into a bleak little town in the Middle West, I said aloud, 'I'd hate to be stuck in this place.' The car promptly burned out a bearing, and I was stuck there for two days.

If Mrs Robertson is right in her prophecy, and the gas engine is really on the way out, it will be no dire blow for me. I will move within roller-skating dis-tance of a grocery, a drugstore, a church, a library, and a movie house. If the worst comes to the worst, I could even walk.

Further Fables
for Our Time

TO ELMER DAVIS
whose comprehension of people
and persons has lighted our time,
so that we can see where we
are going, these fables are dedicated
with admiration, affection
and thankfulness

The Sea and the Shore

A PAIR of gibbous creatures, who had lived in the sea since time began, which hadn't been long before, were washed upon the shore one day and became the discoverers of land. 'The light that never was!' exclaimed the female, lying on the sand in the sun.

'You're always seeing things that never were,' grumbled the male. 'You're always wanting things that aren't yet.'

In the female, lying on the sand in the sun, a dim intuition and prescience began developing. She prefigured mistily things that would one day become rose-point lace and taffeta, sweet perfumes and jewellery. The male, who had a feeling only for wetness and wash, mumbled, 'You're a little moist for things like that, a little moist and shapeless.'

'I only need to lose a little amorphousness around the waist,' she said. 'It won't take more than a million years.' And she began flobbering, almost imperceptibly, toward the scrubby brown growth beyond the sand and toward the sun. 'Come on,' she said. But the male had globbed back into the sea, and was gone.

A couple of eons later, the male, unable to get along alone, reappeared one day upon the shore. He noted with faint satisfaction that the female's shapelessness was beginning to take shape and had become almost shapely. He turned back toward the sea, but a mindless urge deep inside him took on the frail flicker of desire. Suddenly the sea seemed something less than satisfying. He turned about and began flobbering up the sand toward the female, who seemed certain to reach the greening undergrowth in another two thousand years. 'Hey, Mag,' he shouted. 'Wait for baby!'

Moral: *Let us ponder this basic fact about the human: Ahead of every man, not behind him, is a woman.*

The Truth About Toads

O NE MIDSUMMER NIGHT at the Fauna Club, some of the members fell
to boasting, each of his own unique distinction or achievement.

'I am the real Macaw,' squawked the Macaw proudly.

'O.K., Mac, take it easy,' said the Raven, who was tending bar.

'You should have seen the one I got away from,' said the Marlin. 'He must
have weighed a good two hundred and thirty-five pounds.'

'If it weren't for me, the sun would never rise,' bragged the Rooster, 'and
the desire of the night for the morrow would never be gratified.' He wiped a
tear away. 'If it weren't for me, nobody would get up.'

'If it weren't for me, there wouldn't *be* anybody,' the Stork reminded him
proudly.

'I tell them when spring is coming,' the Robin chirped.

'I tell them when winter will end,' the Groundhog said.

'I tell them how deep the winter will be,' said the Woolly Bear.

'I swing low when a storm is coming,' said the Spider. 'Otherwise it
wouldn't come, and the people would die of a drought.'

The Mouse got into the act. 'You know where it says, "Not a creature was
stirring, not even a mouse"?' he hiccuped. 'Well, gentlemen, that little old
mouse was little old me.'

'Quiet!' said the Raven, who had been lettering a sign and now hung it
prominently above the bar: 'Open most hearts and you will see graven upon
them Vanity.'

The members of the Fauna Club stared at the sign. 'Probably means the
Wolf, who thinks he founded Rome,' said the Cat.

'Or the great Bear, who thinks he is made of stars,' said the Mouse.

'Or the golden Eagle, who thinks he's made of gold,' said the Rooster.

'Or the Sheep, who thinks men couldn't sleep unless they counted sheep,'
said the Marlin.

The Toad came up to the bar and ordered a green mint frappé with a
firefly in it.

'Fireflies will make you lightheaded,' warned the bartender.

'Not me,' said the Toad. 'Nothing can make me lightheaded. I have a
precious jewel in my head.' The other members of the club looked at him with
mingled disbelief.

'Sure, sure,' grinned the bartender, 'it's a toadpaz, ain't it, Hoppy?'

'It is an extremely beautiful emerald,' said the Toad coldly, removing the
firefly from his frappé and swallowing it. 'Absolutely priceless emerald. *More*
than priceless. Keep 'em comin'.'

The bartender mixed another green mint frappé, but he put a slug in it this time instead of a firefly.

'I don't think the Toad has a precious jewel in his head,' said the Macaw.

'I do,' said the Cat. 'Nobody could be that ugly and live unless he had an emerald in his head.'

'I'll bet you a hundred fish he hasn't,' said the Pelican.

'I'll bet you a hundred clams he has,' said the Sandpiper.

The Toad, who was pretty well frappéd by this time, fell asleep, and the members of the club debated how to find out whether his head held an emerald, or some other precious stone. They summoned the Woodpecker from the back room and explained what was up. 'If he hasn't got a hole in his head, I'll make one,' said the Woodpecker.

There wasn't anything there, gleaming or lovely or precious. The bartender turned out the lights, the Rooster crowed, the sun came up, and the members of the Fauna Club went silently home to bed.

Moral: *Open most heads and you will find nothing shining, not even a mind.*

The Butterfly, the Ladybug, and the Phoebe

A PHOEBE, bugwinner for a nestful of fledglings, flew out one day to provide dinner for his family, and came upon a ladybug in frantic flight.

'I know you can catch anything smaller than a golf ball and slower than sound,' said the ladybug, 'for you are the fastest of the flycatchers, but my house is on fire and my children will burn unless I fly away home.'

The phoebe, who had sometimes been guilty of wishing that his own house were on fire, let the ladybug fly away, and turned his attention to a beautiful butterfly.

'Is your house on fire and will your children burn?' the phoebe asked.

'Nothing so mundane as all that,' said the butterfly. 'I have no children and I have no house, for I am an angel, as anyone can see.' She fluttered her wings at the world about her. 'This is heaven,' she said.

'This is heaven,' cried the fledglings, as one fledgling, when they had the butterfly for dessert that night.

Moral: *She who goes unarmed in Paradise should first be sure that's where she is.*

The Foolhardy Mouse and the
Cautious Cat

SUCH SPORT there had been that day, in the kitchen and the pantry, for the cat was away and the mice were playing all manner of games: mousy-wants-a-corner, hide-and-squeak, one-old-cat, mouse-in-boots, and so on. Then the cat came home.

'Cat's back!' whispered Father Mouse.

'Into the wainscoting, all of you!' said Mother Mouse, and all of the mice except one hastily hid in the woodwork.

The exception was an eccentric mouse named Mervyn, who had once boldly nipped a bulldog in the ear and got away with it. Mervyn did not know at the time, and never found out, that the bulldog was a stuffed bulldog, and so he lived in a fool's paradise.

The day the cat, whose name was Pouncetta, came back from wherever she had been, she was astonished to encounter Mervyn in the butler's pantry, nonchalantly nibbling crumbs. She crept toward him in her stocking feet and was astounded when he turned, spit a crumb in her eye, and began insulting her with a series of insults.

'How did you get out of the bag?' Mervyn inquired calmly. 'Put on your pyjamas and take a cat nap.' He went back to his nibbling, as blasé as you please.

'Steady, Pouncetta,' said Pouncetta to herself. 'There is more here than meets the eye. This mouse is probably a martyr mouse. He has swallowed poison in the hope that I will eat him and die, so that he can be a hero to a hundred generations of his descendants.'

Mervyn looked over his shoulder at the startled and suspicious cat and began to mock her in a mousetto voice. 'Doodness dwacious,' said Mervyn, 'it's a posse cat, in full pursuit of little me.' He gestured impudently with one foot. 'I went that-a-way,' he told Pouncetta. Then he did some other imitations, including a pretty good one of W. C. Fieldmouse.

'Easy, girl,' said Pouncetta to herself. 'This is a mechanical mouse, a trick mouse with a built-in voice. If I jump on it, it will explode and blow me into a hundred pieces. Damned clever, these mice, but not clever enough for me.'

'You'd make wonderful violin strings, if you had any guts,' Mervyn said insolently. But Pouncetta did not pounce, in spite of the insult unforgivable. Instead, she turned and stalked out of the butler's pantry and into the sitting room and lay down on her pillow near the fireplace and went to sleep.

When Mervyn got back to his home in the woodwork, his father and mother and brothers and sisters and cousins and uncles and aunts were surprised to see him alive and well. There was great jollity, and the finest cheese was served at a family banquet. 'She never laid a paw on me,' Mervyn boasted. 'I haven't got a scratch. I could take on all the cats in the Catskills.' He finished his cheese and went to bed and fell asleep, and dreamed of taking a catamount in one minute and twenty-eight seconds of the first round.

Moral: *Fools rush in where angels fear to tread, and the angels are all in Heaven, but few of the fools are dead.*

The Rose and the Weed

IN A COUNTRY GARDEN a lovely rose looked down upon a common weed and said, 'You are an unwelcome guest, economically useless, and unsightly of appearance. The Devil must love weeds, he made so many of them.'

The unwelcome guest looked up at the rose and said, 'Lilies that fester smell far worse than weeds, and, one supposes, that goes for roses.'

'My name is Dorothy Perkins,' the rose said haughtily. 'What are you – a beetleweed, a bladderweed, a beggarweed? The names of weeds are ugly.' And Dorothy shuddered slightly, but lost none of her pretty petals.

'We have some names prettier than Perkins, or, for my taste, Dorothy, among them silverweed, and jewelweed, and candyweed.' The weed straightened a bit and held his ground. 'Anywhere you can grow I can grow better,' he said.

'I think you must be a burglarweed,' said the disdainful Miss Perkins, 'for you get in where you aren't wanted, and take what isn't yours – the rain and the sunlight and the good earth.'

The weed smiled a weedy smile. 'At least,' he said, 'I do not come from a family of climbers.'

The rose drew herself up to her full height. 'I'd have you know that roses are the emblem of old England,' she said. 'We are the flower of song and story.'

'And of war,' the weed replied. 'The summer winds take you by storm, not you the winds with beauty. I've seen it happen many times, to roses of yesteryear, long gone and long forgotten.'

'We are mentioned in Shakespeare,' said the rose, 'many times in many plays. The lines are too sweet for your ears, but I will tell you some.'

Just then, and before Miss Perkins could recite, a wind came out of the west, riding low to the ground and swift, like the cavalry of March, and Dorothy Perkins' beautiful disdain suddenly became a scattering of petals, economically useless, and of appearance not especially sightly. The weed stood firm, his head to the wind, armoured, or so he thought, in security and strength, but as he was brushing a few rose petals and aphids from his lapels, the hand of the gardener flashed out of the air and pulled him out of the ground by the roots before you could say Dorothy Perkins, or, for that matter, jewelweed.

Moral: Tout, *as the French say, in a philosophy older than ours and an idiom often more succinct*, passe.

The Bat Who Got the Hell Out

Acolony of bats living in a great American cave had got along fine for a thousand generations, flying, hanging head down, eating insects, and raising young, and then one year a male named Flitter, who had fluttered secretly out of his room at night and flown among the haunts of men, told his father that he had decided to get the hell out. The shocked father sent Flitter to Fleder, the great-great-grandfather of all the bats in the cave.

'You should be proud of being a bat among bats,' said old Fleder, 'for we are one of the oldest species on the planet, much older than Man, and the only mammal capable of true flight.'

The discontented young bat was not impressed. 'I want to live like a man among men,' he said. 'Men have the best food, and the most fun, and the cutest females.'

At this, old Fleder stormed about the cave, squeaking unintelligibly. Then he recovered his calm and continued his talk. 'A man got into my room one night,' he said, 'and managed somehow to tangle me in his hair. It was a shattering experience, from which I shall never completely recover.'

'When men die they go to Heaven, but when bats are dead they are dead,' said Flitter. 'I want to go to Heaven when I die.'

This amused old Fleder in a gaunt and gloomy sort of way, and he chittered, quickered, and zickered for some moments before he could say, 'You have no more soul than a moose, or a mouse, or a mole. You should be glad that you will never become an angel, for angels do not have true flight. One wants to *sleep* through eternity, not bumble and flap about forever like a bee or a butterfly.'

But Flitter had made up his mind, and the old bat's words of wisdom were in vain. That night, the discontented young bat quit the bat colony, and flickered out of the cave, in the confident hope of giving up his membership in the Chiroptera and joining the happy breed of men. Unfortunately for his dream, he spent his first night hanging head down from the rafters of an auditorium in which a best-selling Inspirationalist was dragging God down to the people's level. Ushers moved silently among the rapt listeners, selling copies of the speaker's books: *Shake Hands with the Almighty, You Can be Jehovah's Pal* and *Have You Taken Out Eternity Insurance?* The speaker was saying, 'Have a little talk with the Lord while you're waiting for a bus, or riding to work, or sitting in the dentist's chair. Have comfy chats with the Lord in the little cosy corners of spare time.'

Flitter decided that there was something the matter with the acoustics, or

368

with his tragus, caused by hanging head down in the presence of the Eternal Species, but when he began flying about the auditorium, there was no change in the nature of the English sentences. 'Tell the Lord to put it there,' the inspired man went on. 'Give him your duke.' The speaker waved clasped hands above his head and gazed up at the ceiling. 'Keep pitching, God,' he said. 'You've got two strikes on Satan.'

Flitter, who had never felt sick before in his life, felt sick, and decided to get the air. After he had got the air, he realized that he did not want to become a member of the species *Homo sapiens*, because of the danger of bumbling or flapping into the Inspirationalist after they had both become angels. And so Flitter returned to the cave, and everybody was astonished to see him, and nobody said anything, and for a time there was a great silence.

'I've come the hell back,' said Flitter, meekly. And he resumed, without discontent, the immemorial life of the Chiroptera, flying, hanging head down, eating insects, and raising young.

Moral: *By decent minds is he abhorred who'd make a Babbitt of the Lord.*

The Lion and the Foxes

THE LION had just explained to the cow, the goat, and the sheep that the stag they had killed belonged to him, when three little foxes appeared on the scene.

'I will take a third of the stag as a penalty,' said one, 'for you have no hunter's licence.'

'I will take a third of the stag for your widow,' said another, 'for that is the law.'

'I have no widow,' said the lion.

'Let us not split hairs,' said the third fox, and he took his share of the stag as a withholding tax. 'Against a year of famine,' he explained.

'But I am king of beasts,' roared the lion.

'Ah, then you will not need the antlers, for you have a crown,' said the foxes, and they took the antlers, too.

Moral: *It is not as easy to get the lion's share nowadays as it used to be.*

The Wolf Who Went Places

A WEALTHY young wolf, who was oblivious of everything except himself, was tossed out of college for cutting classes and corners, and he decided to see if he could travel around the world in eighty minutes. 'That isn't possible,' his grandmother told him, but he only grinned at her. 'The impossible is the most fun,' he said.

She went with him to the door of the old Wolf place. 'If you go that fast, you won't live to regret it,' she warned him, but he grinned again, showing a tongue as long as a necktie.

'That's an old wolves' tale,' he said, and went on his reckless way.

He bought a 1959 Blitzen Bearcat, a combination motorcar and airplane, with skyrocket getaway, cyclone speedrive, cannonball takeoff, blindall headlights, magical retractable monowings, and lightning pushbutton transformationizer. 'How fast can this crate go without burning up?' he asked the Blitzen Bearcat salesman.

'I don't know,' the salesman said, 'but I have a feeling you'll find out.'

The wealthy young wolf smashed all the ground records and air records and a lot of other things in his trip around the world, which took him only 78.5 minutes from the time he knocked down the Washington Monument on his takeoff to the time he landed where it had stood. In the crowd that welcomed him home, consisting of about eleven creatures, for all the others were hiding under beds, there was a speed-crazy young wolfess, with built-in instantaneous pickup ability, and in no time at all the wolf and his new-found mate were setting new records for driving upside down, backward, blindfolded, handcuffed, and cockeyed, doubled and redoubled.

One day, they decided to see if they could turn in to Central Park from Fifth Avenue while travelling at a rate of 175 miles an hour, watching television, and holding hands. There was a tremendous shattering, crashing, splitting, roaring, blazing, cracking, and smashing, ending in a fiery display of wheels, stars, cornices, roofs, treetops, glass, steel, and people, and it seemed to those spectators who did not die of seizures as they watched the great red portals opened in the sky, swinging inward on mighty hinges, revealing an endless nowhere, and then closed behind the flying and flaming wolves with a clanking to end all clanking, as if those gates which we have been assured shall not prevail had, in fact, prevailed.

Moral: *Where most of us end up there is no knowing, but the hellbent get where they are going.*

The Bluebird and His Brother

IT WAS SAID of two bluebirds that they were unlike as two brothers could be, that one was a pearl in a pod and the other a pea. Pearl was happy-go-lucky, and Pea was gloomy-go-sorry.

'I am in love with love and life,' sang the glad bird.

'I am afraid of sex and flight,' sang the sad bird.

Pearl flaunted his gay colours like a bonnie blue flag, and his song was as bold as the Rebel yell. He went South every winter alone, and came North every spring with a different female. His gay philosophy freed his psyche of the strains of fear and the stresses of guilt, and he attained a serenity of spirit that few male birds and even fewer male human beings ever reach. He did not worry because some of his children were also his nieces, the daughters of one of his sisters. He sat loose, sang pretty, and slept tight, in a hundred honey locusts and cherry trees and lilac bushes. And every winter he went South alone, and every spring he came North with a different female. He did not worry because some of his grandchildren were also his grandnephews, the grandsons of one of his sisters.

At sunset in summertime, the gay bluebird flew higher than the lark or the wild goose, and he was pleased to note that, like himself, heaven wore blue, with a tinge of red.

The gloomy bluebird went South alone in the winter and came North alone in the spring, and never flew higher than you could throw a sofa. While still in his prime he developed agoraphobia and went to live underground, to the surprise and dismay of families of frogs and foxes and moles and gophers and crickets and toads, and of the bewildered dog who dug him up one day while burying a bone, and then hastily buried him again, without ceremony or sorrow.

Moral: *It is more dangerous to straight-arm life than to embrace it.*

The Clothes Moth and the Luna Moth

A CLOTHES MOTH who lived in a closet and had never done anything, or wanted to do anything, except eat wool and fur, flew out of his closet one twilight just in time to see a lovely Luna moth appear on the outside of a windowpane. The Luna moth fluttered against the lighted glass as gracefully as a drifting autumn leaf, and she was dressed in a charming evening gown. What interested her was the flame of a candle burning in the room, burning on the mantelpiece above the fireplace, but the clothes moth thought she was making signs at him, and he conceived a great desire for her.

'I have to have you,' said the clothes moth, but the Luna moth laughed, and her laughter was like the bells of elfland faintly tinkling.

'Go eat a shroud,' said the Luna moth haughtily. 'You are as vulgar as a tent moth, or a gypsy moth, and nowhere near as handsome as a tiger moth.'

'If you come to live with me I will feed you on sweaters and stoles,' said the clothes moth, whose ardour was only increased by the lovely Luna's scorn.

'You are a flug, who can flugger, but not fly or flutter,' said the Luna moth, trying to get through the windowpane and reach the star on the mantelpiece.

'You can have wedding dresses and evening clothes and a mink coat,' panted the clothes moth, and again the Luna moth's laughter was like the bells of elfland faintly tinkling.

'I live on twilight and the stars,' she said.

'It was love at first flight,' the clothes moth protested. 'It was love at first flutter.'

The Luna moth's tiny silvery tone became sharper. 'You are a mulch,' she said, 'a mulbus, a crawg, and a common creeb.'

All these words were words a nice moth rarely uses, but they had no effect upon the passion of the clothes moth.

'I know you have one wing in the grave,' he told her. 'I know you're not long for this world, and so I must have you as soon as I can. A thing of beauty is a joy for such a little time.'

The lovely Luna moth tried to cajole her admirer into opening the window – so that she could fly to the fascinating flame above the fireplace, but she did not tell him this. She let him believe that his drab grey lovemaking had won her heart. In his desire to reach her, he flew against the windowpane time and time again, and finally made a small opening in it, and then fluggered crazily to the floor, dead of a broken head and wings and body. The lovely Luna, whose desire for the star is a matter of immortal record, flew swiftly and gracefully toward the candle on the mantelpiece and was consumed in its flame with a little zishing sound like that made by a lighted cigarette dropped in a cup of coffee.

Moral: *Love is blind, but desire just doesn't give a good goddam.*

The Lover and His Lass

AN ARROGANT grey parrot and his arrogant mate listened, one African afternoon, in disdain and derision, to the lovemaking of a lover and his lass, who happened to be hippopotamuses.

'He calls her snooky-ookums,' said Mrs Grey. 'Can you believe that?'

'No,' said Grey. 'I don't see how any male in his right mind could entertain affection for a female that has no more charm than a capsized bathtub.'

'Capsized bathtub, indeed!' exclaimed Mrs Grey. 'Both of them have the appeal of a coastwise fruit steamer with a cargo of waterlogged basketballs.'

But it was spring, and the lover and his lass were young, and they were oblivious of the scornful comments of their sharp-tongued neighbours, and they continued to bump each other around in the water, happily pushing and pulling, backing and filling, and snorting and snaffling. The tender things they said to each other during the monolithic give-and-take of their courtship sounded as lyric to them as flowers in bud or green things opening. To the Greys, however, the bumbling romp of the lover and his lass was hard to comprehend and even harder to tolerate, and for a time they thought of calling the A.B.I., or African Bureau of Investigation, on the ground that monolithic lovemaking by enormous creatures who should have become decent fossils long ago was probably a threat to the security of the jungle. But they decided instead to phone their friends and neighbours and gossip about the shameless pair, and describe them in mocking and monstrous metaphors involving skidding buses on icy streets and overturned moving vans.

Late that evening, the hippopotamus and the hippopotama were surprised and shocked to hear the Greys exchanging terms of endearment. 'Listen to those squawks,' wuffled the male hippopotamus.

'What in the world can they see in each other?' gurbled the female hippopotamus.

'I would as soon live with a pair of unoiled garden shears,' said her inamoratus.

They called up their friends and neighbours and discussed the incredible fact that a male grey parrot and a female grey parrot could possibly have any sex appeal. It was long after midnight before the hippopotamuses stopped criticizing the Greys and fell asleep, and the Greys stopped maligning the hippopotamuses and retired to their beds.

Moral: *Laugh and the world laughs with you, love and you love alone.*

The Fox and the Crow

A CROW, perched in a tree with a piece of cheese in his beak, attracted the eye and nose of a fox. 'If you can sing as prettily as you sit,' said the fox, 'then you are the prettiest singer within my scent and sight.' The fox had read somewhere, and somewhere, and somewhere else, that praising the voice of a crow with a cheese in his beak would make him drop the cheese and sing. But this is not what happened to this particular crow in this particular case.

'They say you are sly and they say you are crazy,' said the crow, having carefully removed the cheese from his beak with the claws of one foot, 'but you must be nearsighted as well. Warblers wear gay hats and coloured jackets and bright vests, and they are a dollar a hundred. I wear black and I am unique.' He began nibbling the cheese, dropping not a single crumb.

'I am sure you are,' said the fox, who was neither crazy nor nearsighted, but sly. 'I recognize you, now that I look more closely, as the most famed and talented of all birds, and I fain would hear you tell about yourself, but I am hungry and must go.'

'Tarry awhile,' said the crow quickly, 'and share my lunch with me.' Whereupon he tossed the cunning fox the lion's share of the cheese, and began to tell about himself. 'A ship that sails without a crow's nest sails to doom,' he said. 'Bars may come and bars may go, but crow bars last forever. I am the pioneer of flight, I am the map maker. Last, but never least, my flight is known to scientists and engineers, geometrists and scholars, as the shortest distance between two points. Any two points,' he concluded arrogantly.

'Oh, every two points, I am sure,' said the fox. 'And thank you for the lion's share of what I know you could not spare.' And with this he trotted away into the woods, his appetite appeased, leaving the hungry crow perched forlornly in the tree.

Moral: *'Twas true in Aesop's time, and La Fontaine's, and now, no one else can praise thee quite so well as thou.*

Variations on the Theme

I

Aᴏx, attracted by the scent of something, followed his nose to a tree in which sat a crow with a piece of cheese in his beak. 'Oh, cheese,' said the fox scornfully. 'That's for mice.'

The crow removed the cheese with his talons and said, 'You always hate the thing you cannot have, as, for instance, grapes.'

'Grapes are for the birds,' said the fox haughtily. 'I am an epicure, a gourmet, and a gastronome.'

The embarrassed crow, ashamed to be seen eating mouse food by a great specialist in the art of dining, hastily dropped the cheese. The fox caught it deftly, swallowed it with relish, said '*Merci*,' politely, and trotted away.

II

A fox had used all his blandishments in vain, for he could not flatter the crow in the tree and make him drop the cheese he held in his beak. Suddenly, the crow tossed the cheese to the astonished fox. Just then the farmer, from whose kitchen the loot had been stolen, appeared, carrying a rifle, looking for the robber. The fox turned and ran for the woods. 'There goes the guilty son of a vixen now!' cried the crow, who, in case you do not happen to know it, can see the glint of sunlight on a gun barrel at a greater distance than anybody.

III

This time the fox, who was determined not to be outfoxed by a crow, stood his ground and did not run when the farmer appeared, carrying a rifle and looking for the robber.

'The teeth marks in this cheese are mine,' said the fox, 'but the beak marks were made by the true culprit up there in the tree. I submit this cheese in evidence, as Exhibit A, and bid you and the criminal a very good day.' Whereupon he lit a cigarette and strolled away.

IV

In the great and ancient tradition, the crow in the tree with the cheese in his beak began singing, and the cheese fell into the fox's lap. 'You sing like a shovel,' said the fox, with a grin, but the crow pretended not to hear and cried out, 'Quick, give me back the cheese! Here comes the farmer with his rifle!'

'Why should I give you back the cheese?' the wily fox demanded.

'Because the farmer has a gun, and I can fly faster than you can run.'

So the frightened fox tossed the cheese back to the crow, who ate it, and said, 'Dearie me, my eyes are playing tricks on me – or am I playing tricks on you? Which do you think?' But there was no reply, for the fox had slunk away into the woods.

The Bears and the Monkeys

IN A DEEP FOREST there lived many bears. They spent the winter sleeping, and the summer playing leap-bear and stealing honey and buns from nearby cottages. One day a fast-talking monkey named Glib showed up and told them that their way of life was bad for bears. 'You are prisoners of pastime,' he said, 'addicted to leap-bear, and slaves of honey and buns.'

The bears were impressed and frightened as Glib went on talking. 'Your forebears have done this to you,' he said. Glib was so glib, glibber than the glibbest monkey they had ever seen before, that the bears believed he must know more than they knew, or than anybody else. But when he left, to tell other species what was the matter with *them*, the bears reverted to their fun and games and their theft of buns and honey.

Their decadence made them bright of eye, light of heart, and quick of paw, and they had a wonderful time, living as bears had always lived, until one day two of Glib's successors appeared, named Monkey Say and Monkey Do. They were even glibber than Glib, and they brought many presents and smiled all the time. 'We have come to liberate you from freedom,' they said. 'This is the New Liberation, twice as good as the old, since there are two of us.'

So each bear was made to wear a collar, and the collars were linked together with chains, and Monkey Do put a ring in the lead bear's nose, and a chain on the lead bear's ring. 'Now you are free to do what I tell you to do,' said Monkey Do.

'Now you are free to say what I want you to say,' said Monkey Say. 'By sparing you the burden of electing your leaders, we save you from the dangers of choice. No more secret ballots, everything open and aboveboard.'

For a long time the bears submitted to the New Liberation, and chanted the slogan the monkeys had taught them: 'Why stand on your own two feet when you can stand on ours?'

Then one day they broke the chains of their new freedom and found their way back to the deep forest and began playing leap-bear again and stealing honey and buns from the nearby cottages. And their laughter and gaiety rang through the forest, and birds that had ceased singing began singing again, and all the sounds of the earth were like music.

Moral: *It is better to have the ring of freedom in your ears than in your nose.*

The Father and His Daughter

A LITTLE GIRL was given so many picture books on her seventh birth-day that her father, who should have run his office and let her mother run the home, thought his daughter should give one or two of her new books to a little neighbour boy named Robert, who had dropped in, more by design than by chance.

Now, taking books, or anything else, from a little girl is like taking arms from an Arab, or candy from a baby, but the father of the little girl had his way and Robert got two of her books. 'After all, that leaves you with nine,' said the father, who thought he was a philosopher and a child psychologist, and couldn't shut his big fatuous mouth on the subject.

A few weeks later, the father went to his library to look up 'father' in the Oxford English Dictionary, to feast his eyes on the praise of fatherhood through the centuries, but he couldn't find volume F-G, and then he discovered that three others were missing, too – A-B, L-M, and V-Z. He began a probe of his household, and soon learned what had become of the four missing volumes.

'A man came to the door this morning,' said his little daughter, 'and he didn't know how to get from here to Torrington, or from Torrington to Winsted, and he was a nice man, much nicer than Robert, and so I gave him four of your books. After all, there are thirteen volumes in the Oxford English Dictionary, and that leaves you nine.'

Moral: *This truth has been known from here to Menander : what's sauce for the gosling's not sauce for the gander.*

The Cat in the Lifeboat

A FELINE NAMED WILLIAM got a job as copy cat on a daily paper and was surprised to learn that every other cat on the paper was named Tom, Dick, or Harry. He soon found out that he was the only cat named William in town. The fact of his singularity went to his head, and he began confusing it with distinction. It got so that whenever he saw or heard the name William, he thought it referred to him. His fantasies grew wilder and wilder, and he came to believe that he was the Will of Last Will and Testament, and the Willy of Willy Nilly, and the cat who put the cat in catnip. He finally became convinced that Cadillacs were Catillacs because of him.

William became so lost in his daydreams that he no longer heard the editor of the paper when he shouted, 'Copy cat!' and he became not only a ne'er-do-well, but a ne'er-do-anything. 'You're fired,' the editor told him one morning when he showed up for dreams.

'God will provide,' said William jauntily.

'God has his eye on the sparrow,' said the editor.

'So've I,' said William smugly.

William went to live with a cat-crazy woman who had nineteen other cats, but they could not stand William's egotism or the tall tales of his mythical exploits, honours, blue ribbons, silver cups, and medals, and so they all left the woman's house and went to live happily in huts and hovels. The cat-crazy woman changed her will and made William her sole heir, which seemed only natural to him, since he believed that all wills were drawn in his favour. 'I am eight feet tall,' William told her one day, and she smiled and said, 'I should say you are, and I am going to take you on a trip around the world and show you off to everybody.'

William and his mistress sailed one bitter March day on the S.S. *Forlorna*, which ran into heavy weather, high seas, and hurricane. At midnight the cargo shifted in the towering seas, the ship listed menacingly, SOS calls were frantically sent out, rockets were fired into the sky, and the officers began running up and down companionways and corridors shouting, 'Abandon ship!' And then another shout arose, which seemed only natural to the egotistical cat. It was, his vain ears told him, the loud repetition of 'William and Children first!' Since William figured no lifeboat would be launched until he was safe and sound, he dressed leisurely, putting on white tie and tails, and then sauntered out on deck. He leaped lightly into a lifeboat that was being lowered, and found himself in the company of a little boy named Johnny Green and another little boy named Tommy Trout, and their mothers, and other children and their mothers. 'Toss that cat overboard!' cried the sailor in charge of the lifeboat, and Johnny Green threw him overboard, but Tommy Trout pulled him back in.

'Let *me* have that tomcat,' said the sailor, and he took William in his big right hand and threw him, like a long incompleted forward pass, about forty yards from the tossing lifeboat.

When William came to in the icy water, he had gone down for the twenty-fourth time, and had thus lost eight of his lives, so he only had one left. With his remaining life and strength he swam and swam until at last he reached the sullen shore of a sombre island inhabited by surly tigers, lions, and other great cats. As William lay drenched and panting on the shore, a jaguar and a lynx walked up to him and asked him who he was and where he came from. Alas, William's dreadful experience in the lifeboat and the sea had produced traumatic amnesia, and he could not remember who he was or where he came from.

'We'll call him Nobody,' said the jaguar.

'Nobody from Nowhere,' said the lynx.

And so William lived among the great cats on the island until he lost his ninth life in a bar-room brawl with a young panther who had asked him what his name was and where he came from and got what he considered an uncivil answer.

The great cats buried William in an unmarked grave because, as the jaguar said, 'What's the good of putting up a stone reading "Here lies Nobody from Nowhere"?'

Moral: *O why should the spirit of mortal be proud, in this little voyage from swaddle to shroud?*

The Bragdowdy and the Busybody

A FEMALE HARE, who had been born with a foot in everybody's affairs, became known in her community as 'that big Belgian busybody.' She was always listening to the thumpings of her neighbours. 'You're all ears,' her mate snarled one day. 'For God's sake, get some *laissez faire*.' There was no answer, for she had hopped next door to exhort, reproach, and upbraid a female guinea pig who had borne one hundred and seventy-three young and had then let herself go. She had become a bragdowdy, and spent her time weeping over *True Pigtales*.

'Where is your civic spirit?' demanded Mrs Hare. 'And your country, state, federal, and global spirit? Look at me. I am president, or chairwoman, of practically everything, and founder of the Listening Post, an organization of eight hundred females with their ears to the ground.'

The male guinea pig, who had been lying on a lettuce leaf, taking it easy, tried to hide from his nosy neighbour, but she came into the room, buttocky buttocky, before he could get out of bed.

'A big strapping male like you,' she scoffed, 'lying around the house when you ought to be at the laboratory, having injections to see whether some new serum is deadly or not.' The male guinea pig's teeth began to chatter, and when a male guinea pig's teeth chatter it doesn't mean he's afraid, it means he's mad. But the Belgian busybody didn't care how anybody felt except herself. 'You and your mate should join things and do things!' she exclaimed. 'Shoulder to the wheel, nose to the grindstone, best foot forward, finger in the pie, knee on the chest!'

Before many weeks had passed, Mrs Pig developed a guilt complex that manifested itself in an activity compulsion. She gave up reading *True Pigtales*, took her mate's edible bed away from him, straightened up the house, and joined twenty-four up-and-coming organizations. She became famous for keeping everybody on his toes, whether that's where he wanted to be or not. She was made chairman of the Bear a Basket of Babies Committee, secretary of the Get Behind Your Mate and Push Movement, treasurer of the Don't Let Dad Dawdle League, inventor of its slogan, 'He can do twice as much in half the time if he puts your mind to it,' and, in the end, national president of the Daughters of Ambitious Rodents.

The now celebrated Mrs Pig also found time to bear thirty-seven more offspring, which was thirty-seven more than her mate had wanted. They drove him to Distraction, where he found the male Belgian hare, who had been driven there by his own mate's private and public projects, pryings, proddings, and pushings. The two males had such a quiet and peaceful time together without their mates that they decided to keep it that way. Representatives of ninety-six different organizations – the seventy-two Mrs Hare belonged to and Mrs Pig's twenty-four – argued with them in vain. They ran away one night while their mates were addressing the He Could If He Wanted To, He's Just Not Trying Club, without so much as a fare-thee-well or a note on a pillow, and leaving no forwarding address. They decided to go to Tahiti to forget, but long before they reached Tahiti they had forgot.

Moral: *Thou shalt not convert thy neighbour's wife, nor yet louse up thy neighbour's life.*

The Human Being and the Dinosaur

AGES AGO in a wasteland of time and a wilderness of space, Man, in upper case, and dinosaur, in lower, first came face to face. They stood like stones for a long while, wary and watchful, taking each other in. Something told the dinosaur that he beheld before him the coming glory and terror of the world, and in the still air of the young planet he seemed to catch the faint smell of his own inevitable doom.

'Greetings, stupid,' said Man. 'Behold in me the artfully articulated architect of the future, the chosen species, the certain survivor, the indestructible one, the monarch of all you survey, and of all that everyone else surveys, for that matter. On the other hand, you are, curiously enough, for all your size, a member of the inconsequent ephemera. You are one of God's moderately amusing early experiments, a frail footnote to natural history, a contraption in a museum for future Man to marvel at, an excellent example of Jehovah's jejune juvenilia.'

The dinosaur sighed with a sound like thunder.

'Perpetuating your species,' Man continued, 'would be foolish and futile.'

'The missing link is not lost,' said the dinosaur sorrowfully. 'It's hiding.'

Man paid the doomed dinosaur no mind. 'If there were no Man it would be necessary to create one,' said Man, 'for God moves in mysterious, but inefficient, ways, and He needs help. Man will go on forever, but you will be one with the mammoth and the mastodon, for monstrosity is the behemother of extinction.'

'There are worse things than being extinct,' said the dinosaur sourly, 'and one of them is being you.'

Man strutted a little pace and flexed his muscles. 'You cannot even commit murder,' he said, 'for murder requires a mind. You are capable only of dinosaurslaughter. You and your ilk are incapable of devising increasingly effective methods of destroying your own species and, at the same time, increasingly miraculous methods of keeping it extant. You will never live to know the two-party system, the multi-party system, and the one-party system. You will be gone long before I have made this the best of all possible worlds, no matter how possible all other worlds may be. In your highest state of evolution you could not develop the brain cells to prove innocent men guilty, even after their acquittal. You are all wrong in the crotch, and in the cranium, and in the cortex. But I have wasted enough time on you. I must use these fingers which God gave me, and now probably wishes He had kept for Himself, to begin writing those noble volumes about Me which will one day run to several hundred billion items, many of them about war, death, conquest, decline, fall, blood, sweat, tears, threats, warnings, boasts, hopelessness, hell, heels, and whores. There will be little enough about you and your ilk and your kith and your kin, for after all, who were you and your ilk and your kith and your kin? Good day and goodbye,' said Man in conclusion. 'I shall see to it that your species receives a decent burial, with some simple ceremony.'

Man, as it turned out, was right. The dinosaur and his ilk and his kith and his kin died not long after, still in lower case, but with a curious smile of satisfaction, or something of the sort, on their ephemeral faces.

Moral: *The noblest study of mankind is Man, says Man.*

The Hen Party

ALL THE HENS came to Lady Buff Orpington's tea party and, as usual, Minnie Minorca was the last to arrive, for, as usual, she had spent the day with her psychiatrist, her internist, and her beak, comb, and gizzard specialist. 'I'm not long for this barnyard,' she told the other hens. 'What do you suppose I've got *now*?' She went about the room, giving all the hens a peck except her hostess, who pecked her, but without affection.

'I've got blue comb,' Minnie went on.

A chill had fallen upon the gathering, as it always did when Minnie Minorca began reciting her complaints, old and new, real and hysterical. 'Dr Leghorn found out today that I am edentulous, and he told me so,' said Minnie, triumphantly. 'Of course I've always had chronic coryza, Newcastle disease, and laryngotracheitis.'

'Minnie has so many pains she has given each of us one,' said Lady Buff Orpington coldly. 'Isn't that nice?'

'I love you girls,' said Minnie, 'and I love to share my troubles with you. You're such good listeners. I was telling my psychiatrist about my new ailments, including incipient dry feather, and he suddenly blurted out some of the things he has been keeping from me all these years. He said I have galloping aggression, inflamed ego, and too much gall.'

'Now there's a psychiatrist who knows what he's talking about,' said Miss Brahma, and she tried to talk to her hostess about the weather, and the other hens tried to talk to one another, but Minnie Minorca kept on telling how charged with punishments her scroll was. As she rambled on, describing in detail the attack of scale foot she had had in Cadawcutt, Connecticut, one of the hens whispered, 'I've just put some sleeping pills in her teacup.'

'You must have some more tea,' cried Lady Buff Orpington, as she refilled Minnie's cup, and all her guests repeated, 'You must have some more tea,' and Minnie Minorca, delighted to be the centre of attention and, as she thought, concern, hastily drank the slugged tea. After she had passed out, one of the hens suggested that they wring her neck while the wringing was good. 'We could say she broke her neck trying to see what was the matter with her tail,' the conspirator suggested.

Lady Buff Orpington sighed and said, 'We'll draw lots to see who wrings her neck at the next tea party someone gives. Now let's go out and take a dust bath and leave old Fuss and Fevers to her nightmares.' And the hostess and her guests went out into the road, leaving Minnie Minorca to dream of a brand new ailment, called Minnieitis, or Mrs Minorca's disease.

Moral: *Misery's love of company oft goeth unrequited.*

The Rose, the Fountain, and the Dove

IN A GREEN VALLEY, serene as a star and silent as the moon – except for the Saturday laughter of children and the sound of summer thunder – a rose and a fountain grew restless as time crept on.

'This is our sorrow: We're here today and here tomorrow,' sighed the rose. 'I wish I were rootloose and fancy-free, like the dove.'

'I want to see what's in the wood,' the fountain said. 'I want to have adventures to cherish and regret.' He signalled the dove in a cipher of sparkle, and the dove came down from the sky and made a graceful landing.

'What's in the wood?' the fountain asked. 'You have wings and you must know, for there's nowhere you cannot go.'

'I like to fly above the green valley,' said the dove. 'The green valley is all I know, and all I want to know.'

'Stars fall in a pool in the wood,' the rose declared. 'I hear them sputter when they strike the water. I could fish them up and dry them out and sell them to a king, if I had wings like you,' she told the dove.

'I like it where I am,' the dove replied, 'flying above the valley. I watch the stars that do not fall, and would not want to sell them.'

'It is always the same wherever one is,' complained the rose.

'To my eye, it is always changing,' said the dove.

'I am weary of playing in this one spot forever,' whimpered the fountain. 'The same old patterns every day. Help, help, another spray!'

'There's nothing in the wood, I think, but horned owls in hollow oaks,' the dove declared, 'and violets by mossy stones.'

'Violence by mossy stones is what I crave!' the fountain cried. 'I'd love to meet the waterfall in silver combat, and damned be him who first dries up!'

'I have nothing to remember and nothing to forget,' sighed the rose. 'I waste my sweetness on the verdant air.'

'I like it here' was all the dove would say. But the rose and the fountain kept after him every day of every week, and when the summer waned, they convinced the dove he loved the wood, admired horned owls, and ought to spend his life salvaging stars and meeting waterfalls in silver combat.

So the dove flew away into the wood and never came back. There were many varied rumours of the nature of his end. The four winds whispered that the dove had ceased to be because of mossy stones, half-hidden violets, or violence, malicious waterfalls, and owls in trees, but the wood thrush contended the dove had died while playing with burning stars. One thing was sure: The dove had ended the way no other dove had ever ended.

Moral: *He who lives another's life another's death must die.*

The Bachelor Penguin and the
Virtuous Mate

ONE SPRING a bachelor penguin's fancy lightly turned, as it did in every season, to thoughts of illicit love. It was this gay seducer's custom to make passes at the more desirable females after their mates had gone down to the sea to fish. He had found out that all the females in the community made a ritual of rearranging the sitting-room furniture, putting it back where it had been the day before, and they were only too glad to have a strong male help them move the heavier pieces. Their mates had grown less and less interested in housework and more and more addicted to fishing, as time went on. The bachelor penguin proved handy at putting on or taking off screen doors, removing keys wedged in locks meant for other keys, and rescuing the females from other quandaries of their own making. After a few visits, the feathered Don Juan induced the ladies to play Hide-in-the-Dark with him, and Guess Who This Is?, and Webfooty-Webfooty.

As the seasons rolled on, the handsome and well-groomed Casanova became a little jaded by his routine successes with the opposite sex. Then one morning, after the other male penguins had gone to the seashore to fish as usual, Don J. Penguin spied the prettiest female he had ever seen, trying, all by herself, to move a sitting-room sofa back to the spot where it had been the day before. Don gallantly offered to help the matron in distress and she gladly accepted, with a shy look and a faint blush. The next morning the bachelor, who knew how to play his cards, came back and helped the housepenguin put on the screen door, and the following day he fixed the broken catch of her necklace, and the day after that he tightened the glass top of her percolator. Each time that he suggested playing Hide-in-the-Dark or Guess Who This Is?, the object of his desire thought of something else for him to fix, or loosen, or tighten, or take off, or put on. After several weeks of this, the amorist began to suspect that he was being taken, and his intended victim corroborated his fears.

'Unless you keep on helping me take things off, and put things on, and pry things loose, and make things tighter,' she told the dismayed collector of broken hearts, 'I will tell my mate about your improper advances and your dishonourable intentions.' Don Penguin knew that the clever penguin's mate was the strongest male in the community, and also had the shortest temper and the least patience. There wasn't going to be any Hide-in-the-Dark or Guess Who This Is? or Webfooty-Webfooty. And so he spent the rest of his days working for the virtuous and guileful lady of his desire, moving sofas, taking things off and putting things on, loosening this and tightening that, and performing whatever other tasks his fair captor demanded of him. His bow tie became untied, his dinner jacket lost its buttons, his trousers lost their crease, and his eyes lost their dream. He babbled of clocks, and of keys caught in locks, and everybody closed her door when he came waddling down the street except the penguin who had taken him in with a beauty as unattainable as the stars, and a shy look, and a faint blush as phony as a parrot's laugh. One day her mate, returning early from the sea, caught a glimpse of Don leaving the house and said, 'What did old Droop Feather want?'

'Oh, he washes the windows and waxes the floors and sweeps the chimney,' the female replied. 'I believe he had an unhappy love affair.'

Moral: *One man's mate may sometimes be another man's prison.*

The Peacelike Mongoose

IN COBRA COUNTRY a mongoose was born one day who didn't want to fight cobras or anything else. The word spread from mongoose to mongoose that there was a mongoose who didn't want to fight cobras. If he didn't want to fight anything else, it was his own business, but it was the duty of every mongoose to kill cobras or be killed by cobras.

'Why?' asked the peacelike mongoose, and the word went around that the strange new mongoose was not only pro-cobra and anti-mongoose but intellectually curious and against the ideals and traditions of mongoosism.

'He is crazy,' cried the young mongoose's father.

'He is sick,' said his mother.

'He is a coward,' shouted his brothers.

'He is a mongoosexual,' whispered his sisters.

Strangers who had never laid eyes on the peacelike mongoose remembered that they had seen him crawling on his stomach, or trying on cobra hoods, or plotting the violent overthrow of Mongoosia.

'I am trying to use reason and intelligence,' said the strange new mongoose.

'Reason is six-sevenths of treason,' said one of his neighbours.

'Intelligence is what the enemy uses,' said another.

Finally, the rumour spread that the mongoose had venom in his sting, like a cobra, and he was tried, convicted by a show of paws, and condemned to banishment.

Moral: *Ashes to ashes, and clay to clay, if the enemy doesn't get you your own folks may.*

The Godfather and His Godchild

A WORLDLY-WISE COLLECTOR, who had trotted the globe collecting everything he could shoot, or buy, or make off with, called upon his godchild, a little girl of five, after a year of collecting in various countries of the world.

'I want to give you three things,' he said. 'Any three things your heart desires. I have diamonds from Africa, and a rhinoceros horn, scarabs from Egypt, emeralds from Guatemala, chessmen of ivory and gold, mooses' antlers, signal drums, ceremonial gongs, temple bells, and three rare and remarkable dolls. Now tell me,' he concluded, patting the little girl on the head, 'what do you want more than anything else in the world?'

His little godchild, who was not a hesitater, did not hesitate. 'I want to break your glasses and spit on your shoes,' she said.

Moral: *Though statisticians in our time have never kept the score, Man wants a great deal here below and Woman even more.*

The Grizzly and the Gadgets

A GRIZZLY BEAR who had been on a bender for several weeks following a Christmas party in his home at which his brother-in-law had set the Christmas tree on fire, his children had driven the family car through the front door and out the back, and all the attractive female bears had gone into hibernation before sunset returned home prepared to forgive, and live and let live. He found, to his mild annoyance, that the doorbell had been replaced by an ornamental knocker. When he lifted the knocker, he was startled to hear it play two bars of 'Silent Night.'

When nobody answered his knock, he turned the doorknob, which said 'Happy New Year' in a metallic voice, and a two-tone gong rang 'Hello' somewhere deep within the house.

He called to his mate, who was always the first to lay the old aside, as well as the first by whom the new was tried, and got no answer. This was because the walls of his house had been soundproofed by a soundproofer who had soundproofed them so well nobody could hear anybody say anything six feet away. Inside the living room the grizzly bear turned on the light switch, and the lights went on all right, but the turning of the switch had also released an odour of pine cones, which this particular bear had always found offensive. The head of the house, now becoming almost as angry as he had been on Christmas Day, sank into an easy chair and began bouncing up and down and up and down, for it was a brand-new contraption called 'Sitpretty' which made you bounce up and down and up and down when you sat on it. Now thoroughly exasperated, the bear jumped up from the chair and began searching for a cigarette. He found a cigarette box, a new-fangled cigarette box he had never seen before, which was made of metal and plastic in the shape of a castle, complete with portal and drawbridge and tower. The trouble was that the bear couldn't get the thing open. Then he made out, in tiny raised letters on the portal, a legend in rhyme: 'You can have a cigarette on me If you can find the castle key.' The bear could not find the castle key, and he threw the trick cigarette box through a windowpane out into the front yard, letting in a blast of cold air, and he howled when it hit the back of his neck. He was a little mollified when he found that he had a cigar in his pocket, but no matches, and so he began looking around the living room for a matchbox. At last he saw one on a shelf. There were matches in it, all right, but no scratching surface on which to scratch them. On the bottom of the box, however, there was a neat legend explaining this lack. The message on the box read: 'Safety safety matches are doubly safe because there is no dangerous dangerous sandpaper surface to scratch them on. Strike them on a windowpane or on the seat of your pants.'

Enraged, infuriated, beside himself, seeing red and thinking black, the grizzly bear began taking the living room apart. He pounded the matchbox into splinters, knocked over lamps, pulled pictures off the wall, threw rugs out of the broken window, swept vases and a clock off the mantlepiece, and over-turned chairs and tables, growling and howling and roaring, shouting and bawling and cursing, until his wife was aroused from a deep dream of marrying a panda, neighbours appeared from blocks around, and the attractive female bears who had gone into hibernation began coming out of it to see what was going on.

The bear, deaf to the pleas of his mate, heedless of his neighbours' advice, and unafraid of the police, kicked over whatever was still standing in the house, and went roaring away for good, taking the most attractive of the attractive female bears, one named Honey, with him.

Moral: *Nowadays most men lead lives of noisy desperation.*

The Goose That Laid the Gilded Egg

THE GOOSE didn't really lay a gilded egg. She laid an ordinary goose egg, like any other goose egg, and some joker gilded it when she left the nest for a snack or a snail. When she came back and saw the gleaming surprise, she cried, 'Lo, I have laid the golden egg of lore and legend!'

'Lo, my foot,' said a Plymouth Rock hen. 'That is an ordinary goose egg painted yellow, if you ask me.'

'She isn't asking you,' said a rooster. 'She is asking me, and I say that is a solid-gold egg.'

The goose did not seem overjoyed. 'I had my heart set on raising a gosling,' she said.

'You'll have a golden gosling,' said the rooster.

'Golden gosling, my feathers,' said the hen. 'She'll have a yellow gosling, like any other yellow gosling, only punier.'

'I don't care what it looks like,' said the goose. 'I just don't want it to be gold. People would talk. They would snatch my quills for souvenirs. I would be photographed all the time.'

'I will offer you a fabulous sum for that glittering miracle,' said the rooster, and he named a sum fabulous only as things are figured fiscally among the feathered. The goose gladly accepted the offer.

'I wouldn't sit on that egg,' said the hen. 'I wouldn't sit on it if a platinum gander encrusted with diamonds came out of it.'

'I'll sit on it myself,' said the rooster.

And so the hopeful rooster rolled the gilded goose egg to a nest and began sitting on it. At the end of three weeks, all the hens left his bed and board.

'You'll be sorry,' said the rooster, 'when this priceless treasure is hatched. I know it will be a golden goose. I have already named her – Goldie. When she becomes a full-grown goose, I will sell her to the highest bidder for a super-fabulous sum.'

'Oh, sure,' said the Plymouth Rock hen, 'and my family came over on the Mayflower,' and she went away.

The old positivist sat and sat and sat on the gilded egg, and all his friends drifted away, and no hen would look at him, and his feathers began to fall out. One day, being a male and not a female, he clumsily stepped on the egg and broke it, and that was the end of the egg and the end of his dreams.

Moral: *It is wiser to be hendubious than cocksure.*

The Trial of the Old Watchdog

AN OLD experienced collie, who had been a faithful country watchdog for many years, was arrested one summer's day and accused of the first-degree murder of a lamb. Actually, the lamb had been slain by a notorious red fox who had planted the still-warm body of his victim in the collie's kennel.

The trial was held in a kangaroo court presided over by Judge Wallaby. The jury consisted of foxes, and all the spectators were foxes. A fox named Reynard was prosecuting attorney. 'Morning, Judge,' he said.

'God bless you, boy, and good luck,' replied Judge Wallaby jovially.

A poodle named Beau, an old friend and neighbour of the collie, represented the accused watchdog. 'Good morning, Judge,' said the poodle.

'Now I don't want you to be too clever,' the Judge warned him. 'Cleverness should be confined to the weaker side. That's only fair.'

A blind woodchuck was the first creature to take the stand, and she testified that she saw the collie kill the lamb.

'The witness is blind!' protested the poodle.

'No personalities, please,' said the Judge severely. 'Perhaps the witness saw the murder in a dream or a vision. This would give her testimony the authority of revelation.'

'I wish to call a character witness,' said the poodle.

'We have no character witnesses,' said Reynard smoothly, 'but we have some charming character assassins.'

One of these, a fox named Burrows, was called to the stand. 'I didn't actually see this lamb killer kill this lamb,' said Burrows, 'but I almost did.'

'That's close enough,' said Judge Wallaby.

'Objection,' barked the poodle.

'Objection overruled,' said the Judge. 'It's getting late. Has the jury reached a verdict?'

The forefox of the jury stood up. 'We find the defendant guilty,' he said, 'but we think it would be better to acquit him, nonetheless. If we hang the defendant, his punishment will be over. But if we acquit him of such dark crimes as murder, concealing the body, and associating with poodles and defence attorneys, nobody will ever trust him again, and he will be suspect all the days of his life. Hanging is too good for him, and much too quick.'

'Guilt by exoneration!' Reynard cried. 'What a lovely way to end his usefulness!'

And so the case was dismissed and court was adjourned, and everybody went home to tell about it.

Moral: *Thou shalt not blindfold justice by pulling the wool over her eyes.*

The Philosopher and the Oyster

B Y THE SEA on a lovely morning strolled a philosopher – one who seeks a magnificent explanation for his insignificance – and there he came upon an oyster lying in its shell upon the sand.

'It has no mind to be burdened by doubt,' mused the philosopher, 'no fingers to work to the bone. It can never say, "My feet are killing me." It hears no evil, sees no television, speaks no folly. It has no buttons to come off, no zipper to get caught, no hair or teeth to fall out.' The philosopher sighed a deep sigh of envy. 'It produces a highly lustrous concretion, of great price or priceless,' he said, 'when a morbid condition obtains in its anatomy, if you could call such an antic, anomalous amorphousness anatomy.' The philosopher sighed again and said, 'Would that I could wake from delirium with a circlet of diamonds upon my fevered brow. Would, moreover, that my house were my sanctuary, as sound and secure as a safe-deposit vault.'

Just then a screaming sea-gull swooped out of the sky, picked up the oyster in its claws, carried it high in the air, and let it drop upon a great wet rock, shattering the shell and splattering its occupant. There was no lustrous concretion, of any price whatever, among the debris, for the late oyster had been a very healthy oyster, and, anyway, no oyster ever profited from its pearl.

Morals: *Count your own blessings, and let your neighbour count his.*

Where there is no television, the people also perish.

Tea for One

A YOUNG HUSBAND was wakened at five o'clock one morning by his bride. 'Is the house on fire?' he mumbled. She laughed merrily. 'The dawn is here,' she said, 'and I am going to bake a sugar cake.'

'I don't want a sugar cake, I want toast and coffee,' the bridegroom said.

'The sugar cake's for you to take for all the boys to see,' she explained.

'All what boys?' demanded her husband, who was still drowsy.

'The boys at the office, silly,' she said. 'Let them see it, and then bring it home, and maybe we'll have it for dinner.'

He got up and started to dress.

'I'll make tea for both of us now,' she said, singing the line, and adding, 'Coffee doesn't rhyme with anything. You can't have coffee.'

He had tied his shoes and was tying his tie, when her voice brightened and she clapped her hands. 'We'll raise a family,' she said gaily. 'You can have the boy, and I'll take the girl.' And she scampered down the stairs to start to bake the sugar cake for him to take for all the boys to see. When she had gone, the bridegroom glanced at his watch. It was eleven minutes after five. He brushed his teeth and combed his hair, and then he climbed out the bedroom window, dropped to the ground below, and slipped away into the dawn, to find an all-night restaurant where a man could get a meal a man could eat.

Moral: *If life went along like a popular song, every man's marriage would surely go wrong.*

The Mouse and the Money

A CITY MOUSE who moved to the country to live in the walls of an old
house with a lot of country mice began lording it over them from the
start. He trimmed his whiskers, put *mousseline* in his hair, talked with
an accent, and told the country mice that they came from the wrong side of
the mouse tracks.

'My ancestors were of the French aristocracy,' boasted the city mouse. 'Our
name still appears on bottles of great French wine: '*Mise du château*," which
means mice in the chateau, or castle mice.' Every day the newcomer bragged
about his forebears, and when he ran out of ancestors he made some up. 'My
great-great-great-grandfather was a theatre mouse at the Comédie-Francaise,
and he married a cathedral mouse, one of the cathedral mice of Chartres. At
their wedding a dessert named in their honour, *mousse chocolat*, was served to
millions of guests.'

Then the city mouse told how his family had come to America in the bridal
suite of a great French liner. 'My brother is a restaurant mouse at "21," and
my sister's at the Metropolitan,' he said. He went on to tell of other ancestors
of the family who had been in such productions as *The Chauve Souris* and *Die
Fledermaus* and *Les Trois Mousquetaires*. 'Not a mouse in our house was a
common house mouse,' he said.

One day, wandering through forbidden walls of the country house, to show
his inferiors that he knew his way around, he came upon a treasure in currency
which someone had hidden years before between the plaster and the lath. 'I
wouldn't eat that stuff,' warned an old country mouse. 'It is the root of evil and
it will give you greenback bellyache.' But the city mouse did not listen.

'I'm already a mouse of distinction,' said the city mouse, 'and this money
will make me a millionaire. I'll be loaded.' So he began to eat the currency,
which consisted of bills of large denominations, and he drove off one or two of
the young country mice who wanted to help him eat the treasure, saying,
'Finders are not their brothers' keepers.' The city mouse told his country
cousins, 'Blessed are the rich, for they can pay their way into the kingdom of
Heaven,' and he got off a lot of other witticisms, such as 'Legal tender is the
night' and 'Money makes the nightmare go.'

And so he went on living, as he put it, on the fat of the lath. 'When I have
eaten it all,' he said, 'I shall return to the city and live like a king. They say you
can't take it with you, but I'm going to take it with *me*.'

In a few days and nights the arrogant city mouse with the fancy and fanciful
French forebears had eaten all the money, which amounted to an ambassador's

annual salary. Then he tried to leave the walls of the old country house, but he was so loaded with money, and his head was so swelled, that he got caught between the plaster and the lath and could not get out, and his neighbours could not dislodge him, and so he died in the walls, and nobody but the country mice knew that he had been the richest mouse in the world.

Moral: *This is the posture of fortune's slave : one foot in the gravy, one foot in the grave.*

The Wolf at the Door

MR AND MRS SHEEP were sitting in their sitting room with their daughter, who was as pretty as she was edible, when there was a knock at the front door. 'It's a gentleman caller,' said the daughter. 'It's the Fuller Brush man,' said her mother.

The cautious father got up and looked out the window. 'It's the wolf,' he said. 'I can see his tail.'

'Don't be silly,' said the mother. 'It's the Fuller Brush man, and that's his brush.' And she went to the door and opened it, and the wolf came in and ran away with the daughter.

'You were right, after all,' admitted the mother, sheepishly.

Moral: Mother doesn't *always* know best. (The italics are father's and daughter's and mine.)

What Happened to Charles

A FARM HORSE named Charles was led to town one day by his owner, to be shod. He would have been shod and brought back home without incident if it hadn't been for Eva, a duck, who was always hanging about the kitchen door of the farmhouse, eavesdropping, and never got anything quite right. Her farmmates said of her that she had two mouths but only one ear.

On the day that Charles was led away to the smithy, Eva went quacking about the farm, excitedly telling the other animals that Charles had been taken to town to be shot.

'They're executing an innocent horse!' cried Eva. 'He's a hero! He's a martyr! He died to make us free!'

'He was the greatest horse in the world,' sobbed a sentimental hen.

'He just seemed like old Charley to me,' said a realistic cow. 'Let's not get into a moony mood.'

'He was wonderful!' cried a gullible goose.

'What did he ever do?' asked a goat.

Eva, who was as inventive as she was inaccurate, turned on her lively imagination. 'It was butchers who led him off to be shot!' she shrieked. 'They would have cut our throats while we slept if it hadn't been for Charles!'

'I didn't see any butchers, and I can see a burnt-out firefly on a moonless night,' said a barn owl. 'I didn't hear any butchers, and I can hear a mouse walk across moss.'

'We must build a memorial to Charles the Great, who saved our lives,' quacked Eva. And all the birds and beasts in the barnyard except the wise owl, the sceptical goat, and the realistic cow set about building a memorial.

Just then the farmer appeared in the lane, leading Charles, whose new shoes glinted in the sunlight.

It was lucky that Charles was not alone, for the memorial-builders might have set upon him with clubs and stones for replacing their hero with just plain old Charley. It was lucky, too, that they could not reach the barn owl, who quickly perched upon the weathervane of the barn, for none is so exasperating as he who is right. The sentimental hen and the gullible goose were the ones who finally called attention to the true culprit – Eva, the one-eared duck with two mouths. The others set upon her and tarred and unfeathered her, for none is more unpopular than the bearer of sad tidings that turn out to be false.

Moral: *Get it right or let it alone. The conclusion you jump to may be your own.*

The Daws on the Dial

A YOUNG JACKDAW told his father that he was going to build his nest on the minute hand of the town clock. 'That's the most unthinkable thing you ever thought of,' said old John Daw. Young Jack was not deterred. 'We'll build our nest when the minute hand is level,' he said, 'at a quarter of or a quarter after.'

'Those who live in castles in the air have nowhere to go but down,' the old Daw warned, but Jack and his mate built their nest on the clock at a quarter after eight the next morning. At twenty minutes after eight the nest slipped off the minute hand and fell into the street below. 'We didn't start early enough,' the young Daw told his father that evening. 'Better never than late. We'll try again tomorrow at a quarter after six.'

'If at first you don't succeed, fail, fail again,' said the elder Daw. But he might as well have been talking to a gargoyle. Jack and his mate stole some of the elder Daw's silverware and built their nest again the following morning, and again it slipped off the minute hand and fell into the street below.

That evening old John Daw had more to say to his reckless offspring. 'To stick on a dial, you would need three feet, one of them a rabbit's. Don't hang heavy on time's hands, just because it hangs heavy on yours. Clockwise is not wise enough. Even the cyclone and the merry-go-round know that much.'

And again the young Daws did not listen, and again they swiped some silverware from his parents' nest to furnish their own. This time, those human beings known as municipal authorities were concealed in the clock tower, and, with brooms and yells and stones and bells, they frightened the foolish daws away from the clock and the tower and the town.

That night old John Daw's mate counted her silverware and sighed with dismay. 'Gone, alas, with our youth, two spoons,' she said, 'and half the knives, and most of the forks, and all of the napkin rings.'

'If I told him once, I told him a hundred times, "Neither a burglar nor a lender be," ' raged old John, 'but I might as well have been talking to a cast-iron lawn Daw.' Not a word was heard from the young Daws as the weeks went on. 'No news is bad news,' grumbled old John Daw. 'They have probably built their nest this time on a wagon wheel, or inside a bell.'

He was wrong about that. The young Daws had built their last nest in the muzzle of a cannon, and they heard only the first gun of a twenty-one-gun salute fired in honour of a visiting chief of state.

Moral: *The saddest words of pen or tongue are wisdom's wasted on the young.*

The Tiger Who Would Be King

ONE MORNING the tiger woke up in the jungle and told his mate that he was king of beasts.

'Leo, the lion, is king of beasts,' she said.

'We need a change,' said the tiger. 'The creatures are crying for a change.'

The tigress listened but she could hear no crying, except that of her cubs.

'I'll be king of beasts by the time the moon rises,' said the tiger. 'It will be a yellow moon with black stripes, in my honour.'

'Oh, sure,' said the tigress as she went to look after her young, one of whom, a male, very like his father, had got an imaginary thorn in his paw.

The tiger prowled through the jungle till he came to the lion's den. 'Come out,' he roared, 'and greet the king of beasts! The king is dead, long live the king!'

Inside the den, the lioness woke her mate. 'The king is here to see you,' she said.

'What king?' he inquired, sleepily.

'The king of beasts,' she said.

'I am the king of beasts,' roared Leo, and he charged out of the den to defend his crown against the pretender.

It was a terrible fight, and it lasted until the setting of the sun. All the animals of the jungle joined in, some taking the side of the tiger and others the side of the lion. Every creature from the aardvark to the zebra took part in the struggle to overthrow the lion or to repulse the tiger, and some did not know which they were fighting for, and some fought for both, and some fought whoever was nearest, and some fought for the sake of fighting.

'What are we fighting for?' someone asked the aardvark.

'The old order,' said the aardvark.

'What are we dying for?' someone asked the zebra.

'The new order,' said the zebra.

When the moon rose, fevered and gibbous, it shone upon a jungle in which nothing stirred except a macaw and a cockatoo, screaming in horror. All the beasts were dead except the tiger, and his days were numbered and his time was ticking away. He was monarch of all he surveyed, but it didn't seem to mean anything.

Moral: *You can't very well be king of beasts if there aren't any.*

The Chipmunk and His Mate

A MALE CHIPMUNK could sleep like a top or a log or a baby as soon as his head hit the pillow, but his mate was always as wakeful as an owl or a nightwatchman or a burglar. When he turned the lights off, she would turn them on again and read, or worry, or write letters in her head, or wonder where things were. She was often drowsy after supper, and sometimes nodded in her chair, but she became wide awake as soon as her head hit the pillow. She would lie there wondering if her mate had left his pistol in the nursery, what she had done with the Christmas tree ornaments, and whether or not she had left the fire on under the prunes. She was sure the wastebasket was smouldering in the living room, that she had left the kitchen door unlocked, and that someone was tiptoeing around downstairs.

The male chipmunk always slept until the sun was high, but his mate heard all the clocks strike all the hours. She could doze off in the daytime with a glass in her hand, or while her mate was reading aloud, or when his boss came to call, but as soon as she got in bed, she began writing letters in her head, or wondering if she had put the cat out, or where her handbag was, or why she hadn't heard from her mother.

One day she fell asleep while driving the family car, and, after a decent interval, the male chipmunk married her sister. He could still sleep like a top or a log or a baby, but his new mate just lay there as wide awake as an owl or a nightwatchman or a burglar, hearing intruders, smelling something burning, wondering if her mate had let his insurance lapse. One enchanted evening, across a crowded room, he met a stranger, an eight o'clock sleepy-time gal. They ran away to Maracaibo together, where they slept happily ever after. The second mate lay awake every night, wondering what the chipfrump had that she didn't have and what he saw in her, and whether she herself had put out the milk bottles or left the water running in the kitchen sink.

Moral: *A man's bed is his cradle, but a woman's is often her rack.*

The Weaver and the Worm

A WEAVER watched in wide-eyed wonder a silkworm spinning its cocoon in a white mulberry tree.

'Where do you get that stuff?' asked the admiring weaver.

'Do you want to make something out of it?' inquired the silkworm, eagerly.

Then the weaver and the silkworm went their separate ways, for each thought the other had insulted him. We live, man and worm, in a time when almost everything can mean almost anything, for this is the age of gobbledygook, doubletalk, and gudda.

Moral: *A word to the wise is not sufficient if it doesn't make any sense.*

Two Dogs

ONE SULTRY moonless night, a leopard escaped from a circus and slunk away into the shadows of a city. The chief of police dogs assigned to the case a German shepherd named Plunger and a plainclothes bloodhound named Plod. Plod was a slow, methodical sleuth, but his uniformed partner was restless and impatient. Plod set the pace until Plunger snapped, 'We couldn't catch a turtle this way,' and bounded along the trail like a whippet. He got lost. When Plod found him, half an hour later, the bloodhound said, 'It is better to get somewhere slowly than nowhere fast.'

'Repose is for the buried,' said the police dog. 'I even chase cats in my dreams.'

'I don't,' said the bloodhound. 'Out of scent, out of mind.'

As they went along, each in his own way, through the moonlessness, they exchanged further observations on life.

'He who hunts and turns away may live to hunt another day,' commented Plod.

'*Runs* away, you mean,' sneered Plunger.

'I never run,' said the bloodhound. 'It's no good trailing a cat when you're out of breath, especially if the cat isn't. I figured that out myself. They call it instinct.'

'I was taught to do what I do, and not to do what I don't,' the police dog said. 'They call it discipline. When *I* catch cats, cats stay caught,' he added.

'I don't catch them, I merely find out where they are,' the bloodhound said quietly.

The two dogs suddenly made out a great dark house looming in front of them at the end of a lane. 'The trail ends right here, twenty feet from that window,' the bloodhound said, sniffing a certain spot. 'The leopard must have leaped into the house from here.'

The two dogs stared into the open window of the dark and silent house.

'I was taught to jump through the open windows of dark houses,' said Plunger.

'I taught myself not to,' said Plod. 'I wouldn't grab that cat if I were you. I never grab a leopard unless it is a coat.' But Plunger wasn't listening.

'Here goes,' he said jauntily, and he jumped through the window of the dark and silent house. Instantly there was a racket that sounded to the keen ears of the bloodhound like a police dog being forcibly dressed in women's clothes by a leopard, and that is precisely what it was. All of a moment, Plunger, dressed in women's clothes from hat to shoes, with a pink parasol thrust under his collar, came hurtling out the window. 'I had my knee on his chest, too,' said the bewildered police dog plaintively.

The old sleuth sighed. 'He lasteth longest and liveth best who gets not his knee on his quarry's chest,' murmured Plod, in cloudy English but fluent Bloodhound.

Moral: *Who would avoid life's wriest laughter should not attain the thing he's after.*

The Lady of the Legs

IN A POOL NEAR PARIS there lived a frog who thought she was wonderful. 'I have the largest lily pad, the deepest dive, the prettiest eyes, and the finest voice in the world,' she croaked.

'You also have the most succulent legs on earth or water,' said a human voice one day. It was the voice of a renowned Parisian restaurateur, who was passing by when he heard all the bragging.

'I do not know what succulent means,' said the frog.

'You must have the smallest vocabulary in the world,' said the restaurateur, and the foolish frog, who took every superlative for praise, was pleased, and flushed a deeper green than ever.

'I should like to set you before a certain celebrated *bon vivant*,' said the man, 'a distinguished gourmet, a connoisseur of the *grande haute cuisine*.'

The frog almost swooned with delight at the elegant sound of these strange words.

'You will be served like a queen,' said the restaurateur. 'Provençal. Under my personal supervision, of course.'

'Tell me more,' said the rapt and rapturous frog.

'You will be served with the most excellent vintage wine in the world,' said the man. 'A great Montrachet, I should think, would be perfect.'

'Go on,' urged the vain and foolish frog.

'You will be talked about whenever devotees of the culinary art assemble,' said the restaurateur. 'You will be remembered as the daintiest dish in the history of gastronomy.'

At this the frog swooned in a transport of joy and an excess of misplaced self-esteem, and while she was unconscious, the renowned Parisian restaurateur deftly removed her succulent legs and took them to his restaurant, where they were prepared under his personal supervision as he had promised, and served, Provençal, with a bottle of Montrachet, to a celebrated *bon vivant*.

Moral: *Fatua cruraque mox separabuntur.*

The Kingfisher and the Phoebe

A PROUD MOTHER PHOEBE who had raised two broods of fledglings in the fair weather was at first dismayed and then delighted when one of the males of the second brood refused to leave the nest and fly away like the others. 'I have raised a remarkable phoebe unlike any other phoebe,' the mother bird decided. 'He will become a great singer, greater than the nightingale.'

She brought in a nightingale to teach her son to sing, and then a catbird, and then a mockingbird, but all the young phoebe could learn to sing was 'Phoebe, Phoebe.' And so the mother bird sent for Dr Kingfisher, a bird psychologist, who examined the young phoebe carefully. 'This phoebe is a phoebe like any other phoebe,' he told the mother. 'And all he will ever sing is "Phoebe, Phoebe."'

But the ambitious mother did not believe Dr Kingfisher's prognosis. 'Maybe he won't be a great singer, but he will be a great something,' she insisted. 'He will take the place of the eagle on the dollar, or the canary in the gilded cage, or the cuckoo in the cuckoo clock. You just wait.'

'I'll wait,' said Dr Kingfisher, and he waited. But nothing happened. The phoebe went on being a phoebe and singing 'Phoebe, Phoebe' like any other phoebe, and that was all.

Moral: *You can't make anything out of cookie dough except cookies.*

The Turtle Who Conquered Time

A TURTLE appeared in a meadow one summer's day and attracted the
attention of all the creatures in the grass and in the trees, because the
date 44 B.C. was carved on his shell. 'Our meadow is honoured indeed,'
exclaimed a grasshopper, 'for our visitor is the oldest of all living creatures.'

'We must build a pavilion in his honour,' said a frog, and the catbirds and
the swallows and the other birds built a stately pleasure dome out of twigs and
leaves and blossoms for the very important turtle. An orchestra of crickets
played music in his honour, and a wood thrush sang. The sounds of jubilee
were heard in nearby fields and woods, and as more and more creatures turned
up from farther and farther away to have a look at the ancient turtle, the grasshopper decided to charge admission to the pavilion.

'I will be the barker,' said the frog, and, with the help of the grasshopper,
he composed an impressive spiel. 'Yesterday and yesterday and yesterday,' it
began, 'creeps in this carapace from day to day to the first syllable of recorded
time. This great turtle was born two thousand years ago, the year the mighty
Julius Caesar died. Horace was twenty-one in 44 B.C., and Cicero had but a
single year to live.' The bystanders did not seem very much interested in the
turtle's ancient contemporaries, but they gladly paid to go in and have a look
at his ancient body.

Inside the pavilion, the grasshopper continued the lecture. 'This remarkable turtle is a direct descendant of one of the first families of Ooze,' he
chanted. 'His great-grandfather may have been the first thing that moved in
the moist and muddy margins of this cooling planet. Except for our friend's
ancestors, there was nothing but coal and blobs of glob.'

One day a red squirrel who lived in a neighbouring wood dropped in to look
at the turtle and to listen to the ballyhoo. 'Forty-four B.C., my foot!' scoffed
the squirrel, as he glared at the grasshopper. 'You are full of tobacco juice, and
your friend the frog is full of lightning bugs. The carving of an ancient date on
the carapace of a turtle is a common childish prank. This creep was probably
born no earlier than 1902.'

As the red squirrel ranted on, the spectators who had paid to get into the
pavilion began departing quietly, and there was no longer a crowd listening to
the frog out front. The crickets put away their instruments and disappeared as
silently as the Arabs, and the wood thrush gathered up his sheet music and
flew off and did not return. The sounds of jubilee were no longer heard in the
once merry meadow, and the summer seemed to languish like a dying swan.

'I knew all the time he wasn't two thousand years old,' admitted the grasshopper, 'but the legend pleased the people, young and old, and many smiled who had not smiled for years.'

'And many laughed who had not laughed for years,' said the frog, 'and many eyes sparkled and many hearts were gay.' The turtle shed a turtle tear at this and crawled away.

'The truth is not merry and bright,' said the red squirrel. 'The truth is cold and dark. Let's face it.' And, looking smug and superior, the iconoclast scampered impudently back to his tree in the wood. From the grass of the meadow voices once carefree and gay joined in a rueful and lonely chorus, as if someone great and wonderful had died and was being buried.

Moral: *Oh, why should the shattermyth have to be a crumplehope and a dampenglee?*

The Lion and the Lizard

A LION and a lizard kept the halls where once a prince had slept. The prince had died, as even princes do, and his palace had fallen to rats and ruin. The lion destroyed the rats, but he could never find the lizard, who lived in a crevice in the wall. There was royal food in the ruined kitchen, and royal wine in the ruined cellar, but the lion got it all, for the lizard was afraid to emerge from his hiding place. So the lion got fatter and fatter, and drunker and drunker, and the lizard grew thinner and thinner, and soberer and soberer. Weeks went by, and the weeds grew and the walls crumbled, as the lion ate six meals a day, washing them down with a total of eighteen different wines. One night, as the tawny master of the palace was topping off his sixth meal of the day with a tankard of brandy, he fell asleep on his golden chair at the head of the ornate table. The lizard, with his remaining strength, which wasn't much, crawled up on the table and tried to nibble a crumb, but he was too weak to eat. The lion, awakened by a tiny tinkle of spoons, tried to crush the unwelcome guest with one blow of his mighty paw, but he was sated and obese, and his paw was no longer mighty. He passed away in his golden chair, spilling the last of the brandy, as the lizard gave up the ghost among the crumbs and silver.

Moral: *He who dies of a surfeit is as dead as he who starves.*

The Tigress and Her Mate

PROUDFOOT, a tiger, became tired of his mate, Sabra, a few weeks after they had set up housekeeping, and he fell to leaving home earlier and earlier in the morning, and returning later and later at night. He no longer called her 'Sugar Paw,' or anything else, but merely clapped his paws when he wanted anything, or, if she was upstairs, whistled. The last long speech he ever made to her at breakfast was 'What the hell's the matter with you? I bring you rice and peas and coconut oil, don't I? Love is something you put away in the attic with your wedding dress. Forget it.' And he finished his coffee, put down the *Jungle News*, and started for the door.

'Where are you going?' Sabra asked.

'Out,' he said. And after that, every time she asked him where he was going, he said, 'Out,' or 'Away,' or 'Hush.'

When Sabra became aware of the coming of what would have been, had she belonged to the chosen species, a blessed event, and told Proudfoot about it, he snarled, 'Growp.' He had now learned to talk to his mate in code, and 'growp' meant 'I hope the cubs grow up to be xylophone players or major-generals.' Then he went away, as all male tigers do at such a moment, for he did not want to be bothered by his young until the males were old enough to box with and the females old enough to insult. While waiting for the unblessed event to take place, he spent his time fighting water buffaloes and riding around with plainclothes tigers in a prowl car.

When he finally came home, he said to his mate, 'Eeps,' meaning 'I'm going to hit the sack, and if the kids keep me awake by yowling, I'll drown them like so many common house kittens.' Sabra stalked to the front door of their house, opened it, and said to her mate, 'Scat.' The fight that took place was terrible but brief. Proudfoot led with the wrong paw, was nailed with the swiftest right cross in the jungle, and never really knew where he was after that. The next morning, when the cubs, male and female, tumbled eagerly down the stairs demanding to know what they could do, their mother said, 'You can go in the parlour and play with your father. He's the tiger rug just in front of the fireplace. I hope you'll like him.'

The children loved him.

Moral: *Never be mean to a tiger's wife, especially if you're the tiger.*

The Magpie's Treasure

ONE DAY when the sun made everything that glitters glitter and every-thing that sparkles sparkle, a magpie picked up something from a gutter and carried it off to her nest. A crow and a rabbit had seen her swoop down and fly away, and each decided she had found something good to eat. 'I'm sure it's a carrot,' said the rabbit, 'for I heard her say something about carrots.'

'I saw it glitter,' said the crow, 'and it glittered edibly, like a yellow grain of corn.'

'Corn is for the commoner,' said the rabbit scornfully.

'You can have your carrots, and welcome to them,' said the crow. They smacked their lips as they approached the magpie's nest. 'I'll find out what she's got,' said the crow. 'If it's a grain of corn, I'll eat it. If it's a carrot, I'll throw it down to you.'

So the crow flew to the edge of the magpie's nest while the rabbit waited below. The magpie happily showed the crow what she had found in the gutter. 'It's a fourteen-carat diamond set in a golden ring,' she said. 'I wanted rings from the time I could fly, but my parents were worm collectors. If I had had my way, I'd be a wealthy bird today, surrounded by rings and other lovely things.'

'You are living in the pluperfect subjunctive,' said the crow disdainfully.

'It's serene there, and never crowded, except for old regrets,' the magpie said.

The crow dropped down to the ground and explained to the rabbit that the 'carrots' the magpie had talked about were only carats. 'One carrot is worth fourteen carats,' the rabbit said. 'You can multiply that by twenty and it will still be true.'

'If I can't eat it, I don't want it,' said the crow. 'Seeing is deceiving. It's eat-ing that's believing.' And the crow and the rabbit swallowed their disappoint-ment, for want of anything else, and left the magpie to the enjoyment of her treasure. The light made everything that sparkles sparkle, and everything that glitters glitter, and the magpie was content until the setting of the sun.

Moral: Chacun à son gout *is very very true, but why should we despise the apples of other eyes?*

The Cricket and the Wren

AT A MUSIC FESTIVAL one summer in Tangletale Wood, a score of soloists came together to compete for the annual Peacock Awards. The Cricket was asked to pick the winner because of his fame as a fiddler and his many appearances on radio, where he is employed to let audiences know when it is night.

The Cricket was met at the station by the Wren, who flew him to an inn, bought him a drink, carried his bags upstairs to his room, and was in general so courteous and attentive that the Cricket thought he was the proprietor of the inn.

'I am not a proprietor, but a competitor,' the Wren said. 'It is a greater honour to be judged by you, even if I should lose, than to win the highest award from a lesser critic and cricket. As small tokens of my esteem, here are a bottle of wine and a cherry pie, and the key to the boudoir of as charming a lady cricket as you would attract in a year of chirping.'

That afternoon, the Wren flew the Cricket out to the concert field, where he heard the Frog scrape his cello, the Lark blow his clarion trumpet, the Nightingale strum his lyre of gold, the Blackbird play his boxwood flute, the Catbird run his bright piano arpeggios, and the Partridge show off on his drums. The vocalists came next, beginning with the Canary, a temperamental visitor from abroad, who had sat up all night bragging of his ability and was, as a consequence, in lousy voice. 'The Owl can do better than that even if all he can sing is "Who," ' said the Wren, who had slipped quietly into a chair next to the Cricket's. He gave the critic a cigar, a light, and a swig from a flask. 'I shall sing a group of *Lieder*,' said the Wren, 'all of them Henley's "Take, Dear, This Little Sheaf of Songs." I composed the music myself, and dedicated it to my mate and to you.'

The Mockingbird sang next, and those in the audience who hoped the amiable Wren would win with his bright little group of songs, all of them the same song, began to worry, for the Mockingbird had slept all night, dreaming of victory, and as a consequence, was in heavenly voice. 'I should say his tongue is sharp rather than sweet,' whispered the Wren. 'When I told him last night that you were a finer fiddler than all the finest fiddlers in the field, he remarked that, to him, you looked like a limousine come to grief at an intersection.' The Cricket rubbed his legs together angrily, producing two low, ominous notes. 'In my opinion,' the Wren went on, 'you look like a shining piece of mechanism, handsome and authoritative, such as the trigger action of a Colt. Here is a lozenge for your cough, and a pillow for your chair, and a footstool for your feet.'

When it came time for the Wren to sing, his group of songs, all of them the same song, delighted everybody in the audience except the other soloists and their friends and families.

'I could do better than that,' sneered the Mockingbird, 'with my beak closed.'

'I have thrashed singers with voices ten times better than that,' said the Brown Thrasher.

'*Gott im Himmel!*' cried the Canary. '*Er klingt wie ein rostiges eisernes Tor das geölt werden muss.*'

In awarding first prize to the Wren, the Cricket said, in part and in parting, 'His voice is like some bright piece of mechanism, such as the works of a golden music box, and he gives his group of one song an infinite variety. This artist also has a keen appreciation of values and a fine critical perception.'

In departing, or, to be precise, escaping from, the music festival, the Cricket was fortunate enough to have at his disposal a private airplane, none other than the victorious Wren himself.

Moral: *It is not always more blessed to give than to receive, but it is frequently more rewarding.*

The Crow and the Scarecrow

ONCE upon a farm an armada of crows descended like the wolf on the fold. They were after the seeds in the garden and the corn in the field. The crows posted sentinels, who warned them of the approach of the farmer, and they even had an undercover crow or two who mingled with the chickens in the barnyard and the pigeons on the roof, and found out the farmer's plans in advance. Thus they were able to raid the garden and the field when he was away, and they stayed hidden when he was at home. The farmer decided to build a scarecrow so terrifying it would scare the hateful crows to death when they got a good look at it. But the scarecrow, for all the work the farmer put in on it, didn't frighten even the youngest and most fluttery female. The marauders knew that the scarecrow was a suit of old clothes stuffed with straw and that what it held in its wooden hand was not a rifle but only a curtain rod.

As more and more corn and more and more seeds disappeared, the farmer became more and more eager for vengeance. One night, he made himself up to look like a scarecrow and in the dark, for it was a moonless night, his son helped him to take the place of the scarecrow. This time, however, the hand that held the gun was not made of wood and the gun was not an unloaded curtain rod, but a double-barrelled 12-gauge Winchester.

Dawn broke that morning with a sound like a thousand tin pans falling. This was the rebel yell of the crows coming down on field and garden like Jeb Stuart's cavalry. Now one of the young crows who had been out all night, drinking corn instead of eating it, suddenly went into a tailspin, plunged into a bucket of red paint that was standing near the barn, and burst into flames.

The farmer was just about to blaze away at the squadron of crows with both barrels when the one that was on fire headed straight for him. The sight of a red crow, dripping what seemed to be blood, and flaring like a Halloween torch, gave the living scarecrow such a shock that he dropped dead in one beat less than the tick of a watch (which is the way we all want to go, *mutatis*, it need scarcely be said, *mutandis*).

The next Sunday the parson preached a disconsolate sermon, denouncing drink, carryings on, adult delinquency, front page marriages, golf on Sunday, adultery, careless handling of firearms, and cruelty to our feathered friends. After the sermon, the dead farmer's wife explained to the preacher what had really happened, but he only shook his head and murmured sceptically, 'Confused indeed would be the time in which the crow scares the scarecrow and becomes the scarescarecrow.'

Moral: *All men kill the thing they hate, too, unless, of course, it kills them first.*

Ivory, Apes and People

A BAND of ambitious apes in Africa once called upon a herd of elephants with a business proposition. 'We can sell your tusks to people for a fortune in peanuts and oranges,' said the leader of the apes. 'Tusks are tusks to you and us, but to people they are merchandise – billiard balls and piano keys and other things that people buy and sell.' The elephants said they would think it over. 'Be here tomorrow at this time and we will swing the deal,' said the leader of the apes, and the apes went away to call on some people who were hunting for merchandise in the region.

'It's the very best ivory,' the leader of the apes told the leader of the people. 'One hundred elephants, two hundred tusks. All yours for oranges and peanuts.'

'That's enough ivory for a small ivory tower,' said the leader of the people, 'or four hundred billiard balls and a thousand piano keys. I will cable my agent to ship your nuts and oranges, and to sell the billiard balls and piano keys. The business of business is business, and the heart of the matter is speed.'

'We will close the deal,' said the leader of the apes.

'Where is the merchandise now?' inquired the leader of the people.

'It's eating, or mating, but it will be at the appointed place at the appointed hour,' replied the chief ape. But it wasn't. The elephants had thought it over, and reconsidered, and they forgot to show up the following day, for elephants are good at forgetting when forgetting is good. There was a great to-do in the marts of world trade when the deal fell through, and everybody, except the elephants, got into the litigation that followed: the Better Business Bureau, the Monkey Business Bureau, the Interspecies Commerce Commission, the federal courts, the National Association of Merchandisers, the African Bureau of Investigation, the International Association for the Advancement of Animals, and the American Legion. Opinions were handed down, rules were promulgated, subpoenas were issued, injunctions were granted and denied, and objections were sustained and overruled. The Patriotic League of American Women Against Subversion took an active part until it was denounced as subversive by a man who later withdrew his accusation and made a fortune on the sale of two books, 'I Made My Bed' and 'I Lie in My Teeth.'

The elephants kept their ivory, and nobody got any billiard balls or piano keys, or a single nut or an orange.

Moral: *Men of all degrees should form this prudent habit: never serve a rabbit stew before you catch the rabbit.*

Oliver and the Other Ostriches

AN AUSTERE OSTRICH of awesome authority was lecturing younger ostriches one day on the superiority of their species to all other species. 'We were known to the Romans, or, rather, the Romans were known to us,' he said. 'They called us *avis struthio*, and we called them Romans. The Greeks called us *strouthion*, which means "truthful one," or, if it doesn't, it should. We are the biggest birds, and therefore the best.'

All his listeners cried, 'Hear! Hear!' except a thoughtful one named Oliver. 'We can't fly backward like the hummingbird,' he said aloud.

'The hummingbird is losing ground,' said the old ostrich. 'We are going places, we are moving forward.'

'Hear! Hear!' cried all the other ostriches except Oliver.

'We lay the biggest eggs and therefore the best eggs,' continued the old lecturer.

'The robin's eggs are prettier,' said Oliver.

'Robins' eggs produce nothing but robins,' said the old ostrich. 'Robins are lawn-bound worm addicts.'

'Hear! Hear!' cried all the other ostriches except Oliver.

'We get along on four toes, whereas Man needs ten,' the elderly instructor reminded his class.

'But Man can fly sitting down, and we can't fly at all,' commented Oliver.

The old ostrich glared at him severely, first with one eye and then the other. 'Man is flying too fast for a world that is round,' he said. 'Soon he will catch up with himself, in a great rear-end collision, and Man will never know that what hit Man from behind was Man.'

'Hear! Hear!' cried all the other ostriches except Oliver.

'We can make ourselves invisible in time of peril by sticking our heads in the sand,' ranted the lecturer. 'Nobody else can do that.'

'How do we know we can't be seen if we can't see?' demanded Oliver.

'Sophistry!' cried the old ostrich, and all the other ostriches except Oliver cried 'Sophistry!' not knowing what it meant.

Just then the master and the class heard a strange alarming sound, a sound like thunder growing close and growing closer. It was not the thunder of weather, though, but the thunder of a vast herd of rogue elephants in full stampede, frightened by nothing, fleeing nowhere. The old ostrich and all the other ostriches except Oliver quickly stuck their heads in the sand. Oliver took refuge behind a large nearby rock until the storm of beasts had passed, and when he came out he beheld a sea of sand and bones and feathers – all that was

419

left of the old teacher and his disciples. Just to be sure, however, Oliver called the roll, but there was no answer until he came to his own name. 'Oliver,' he said.

'Here! Here!' said Oliver, and that was the only sound there was on the desert except for a faint, final rumble of thunder on the horizon.

Moral: *Thou shalt not build thy house, nor yet thy faith, upon the sand.*

The Shore and the Sea

A SINGLE excited lemming started the exodus, crying, 'Fire!' and running toward the sea. He may have seen the sunrise through the trees, or waked from a fiery nightmare, or struck his head against a stone, producing stars. Whatever it was, he ran and ran, and as he ran he was joined by others, a mother lemming and her young, a nightwatchlemming on his way home to bed, and assorted revellers and early risers.

'The world is coming to an end!' they shouted, and as the hurrying hundreds turned into thousands, the reasons for their headlong flight increased by leaps and bounds and hops and skips and jumps.

'The devil has come in a red chariot!' cried an elderly male. 'The sun is his torch! The world is on fire!'

'It's a pleasure jaunt,' squeaked an elderly female.

'A what?' she was asked.

'A treasure hunt!' cried a wild-eyed male who had been up all night. 'Full many a gem of purest ray serene the dark unfathomed caves of ocean bear.'

'It's a bear!' shouted his daughter. 'Go it!' And there were those among the fleeing thousands who shouted 'Goats!' and 'Ghosts!' until there were almost as many different alarms as there were fugitives.

One male lemming who had lived alone for many years refused to be drawn into the stampede that swept past his cave like a flood. He saw no flames in the forest, and no devil, or bear, or goat, or ghost. He had long ago decided, since he was a serious scholar, that the caves of ocean bear no gems, but only soggy glub and great gobs of mucky gump. And so he watched the other lemmings leap into the sea and disappear beneath the waves, some crying 'We are saved!' and some crying 'We are lost!' The scholarly lemming shook his head sorrowfully, tore up what he had written through the years about his species, and started his studies all over again.

Moral: *All men should strive to learn before they die what they are running from, and to, and why.*

The Thurber Album

TO

HERMAN ALLEN MILLER

OCTOBER 25, 1896 – APRIL 20, 1949

whose friendship was an

early and enduring inspiration

Adam's Anvil

IT WAS about fifteen years ago, just after Mahlon Taylor left Columbus to live in Punxsutawney, that I came across a faded obituary of my great-grandfather, Jacob Fisher, preserved in an old family scrapbook. Jacob, I learned, was born in 1808, one of the eleven children of Michael Fisher, who had built his cabin on the east shore of the Scioto River, south of Columbus, in 1799, the year George Washington died. This Michael was one of the six sons – the most restless one – of Adam Fisher, a blacksmith, of Hampshire County, Virginia, who died there in the year 1782. I have no yellowing eulogy of old Adam, or any other report of him except a copy of his last will and testament, which I found not long ago, while digging into ancient family records. The original will was filed in the Hampshire County courthouse at Romney, which became a part of West Virginia after General George Brinton McClellan smashed across the Ohio River, during the Civil War, and seized the western end of the Old Dominion in the name of the Federal Union. The document disposing of the blacksmith's earthly possessions is dated the 14th day of May in the year of our Lord 1778. It contains some curious spellings which I respectfully preserve.

'In the name of God Amen,' it begins. 'I Adam Fisher, Black Smith of the County of Hampshire and Colloney of Virginia being weak in body, but of sound mind and memory blessed be God, Do here make this my last Will and Testament in manner and form as follows. That is to say, that it is my desire that in the first place, that after my Decease, I be deacently buried after a Christian manner, and my funeral charges to be paid and all my Just Debts . . . Imprimis I do leave and bequeath unto my well beloved Wife Christian Fisher, the benefit of as much of the plantation I now live on (in the manor) as she shall stand in need of during her widowhood, and likewise one Negro wench named Fan, to be hers during her widowhood and no longer, and if she should marry again she is to have what the law allows.' The will then goes on to provide for the six sons and two daughters of Adam and his beloved wife, whose name appears three times as 'Christian' and once as 'Christina.' The will was probated in 1783 and it ends in a mysterious renunciation of all rights by Christian, or Christina. She refused to join in the probate, declaring that 'she would not accept, receive, or take any Legacy or legacies to her given or bequeathed by this Will or any part thereof and renounced all benefit and advantage which she might claim by the same.' It is probable that Christian, or Christina, was married again, or intended to be, for she must still have been a young woman and she was, after all, the mother of only eight children.

I don't know what became of Fan, or of any of the rest of Adam Fisher's 'movable property,' except his old smithy anvil. Uncle Mahlon tells me that the iron block was bequeathed to Michael Fisher, a blacksmith as well as a farmer, who passed it on to his son Jacob when he died. Jake could shoe a horse as well as his father and grandfather, and Uncle Mahlon, as a boy, used to watch him hammering iron shoes into shape on the anvil. Jake's sons, one of whom, William M. Fisher, became my grandfather, all grew up to be city fellows, and they had no use for an anvil or any knowledge of how to use one. I am sure this did not please old Jake, and it is a fond notion of mine, although I have no facts to support it, that he picked up the anvil one day, in a fit of temper and disdain, and threw it away. For Jake Fisher, as we shall see, was a mighty man, with large and sinewy hands.

Jacob Fisher's death notice, headed simply 'Memorial,' recorded that he was survived by three sisters and a brother, six of his thirteen children, thirty-two grandchildren, and six great-grandchildren. The rest of the story, except for a single arresting sentence, praised the deceased's homely virtues – a persistent devotion to the Lord, kindliness to his neighbours, and generosity to those in want. The sentence that caught my eye and interest, set austerely apart in a paragraph by itself, read, 'In his prime Jacob Fisher was the strongest man for many miles below the city.' That was all; no instances were given of my great-grandfather's physical prowess. In the severe and solemn memorials of 1885 in Ohio there was no place for vain glorification of the pitiful and transitory clay. I wondered, when I read the obituary, what lay behind that cautious tribute to the earthly power of old Jake Fisher's flesh. It wasn't until I asked Mahlon Taylor that I found out.

A far lesser breed of men has succeeded the old gentleman on the American earth, and I tremble to think what he would have said of a great-grandson who turned out to be a writer. Perhaps I can make up for it a little by giving the substance of the story that should have followed that topic sentence left hanging mute and lonely in old Jake's obituary. He would have wanted it there in place of the list of his virtues. He didn't care if his neighbours knew that he could heft a bigger load of stone or iron than any other man for miles south of the city, or in any other direction, or that he had once picked up an old locomotive wheel and throwed it thirty-four inches farther than the next strongest man in the countryside; but his acts of kindness and generosity were his own private business, and not to be bragged about. He had a clean conscience, a good appetite, and sound common sense – except for his habit of taking a homemade physic, compounded of bitter roots, that was strong enough to singe a brigadier's moustache – and he stayed young-looking all the years of his long life. 'I don't know what old Jake used on his hair,' said Mahlon, that Old Dutch Cleanser man, 'but it stayed full and black up to his death. Beard turned grey, but his hair didn't. He died with all his own teeth in his head, too – all except one. That'd been knocked out with a brick in a fight.'

Jake Fisher fought a thousand fights in his time. In those days, if you went west of the Alleghenies, there was only one way of settling an argument or a

difference of opinion. Farther west they wrassled and gouged out eyes with
their thumbnails, but in the Northwest Territory they fought standing up,
with their fists. Some men would pick up a club or a rock or even a broadaxe,
and a few grabbed for their guns, but mostly they slugged it out toe to toe.

'Jake never lost a fight,' Mahlon said. 'He fought men who were hard on
their womenfolk or were cruel to dumb animals, but mostly he fought to back
up his political beliefs or to defend the divine inspiration of Scripture. "There
is too goddam much blasphemin' goes on," he used to say. He was a good man.'

Jacob Fisher, born in a log cabin when Jefferson was President, was twenty-
one when Andrew Jackson took office. 'Your great-grandpa's prime that the
fella speaks of,' said Uncle Mahlon, 'began about then and lasted up to Cleveland's first term. He couldn't go through another Democratic administration,
and so he died.' Jake's political bias, it seems, was partly determined by an
incident of the War of 1812. General Jackson had ordered the execution of a
young soldier who had deserted to visit his dying mother. Jake heard about it
from his father and he never got it out of his mind. He licked every Jackson
man he met, once going up on to the platform of a meeting house to knock
down a visiting speaker from the East who praised Old Hickory. Afterwards
he stopped his buggy beside the man, who was walking along the road, holding
his jaw. 'Git in the buggy and I'll take you to the hotel,' said Jake. The man
refused. 'Git in the buggy!' roared Jake. The man got in. A fist fight settled an
issue once and for all, and subsequent hard feelings were not to be tolerated.
If Jake broke a man's ribs or fractured his jaw, he took the man home. Often
he sat up all night at the bedside of a vanquished foe, applying arnica or
changing bandages. He could assist at the birth of a child, and he had a comforting voice in a house of death. 'About all the graves in the old Walnut Hill
Cemetery were dug single-handed by Jake,' said Uncle Mahlon. 'He never
allowed nobody to help him.'

Jacob Fisher built one of the first stone houses south of Columbus, and
people used to go out from the town to watch him pick up a three-hundred-
pound granite sill and set it in place. 'He was only a hair over five foot ten,'
said Uncle Mahlon, 'but he weighed a hundred and ninety-eight pounds, most
of it bone and muscle. You couldn't lay your finger between his hip-bone and
his ribs, he was that close-built. He walked so straight he never run his shoes
over, heel or sole – they wore out even.' Around the house that Jake built grew
up a farm of ten thousand acres. Through a part of his vast fields drifted the
barges of the Ohio Canal on their way to and from Athens, and across one end
of his property the Chillicothe tollpike was cut. Jake owned a great gravel pit
and he allowed the road contractor to use all the gravel he needed, with the
understanding that Jake would never have to pay toll. When the pike was
finished and the tollgate put up, the agreement was forgotten. The pole would
be kept in place across the road when Jake drove along in his buggy. 'He'd git
out and beat up the tollgate keeper,' Uncle Mahlon told me, 'and then raise
the gate and drive on. They kept puttin' bigger and stronger men on the gate.
Jake licked eight of 'em all told, and finally his patience gave out and he

threatened to go over their heads to their bosses and lick *them*, and after that they didn't molest him. The gatekeeper would h'ist the gate when Jake's rig was still a quarter-mile away.'

The canal wove itself into my great-grandfather's saga, too. If you stood on his back porch, you could see the slow boats passing through the land, half a mile away. Once in a while, when a barge came along, Jake would cup his hands around his mouth and bellow, 'Git me some whisky!' On the return trip five barrels would be tossed off on to Jake's land. He didn't drink or smoke or chew, but his hired hands did. When he was not yet forty, Jake had half a hundred Negroes working for him. Each man had a jug and a tin cup and the barrels were set in a lean-to and you could get whisky whenever you wanted it. If a man got mean drunk or lazy drunk, Jake would whip him sober with a hickory withe. The men learned to drink moderately, out of fear of the big man's lash, and also out of a real devotion to him. 'Your great-grandpa,' said Uncle Mahlon, 'was the first man in Franklin County to sit down at table with a Negro. This caused a stew and a fret in the Presbyterian Church, but Jake just said, "If a man's good enough to work for me, he's good enough to eat with me," and that settled that.'

One day there was hell and a battle royal along the canal. Jake wandered down to the waterway and witnessed a dismaying spectacle. The bargemen were 'whippin' up ducks.' Each of the men held in his hand a long-lashed bull-whip. Their sport consisted of casting the whip at ducks floating in the canal in such a way that the end of the lash wrapped itself several times about a duck's neck. Then they would jerk the bird up on to the barge. The bargemen were expert at this curious pastime. They caught a great many ducks. The ducks were Jake's. He ran down to the towpath, grabbed the towrope away from the drowsy boy on the mule, and hauled the boat into shore. Then he leaped on board and began to throw men into the water and on to the land. 'He could throw a six-foot grown man as far as twenty-five feet when he was in a rage,' said Uncle Mahlon. 'A lot of heads cracked and bones broke that day, but nobody was killed. Your great-grandpa never tried to kill anybody – except one Indian. He was a good man.'

I asked about the Indian. There were a great many Indians in central Ohio in the first thirty years of Jake Fisher's prime, descendants, perhaps, of the braves who fought at the Battle of Fallen Timbers. They plagued Jake because, although they couldn't outwrassle or outhoist him, they could outrun him. 'If I could catch 'em,' he used to say wistfully, 'I could hold 'em.' He never gave up trying. 'Once, over by the old deer lick west of the river,' Uncle Mahlon told me, 'he challenged an Indian to a foot race – see which one could reach an old elm tree first. The Indian won by a couple of strides. Your great-grandpa ran back and got his gun where he had left it and shot the Indian. He wasn't killed, but he was hurt bad. Jake carried him to his own home and nursed him back to life. Old Fisher didn't get more than two, three hours' sleep a night for weeks, sittin' up with that Indian. The fella thought he was going to die, so he

confessed to his sins and crimes, which included most of the thievin' and skul-
duggery that'd gone on in the county for the past five years. Your great-
grandpa never gave him away to the authorities. Jake always said the Lord
God Almighty disturbed his aim the day he shot that Indian.'

Shortly after that, Jake became captain of a horse militia company, whose
main duty was to keep order at public hangings. Captain Fisher, in his official
capacity, wore a sabre, but he never picked up a gun again, even to face an
armed man. There was the November evening when Stambaugh showed up
on the road outside the Fisher house. He was a quick-moving, broad-shoul-
dered neighbour, and there was bad blood between him and Milt Fisher, one of
Jake's sons. It was suppertime and Jake had just finished saying grace. One of
his darkies came running into the dining room. 'Stambaugh's come to git Mr
Milt!' he said. 'He got a shotgun in one hand and a broadaxe in t'other!' Jake
told Milt and his other sons to sit still. He took his napkin out of his collar and
went out the door, empty-handed. 'Jake took Stambaugh's gun away from him
and broke it in two,' said Uncle Mahlon. 'Then he snapped the axe-handle and
throwed the pieces away. He broke that gun and axe in his hands, like you'd
break a stick.'

When Fort Sumter was fired on, Jake Fisher, still hard as a boulder, had just
turned fifty-three. They wouldn't take him in the Army, so he stayed at home
and fought Copperheads and mealymouthed patriots with his fists. 'On a
market day Jake would lick as many as six, eight men,' Uncle Mahlon said.
'Mostly men who questioned Lincoln's policies or turned scared after a
Rebel victory. Once a fella that was ridin' on a horse yelled something that
angered your great-grandpa and Jake ordered him down off his horse. The fella
was just takin' off his coat to square away when Jake walked over to the
horse. "We gotta have more room," he said. "I don't want you to hit this horse
when I throw you." Thereupon he picked the animal up in his arms and moved
it eight or ten feet away. He was used to doing that in his own blacksmith
shop – it was easier to move 'em that way than to lead 'em sometimes. Well,
when the fella saw that, he took to his heels and ran faster than an Indian.'

On another occasion during the war years, a friend of Jake's told him that
five men, probably Copperheads, were conspiring to beat Jake up. They were
in the back room of Frick's saloon, laying plans for a mass assault. Jake jumped
on a horse and rode over to the place. 'He didn't knock them fellows down,'
said Uncle Mahlon. 'He throwed 'em. Jake only fought with his fists over
political or religious questions. He throwed fellas that whipped up ducks or
were just plain ornery.' It was also during the Civil War, when Morgan's
raiders had crossed over into Ohio, that a train of boxcars on its way to Cincin-
nati stopped in the yards in Columbus. Jake found out that they were crowded
with men, Home Guards, on their way to protect the Ohio-Kentucky border.
'The goddam Copperheads has cooped them boys up in there without no air!'
said Jake. He tore a rail loose from a siding and, swinging it like a tennis racket,
beat holes in the sides of each car. The authorities always looked the other way

when Jake started out on one of his rampages. 'Nobody wanted to arrest a man as good as Jake,' Uncle Mahlon said. He kept trying to enlist in the Union Army almost up to the day of Lee's surrender, and once demonstrated his fitness to a couple of recruiting officers by pulling a thick oak door loose from its hinges as easily as if it had been a petal he was plucking from a daisy. After the war was over, and Jake was either sixty or sixty-one, Uncle Mahlon can't be sure about that, he throwed his last man, an impudent gatekeeper at a county fair. 'It wasn't his best throw,' said Uncle Mahlon, 'but the fella went a good twenty feet.'

In his seventies, Jake Fisher could still lift two hundred pounds' dead weight from the ground and hold it at arm's length above his head. Three years before he died he performed his last exploit in public. The drunken driver of a team of horses on High Street tumbled over on to the doubletree and the horses took off. Jake outran the other men who saw it happen and pulled the team to a stop. 'I can still catch 'em,' he said proudly, 'and if I catch 'em, I can hold 'em.' In his last days he had little respect for the soft race of men he saw growing up around him. When he was taken to see a newborn great-grandchild, a puny boy weighing seven pounds, Jake snorted. 'Goddam it,' he said, 'the next generation of Fishers is goin' to be squirrels.'

In his seventy-seventh year, Jake took to his bed for the last time. As he lay dying, the preacher called on him. 'Don't you want to forgive your enemies?' he asked. Jake smiled. 'I ain't got none,' he said. 'I licked 'em all.'

Daguerreotype of a Lady

WHEN I FIRST BECAME aware of Mrs Albright in my world – at the age of three or four, I suppose – she was almost seventy, and a figure calculated to excite the retina and linger in the consciousness of any child. Aunt Margery, as everybody called her, was stout and round, and, in the phrase of one of her friends, set close to the ground, like a cabbage. Her shortness was curiously exaggerated by the effect of an early injury. She had fractured her right kneecap in a fall on the ice when she was in her late teens, and the leg remained twisted, so that, when she was standing, she bent over as if she were about to lean down and tie her shoelace, and her torso swayed from side to side when she walked, like the slow pendulum of an ancient clock, arousing sympathy in the old and wonder in the young. I used to marvel at the way she kept her balance, hobbling about in her garden after sundown, with a trowel in one hand and a sprinkling can in the other, her mouth tightening and her eyes closing every now and then when the misery seized her knee. She scorned the support of a cane; canes were for men, who were often feeble and tottery as early as their sixties. It took her a good ten minutes to mount the short staircase that led to the second floor of her home. She would grasp the banister with one hand and, with the other, pull her bad leg up beside her good one, pausing every few steps to catch her breath. She had to come downstairs backward, and this journey was even more laborious and painful. She got up before dawn every morning except Sunday the year around, and she rarely went to bed until after ten o'clock at night.

Aunt Margery was an active woman who got things done, and she did not always carry her cross with meekness and equanimity. She was capable of cursing her bad leg in good, round words that shocked women of more pious vocabulary. In her moments of repose, which were rare enough in a long and arduous lifetime, the gentleness of her face, enhanced by white hair smoothly parted in the middle, belied the energy of her body and the strength of her spirit, but her mouth grew firm, her eyes turned serious or severe, and her will overcame her handicap when she felt called upon, as she often did, to take up some burden too heavy for the shoulders of lesser women, or too formidable for mere menfolks to cope with. Her neighbours often summoned her in an hour of crisis, when there was illness in their homes, or a wife in labour, or a broken bone to set, for she was a natural nurse, renowned for her skill and wisdom and, as we shall see, for many an earthy remedy and forthright practice.

*

Mrs Albright, born Margery Dangler nearly a hundred and thirty years ago, in a time of stout-hearted and self-reliant women, came West in a covered wagon driven by her father, during the Presidency of Martin Van Buren, when she was only nine. The Danglers, before their westward venture, had lived in Long Branch, in New Jersey – she always used 'in' before a state or county. The family settled for a time in Kokomo, in Indiana, and then retraced its steps to Ohio, to live in Lebanon, in Warren County, Degraff, in Logan County, and Arcanum and Greenville, in Darke County. Shortly after the Civil War, Mrs Albright came to Columbus, where she spent the last forty years of her life in the north half of a two-family frame house at the corner of Fifth Street and Walnut Alley. Her husband had died in Greenville the year the war ended, and she lived with her daughter Belle. When I first knew the neighbourhood, at the turn of the century, Fifth Street was paved with cobble-stones and a genial City Council allowed a tall sycamore tree to stand squarely in the middle of the brick sidewalk in front of Mrs Albright's house, dropping its puffballs in season. On the opposite side of the street, the deep-toned clock in the steeple of Holy Cross Church marked, in quarter hours, the passing of the four decades she lived there. It was a quiet part of town in those days, and the two-storey frame house was one of the serene, substantial structures of my infancy and youth, for all its flimsy shabbiness.

Mrs Albright and her daughter were poor. They took in sewing and washing and ironing, and there was always a roomer in the front room upstairs, but they often found it hard to scrape together ten dollars on the first of the month to pay Mr Lisle, a landlord out of Horatio Alger, who collected his rents in person, and on foot. The sitting-room carpet was faded and, where hot coals from an iron stove had burned it, patched. There was no hot water unless you heated it on the coal stove in the dark basement kitchen, and light was supplied by what Mrs Albright called coal-oil lamps. The old house was a firetrap, menaced by burning coal and by lighted lamps carried by ladies of dimming vision, but these perils, like economic facts, are happily lost on the very young. I spent a lot of time there as a child, and I thought it was a wonderful place, different from the dull formality of the ordinary home and in every difference enchanting. The floors were uneven, and various objects were used to keep the doors from closing: a fieldstone, a paving brick that Mrs Albright had encased in a neat covering made of a piece of carpet, and a conch shell, in which you could hear the roaring of the sea when you held it to your ear. All the mirrors in the house were made of wavy glass and reflected images in fascinating distortions. In the coal cellar, there was what appeared to be an outside toilet moved inside, miraculously connected with the city sewage system; and the lower sash of one of the windows in the sitting room was flush with the floor – a perfect place to sit and watch the lightning or the snow. Furthermore, the eastern wall of Jim West's livery stable rose less than fifteen feet away from Mrs Albright's back stoop. Against this wall, there was a trellis of moon-flowers, which popped open like small white parachutes at twilight in the summertime, and between the trellis and the stoop you could pull up water from a cistern in the veritable oaken bucket of the song. Over all this presided a great lady, fit, it seemed to me, to be the mother of King Arthur or, what was more, of Dick Slater and Bob Estabrook, captain and lieutenant, respectively, in the nickel novels, 'Liberty Boys of '76.'

I was reminded of Mrs Albright not long ago when I ran across an old query of Emerson's: 'Is it not an eminent convenience to have in your town a person who knows where arnica grows, or sassafras, or pennyroyal?' Mrs Albright was skilled in using the pharmacopoeia of the woods and fields. She could have brought the great philosopher dozens of roots and leaves and barks, good for everything from ache to agony and from pukin' spells to a knotted gut. She could also have found in the countryside around Concord the proper plants for the treatment of asthma and other bronchial disturbances. She gathered belladonna, Jimson weed, and digitalis, made a mixture of them, added a solution of saltpetre, put the stuff in a bowl, and set it on fire. The patient simply bent over the bowl and inhaled the fumes. She knew where sour grass grew, which you chew for dyspepsy, and mint, excellent for the naushy, and the slippery elm, whose fragrant inner bark was the favourite demulcent of a hundred years ago – the thing to use for raw throat and other sore tishas. I don't think she ever mentioned goldthread, also known as dodder, but the chances are that she knew it by one or both of its other aliases, devil's-guts and creeping crowfoot.

Mrs Albright's sitting room was often redolent of spirits of camphor, which could be applied to minor cuts (wet baking soda or cold mashed potato was the stuff for burns); rubbed on the forehead, for headache; used as a gargle or mouthwash, in a mild solution that was never mild enough for me; and sniffed, for attacks of dizzy spells or faintness. Such attacks in Mrs Albright's own case might have been the result of lack of sleep or overwork, but they were never symptoms of the vapours or other feminine weaknesses. A dab of camphor on the back of each hand acted to break affectionate dogs of the habit of licking. Aunt Margery had owned a long line of affectionate dogs, the first of which, Tuney – named after her brother Tunis, who was later killed at Shiloh by a ramrod fired from a nervous Southern farmboy's musket – made the westward trip from Long Branch in the wagon with the Danglers. The last of the line, Cap, a brindle mongrel who looked like a worn carpet-bag, caught the secret of vitality from his indomitable mistress and lived to be sixteen, when Aunt Margery, with heavy heart but steady hand, administered the ether that put a merciful end to the miserable burden of his years. That was the year Mrs Albright adopted, fed, and reared a newborn mouse, whose mother had been annihilated in a trap set in the cellar to catch the largest rats I have ever seen. I say annihilated because it was surely the deadliest rat trap in the world, made of a hickory plank, a powerful spring, and a heavy iron ring that could have killed a full-grown cat when it let go. Once Mrs Albright cornered in the cellar the ugly patriarch of all rats, who had found a safe way to get at the cheese in the trap, and she whammed its life out with a lump of coal.

Shelves in Mrs Albright's sitting room, where they were handy to get at,

held alum, for canker sores; coca butter, for the chest; paregoric, for colic and
diarrhoea; laudanum, for pain; balsam apples, for poultices; bismuth, for the
bowels; magneeshy (carbonate of magnesium), a light, chalky substance,
wrapped in blue paper, that was an antacid and a gentle laxative; and calomel
and blue mass, regarded by women of Aunt Margery's generation as infallible
regulators of the liver. Blue mass came in the form of pills, and she made it by
rubbing up metallic mercury with confection of roses. Blue mass and calomel
are no longer found in every house, as they were in Mrs Albright's day, and the
free and easy use of paregoric and laudanum, both tinctures of opium, has long
been frowned upon by doctors. Your druggist may have heard of balsam
apples, alias balsam pears, but unless he is an elderly man, he has probably
never seen one. The poultice of today has no source so picturesque as the
balsam apple, a warty, oblong West Indian fruit, tropical red or orange in
colour. It was used for decoration, too, a hundred years ago and more, and
looked nice on a window sill with love apples turning from green to red. One
legend has it, by the way, that the first American tomato was eaten in 1820, by
a gentleman of Salem, in New Jersey, a town not far from Long Branch, where
Margery Albright was born ten years after this startling and foolhardy act. I
was pleased to find out from my pharmacist, Mr Blakely, of Crutch & Macdonald's drugstore, in Litchfield, Connecticut, that folks in small towns and
rural regions still favour slippery elm for sore throat. No housewife actually
strips the bark from the tree nowadays, the way Mrs Albright did, but slippery-
elm lozenges, manufactured by the Henry Thayer Company (founded 1847)
from a formula more than ninety years old, are bought by many people in wet
or wintry weather. I got a box of the lozenges from Mr Blakely myself and
tried a couple. They smelled faintly like fertilizer to my snobbish city nose, but
their taste was bland enough and inoffensive. I am sure they soothe the inflamed tishas of the throat. Mr Blakely also said that people from seventy to a
hundred years old drop in now and then for blue pills when their liver is
kicking up. When I asked him about balsam apples, he told me he knew what
they were, but he confessed that he had never seen one. It made me feel old
and odd, suddenly, as if I were a contemporary of Aunt Margery's who had
lived beyond his time.

Aunt Margery held that cold black coffee – not iced, just cold – was fine for
torpor, depression of the spirits, and fatigue. She also used it to disguise the
taste of castor oil for timid palates, but she drank the oil straight from the bottle
herself, in great, gulping dollops that made me flinch and shudder when I was
a boy. For gas on the stomach, and for gentlemen who had brought out the
jugs the night before, she made a fizzing mixture of vinegar, sugar, and baking
soda. Soda crackers soaked in water were excellent for thinning out the blood
in cases that were not severe enough for leeches or the letting of a vein. If you
fell down and broke the skin on your elbow or your knee, she kept a sharp
lookout for the appearance of proud flesh. In the event of serious injuries, such
as gunshot wounds or axe cuts, you had to beware of gangrum. It was easy
enough to identify this awful disease as gangrene, but I was well out of my teens

before I discovered what 'blue boars' are, or, rather, is. Mrs Albright had described it as a knotted groin, a symptom of the Black Death, at least one siege of which she had survived somewhere in her travels. The true name is 'buboes,' from which the word 'bubonic' is derived, and Webster supports Mrs Albright in her definition of the malady as a knotted groin. Then there was cholera morbus, which sounds Asiatic and deadly, but is really no more serious, I found in looking it up the other day, than summer complaint accompanied by green-apple bellyache. If you had the jumpin' toothache, there was nothing better than a large chaw of tobacco. Once, when she was sixteen, Margery Albright was out horseback-riding with a gallant of her acquaintance who bore the gloomy name of Aubrey Hogwood. A jumpin' toothache nearly knocked her from the saddle, and Hogwood, not knowing what the trouble was, paled and stammered when she demanded his tobacco pouch. ('I says to him, "Hogwood," says I, "hand me your pouch." ') She took a man-sized helping of the weed and chewed it lustily. The toothache went away, and so did Hogwood. A pallid romantic of queasy stomach, he drifted out of the realistic maiden's life. In Greenville, in Darke County, not long afterward, she married one John Albright, a farmer, whom she was destined to pull out of what I will always think of as the Great Fever.

One day in Darke County, Albright – his wife always called him by his last name – staggered in from the fields, pale and ganted – this was her word for 'gaunt' – and took to his bed with an imposing fever and fits of the shakes that rattled the china in the cupboard. She was not yet thirty at the time, but already a practical nurse of considerable experience, famous in her neighbourhood for her cool presence at sickbeds and her competence as a midwife. She had nursed Albright through a bad case of janders – jaundice to you and me. Her celebrated chills-and-fever medicine, with which she dosed me more than once fifty years after Albright's extremity, failed to do any good. It was a fierce liquid, compounded of the bitterest roots in the world and heavily spiked with quinine, and it seared your throat, burned your stomach, and set your eyes to streaming, but several doses left Albright's forehead still as hot as the bottom of a flatiron. His wife was jubrous – her word for 'dubious' – about his chances of pulling through this strange seizure. Albright tossed all night and moaned and whinkered – a verb she made up herself out of 'whinny' and 'whicker' – and in the morning his temperature had not gone down. She tested his forehead with the flat of her sensitive hand, for she held that thermometers were just pieces of glass used to keep patients' mouths closed while the doctors thought up something to say about conditions that baffled them. The average doctor, in her opinion, was an educated fool, who fussed about a sickroom, fretted the patient, and got in a body's way. The pontifical doctor was likely to be named, in her pungent idiom, a pusgut, and the talkative doctor, with his fluent bedside manner, was nothing more than a whoop in a whirlwind.

In the afternoon of the second day of the Great Fever, John Albright's wife knew what she had to do. She went out into the pasture and gathered a pailful of sheep droppings, which she referred to in the flattest possible terms. Sheep droppings were not the only thing that Mrs Albright looked for in the pasture and the barnyard to assist her ministrations as a natural nurse. Now and then, in the case of a stubborn pregnancy, she would cut a quill from a chicken feather, fill it with powdered tobacco, and blow the contents up one nostril of the expectant mother. This would induce a fit of sneezing that acted to dislodge the most reluctant baby. Albright, whinkering on his bed of pain, knew what she was up to this time, and he began to gag even before the terrible broth was brewing on the kitchen stove. She got it down him somehow, possibly with a firm hand behind his neck and one knee on his stomach. I heard the story of this heroic cure – for cure it was – a dozen times. Albright lay about the house for a day or two, retching and protesting, but before the week was out, he was back at his work in the fields. He died, a few years later, of what his widow called a jaggered kidney stone, and she moved, with her daughter, to Columbus where she worked for a while as housekeeper of the old American House, a hotel that nobody now remembers. She liked to tell about the tidiest lodger she ever had to deal with, the Honourable Stephen A. Douglas, who kept his room neat as a pin and sometimes even made his own bed. He was a little absent-minded, though, and left a book behind him when he checked out. She could not remember the title of the book or what became of it.

Margery Albright was a woman's woman, who put little faith in the integrity and reliability of the average male. From farmhand to physician, men were the frequent object of her colourful scorn, especially the mealy-mouthed, and the lazy, the dull, and the stupid, who 'sat around like Stoughton bottles' – a cryptic damnation that charmed me as a little boy. I am happy to report that Webster has a few words to say about Dr Stoughton and the bottle that passed into the workaday idiom of the last century. Stoughton, an earlier Dr Munyon or Father John, made and marketed an elixir of wormwood, germander, rhubarb, orange peel, cascarilla, and aloes. It was used to flavour alcoholic beverages and as a spring tonic for winter-weary folks. It came in a bottle that must have been squat, juglike, and heavy. Unfortunately, my Webster does not have a picture, or even a description, of the old container that became a household word. The dictionary merely says, 'To sit, stand, etc., like a Stoughton bottle: to sit, stand, etc., stolidly and dumbly.' Mrs Albright's figure of speech gave the Stoughton bottle turgid action as well as stolid posture. Only a handful of the husbands and fathers she knew were alert or efficient enough to escape the name of Stoughton bottle.

Aunt Margery lived to be eighty-eight years old, surviving, I am constrained to say, the taking of too much blue mass and calomel. She was salivated, as she called it, at least once a year. This, according to my pharmacist, means that she suffered from mercurial poisoning, as the result of an incautious use of calomel. In spite of everything, her strength and vigour held out to the end, and I can remember no single time that she permitted a doctor to look after her. Her daughter Belle held the medical profession in less contempt, and once, in her fiftieth year, after ailing for several months, she went to see a physician in the neighbourhood. He was greatly concerned about her condition and called a colleague into consultation. The result of their joint findings was a dark prognosis indeed. The patient was given not more than a year to live. When Mrs Albright heard the news, she pushed herself out of her rocking chair and stormed about the room, damning the doctors with such violence that her right knee turned in on her like a flamingo's and she had to be helped back to her chair. Belle recovered from whatever it was that was wrong, and when she died, also at the age of eighty-eight, she had outlived by more than fifteen years the last of the two doctors who had condemned her to death. Mrs Albright never forgave, or long forgot, the mistaken medical men. Every so often, apropos of little or nothing, she would mutter imprecations on their heads. I can remember only two doctors whom she treated with anything approaching respect. She would josh these doctors now and then, when their paths crossed in some sickroom, particularly on the subject of their silly theory that air and water were filled with invisible agencies of disease. This, to a natural nurse who had mastered the simple techniques of barnyard and pasture, was palpable nonsense. 'How, then,' Dr Rankin asked her once, 'do you account for the spread of an epidemic?' 'It's just the contagion,' said Mrs Albright. The doctor gave this a moment of studious thought. 'It's just possible,' he said, 'that we may both be right.'

Dr Dunham, one of her favourites – if I may use so strong a word – arrived late at a house on Parsons Avenue on the night of December 8, 1894. I had got there ahead of him, with the assistance of Mrs Albright. 'You might have spared your horse,' she snapped when he finally showed up. 'We managed all right without you.' But she was jubrous about something, and she decided to take it up with the doctor. 'He has too much hair on his head for a male child,' she told him. 'Ain't it true that they don't grow up to be bright?' Dr Dunham gave the matter his usual grave consideration. 'I believe that holds good only when the hair is thicker at the temples than this infant's,' he said. 'By the way, I wouldn't discuss the matter with the mother.' Fortunately for my own peace of mind, I was unable to understand English at the time. It was a source of great satisfaction to Margery Albright, and not a little surprise, when it became evident, in apt season, that I was going to be able to grasp my mother tongue and add, without undue effort, two and two. I have had my own jubrous moments, however. There was the time when, at forty-three, I sweated and strained to shove an enormous bed nearer the lamp on a small table, instead of merely lifting the small table and placing it nearer the enormous bed. There have been other significant instances, too, but this is the story of Aunt Margery Albright.

I remember the time in 1905 when the doctors thought my father was dying, and the morning someone was wise enough to send for Aunt Margery. We went to get her in my grandfather's surrey. It was an old woodcut of a morning. I can see Mrs Albright, dressed in her best black skirt and percale blouse (she pronounced it 'percal'), bent over before the oval mirror of a cherrywood bureau, tying the velvet ribbons of an antique bonnet under her chin. People turned to stare at the lady out of Lincoln's day as we helped her to the kerb. The carriage step was no larger than the blade of a hoe, and getting Aunt Margery, kneecap and all, into the surrey was an impressive operation. It was the first time she had been out of her own dooryard in several years, but she didn't enjoy the April drive. My father was her favourite person in the world, and they had told her he was dying. Mrs Albright's encounter with Miss Wilson, the registered nurse on the case, was a milestone in medical history – or, at least, it was for me. The meeting between the starched young lady in white and the bent old woman in black was the meeting of the present and the past, the newfangled and the old-fashioned, the ritualistic and the instinctive, and the shock of antagonistic schools of thought clashing sent out cold sparks. Miss Wilson was coolly disdainful, and Mrs Albright plainly hated her crisp guts. The patient, ganted beyond belief, recognized Aunt Margery, and she began to take over, in her ample, accustomed way. The showdown came on the third day, when Miss Wilson returned from lunch to find the patient propped up in a chair before a sunny window, sipping, of all outrageous things, a cup of cold coffee, held to his lips by Mrs Albright, who was a staunch believer in getting a patient up out of bed. All the rest of her life, Aunt Margery, recalling the scene that followed, would mimic Miss Wilson's indignation, crying in a shrill voice, 'It shan't be done!' waving a clenched fist in the air, exaggerating the young nurse's wrath. 'It shan't be done!' she would repeat, relaxing at last with a clutch at her protesting kneecap and a satisfied smile. For Aunt Margery won out, of course, as the patient, upright after many horizontal weeks, began to improve. The doctors were surprised and delighted, Miss Wilson tightly refused to comment, Mrs Albright took it all in her stride. The day after the convalescent was able to put on his clothes and walk a little way by himself, she was hoisted into the surrey again and driven home. She enjoyed the ride this time. She asked the driver to stop for a moment in front of the marble house at Washington and Town, built by Dr S. B. Hartman out of the profits of Peruna, a tonic far more popular than Dr Stoughton's, even if the bottle it came in never did make Webster's Dictionary.

The old frame house in Columbus and the old sycamore tree that shaded it disappeared a long time ago, and a filling station now stands on the northwest corner of Fifth Street and Walnut Alley, its lubricating pit about where Mrs Albright's garden used to be. The only familiar landmark of my youth is the church across the way, whose deep-toned clock still marks the passing of the quarter hours as tranquilly as ever. When Belle died in 1937, in another house on Fifth Street, the family possessions were scattered among the friends who had looked after her in her final years. I sometimes wonder who got the photograph album that had been promised to me; the card table, bought for a dollar or two before the Civil War, but now surely an antique of price and value; the two brown plaster-of-Paris spaniels that stood on either end of the mantel in Mrs Albright's bedroom; and the muddy colour print that depicted the brave and sturdy Grace Darling pulling away from a yellow lighthouse on her famous errand of mercy. I have no doubt that some of the things were thrown away: the carpet-covered brick, the fieldstone, the green tobacco tin that Aunt

Margery used for a button box, and the ragbag filled with silk cuttings for the crazy quilts she made. Who could have guessed that a writer living in the East would cherish such objects as these, or that he would have settled for one of the dark and wavy mirrors, or the window sash in the sitting room that was flush with the floor?

I sometimes wonder, too, what has happened to the people who used to call so often when Aunt Margery was alive. I can remember all the tenants of the front room upstairs, who came and went: Vernie, who clerked in a store; the fabulous Doc Marlowe, who made and sold Sioux Liniment and wore a ten-gallon hat with kitchen matches stuck in the band; the blonde and mysterious Mrs Lane, of the strong perfume and the elegant dresses; Mr Richardson, a guard at the penitentiary, who kept a gun in his room; and a silent, thin, smiling man who never revealed his business and left with his rent two weeks in arrears. I remember Dora and Sarah Koontz, daughters of a labourer, who lived for many years in the other half of the two-family house, and the visitors who dropped in from time to time: Mr Pepper and his daughter Dolly, who came to play cards on summer evenings; Mrs Straub, who babbled of her children – her Clement and her Minna; Joe Chickalilli, a Mexican rope thrower; and Professor Fields, a Stoughton bottle if there ever was one, who played the banjo and helped Doc Marlow sell the liniment that Mrs Albright and Belle put up in bottles; and the Gammadingers and their brood, who lived on a farm in the Hocking Valley. Most of them were beholden to Mrs Albright for some service or other in time of trouble, and they all adored her.

When Margery Albright took to her bed for the last time – the bed in the front room downstairs, where she could hear people talking and life stirring in the street outside her window – she gave strict orders that she was not to be 'called back.' She had seen too much of that, at a hundred bedsides, and she wanted to die quietly, without a lot of unseemly fuss over the natural ending of a span of nearly ninety complete and crowded years. There was no call, she told her daughter, to summon anybody. There was nothing anybody could do. A doctor would just pester her, and she couldn't abide one now. Her greatest comfort lay in the knowledge that her plot in Green Lawn Cemetery had been paid for, a dollar at a time, through the years, and that there was money enough for a stone marker, tucked away in a place her daughter knew about. Mrs Albright made Belle repeat to her the location of this secret and precious cache. Then she gave a few more final instructions and turned over in bed, pulling her bad leg into a comfortable position. 'Hush up!' she snapped when her daughter began to cry. 'You give a body the fidgets.'

Women who were marked for death, Aunt Margery had often told me, always manifested, sooner or later, an ominous desire to do something beyond the range of their failing strength. These ladies in the very act of dying fancied, like Verdi's Violetta, that life was returning in full and joyous tide. They wanted to sit up in bed and comb their hair, or alter a dress, or bathe the cat, or change the labels on the jam jars. It was an invariable sign that the end was not far off. Old Mrs Dozier, who had insisted on going to the piano to play

'Abide with Me,' collapsed with a discordant jangle on the keys and was dead
when they carried her back to the bed. Mrs Albright's final urge, with which
her ebbing sense no doubt sternly dealt, might easily have been to potter about
in her garden, since it was coming summer and the flowers needed constant
attention. It was a narrow plot, occasionally enlivened with soil from the
country, that began with an elephant ear near the rickety wooden fence in front
and extended to the trellis of moonflowers against the wall of Jim West's stable.
It was further shaded by her own house and the Fenstermakers', and it caught
only stingy glimpses of the sun, but, to the wonder of the jubrous, it sustained
for forty summers Canterbury bells and bluebells, bleeding hearts and fuch-
sias, asters and roses. There were tall stalks of asparagus, raised for ornament,
and castor-oil plants six feet high (I doubt that she made the castor oil that she
disguised in coffee for timid palates and drank neat from the bottle herself,
but I have no doubt she could have). 'This garden,' said Dr Sparks, pastor of
the old Third Street Methodist Church, one day, 'is a testament of faith.' 'It
takes faith, and it takes work, and it takes a lot of good, rich manure,' said Mrs
Albright, far and away the most distinguished manurist of her time.

Since there had to be services of some kind, in accordance with a custom that
irked her, Mrs Albright would have preferred a country parson, who rode a
horse in any weather and could lend a hand at homely chores, if need be. She
liked what she called a man of groin, who could carry his proper share of the
daily burden and knew how to tell a sow from a sawbuck. City ministers, in her
estimation, were delicate fellows, given to tampering with the will of God, and
with the mysteries of life after death, which the Almighty would have cleared
up for people Himself if He had had a mind to. It was her fancy that urban
reverends were inclined to insanity, because of their habit of studying.
'Studying,' in Mrs Albright's language, meant that form of meditation in
which the eyes are lifted up. The worst cases let their gaze slowly follow, about
a room, the juncture of ceiling and walls, and once a pastor developed this symptom, he was in imminent danger of going off his worshipful rocker. Such
parsons, whether they studied or not, made Mrs Albright uneasy, except for
the Reverend Stacy Matheny, a first cousin of my mother's. He had been born
on a farm in Fairfield County, and he knew how to hitch a horse, split a rail,
and tell a jaybird from a bootjack. Mrs Albright wanted him to read her funeral
service because he was a man of few words, and he would get it over with and
not whinker all afternoon, keeping people away from their jobs. Aunt Margery
never discussed religion with me or with anyone else. She seemed to take it for
granted that the Lord would find a fitting place in Heaven for women who devoted their lives to good works, and she let it go at that. Tales of ghosts and
haunted houses annoyed her. Earthbound spirits, in her pragmatic view, had
no business puttering about among the living. A certain house in Kokomo, she
told me once when I was ten, was supposed to be haunted by a woman, but her
ghost was laid by a peremptory command from the great nurse. 'I never seen
her myself,' she told me, 'but I went into the room they said she hanted, and I
says, "Rest, Mrs Detweiler," said I.' As I remember the tale after more than

fifty years, the ghost of Mrs Detweiler rested. Women, in any shape or form, were accustomed to obey Margery Albright's commands.

The Reverend Stacy Matheny compared the late Margery Albright to the virtuous woman of Proverbs, who rose while it was yet night, worked willingly with her hands, and ate not the bread of idleness. The original lady of the tribute was, of course, far richer in worldly goods than Mrs Albright, whose clothing was not silk and purple, but in trait and toil and temper they were rare and similar examples of that noble breed of women the French call *brave et travailleuse*. I wished that some closer student of Aunt Margery could have taken over those final rites, whose formality would have annoyed the great lady as much as the lugubrious faces of her friends and neighbours. Somebody should have told how she snatched up a pair of scissors one day and cut a hornet in two when it lighted on the head of a sleeping baby; and how she took an axe and chopped off the head of a savage outlaw cat that killed chickens, attacked children, and, blackest sin of all, disturbed the sleep of a woman patient; and about the time she whipped off her calico blouse, put it over the eyes of a frightened horse, and led him out of a burning barn while the men-folks, at a safe distance, laughed at her corset cover and cheered her courage. But it would have taken all afternoon to do even faint justice to the saga of Mrs Albright, born Margery Dangler, nearly a hundred and thirty years ago, in Long Branch, in New Jersey, who departed this earthly scene June 6, 1918, in the confident hope – as old epitaphs used to say – of the blessed resurrection and the life eternal. It seemed to me, standing there in the dim parlour of the old frame house, that something as important as rain had gone out of the land.

The services came to a close with the singing of 'No Night There' by two tearful women, who sang it as only middle-aged Methodist females in Ohio can sing a hymn – upper register all the way, nasal, tremulous, and loud. Mrs Albright, I reflected, would enjoy the absence of night in Paradise only because everlasting light would give her more time to look after people and to get things done. I still like to believe, after all these years, that chalcedony is subject to cleaning, and that a foolish angel falls now and then and breaks a wing, for glory, as mere reward of labours ended, would make Margery Albright uncomfortable and sad. I trust that Providence has kept this simple truth in mind.

Lavender with a Difference

BELINDA WOOLF TELEPHONED my mother at the Southern Hotel in Columbus one morning ten years ago, and apologized, in a faintly familiar voice, for never having run in to call on her. Something always seemed to turn up, she declared, to keep her from dropping by for a visit, and she was sorry. 'I've thought of you, Mrs Thurber,' said Belinda. 'I've thought of you every day since I worked for you on Champion Avenue. It's been a long time, hasn't it?' It certainly had. Belinda Woolf was only twenty-three years old when she came to work for us as cook in the spring of 1899, and she was seventy-three when she finally got around to calling her former employer. Half a century had gone by since my mother had heard her voice. Belinda had thought of telephoning for more than eighteen thousand days but, as she indicated, more than eighteen thousand things had turned up to prevent her.

About a year after Belinda's appearance out of the past, I went to Columbus, and my mother and I drove out to see her. She was then the wife of Joe Barlow, master carpenter of the Neil House, where Charles Dickens used to stay, during his western trips a hundred years ago. In fifty years Belinda had not wandered very far. She was living only two blocks from our old house on South Champion Avenue. The weather was warm, and we sat on the verandah and talked about a night in 1899 that we all remembered. It was past midnight, according to an old clock in the attic of my memory, when Belinda suddenly flung open a window of her bedroom and fired two shots from a .32-calibre revolver at the shadowy figure of a man skulking about in our back yard. Belinda's shooting frightened off the prowler and aroused the family. I was five years old, going on six, at the time, and I had thought that only soldiers and policemen were allowed to have guns. From then on I stood in awe, but not in fear, of the lady who kept a revolver under her pillow. 'It was a lonesome place, wasn't it?' said Belinda, with a sigh. 'Way out there at the end of nowhere.' We sat for a while without talking, thinking about the lonesome place at the end of nowhere.

No. 921 South Champion Avenue is just another house now, in a long row of houses, but when we lived there in 1899 and 1900, it was the last house on the street. Just south of us the avenue dwindled to a wood road that led into a thick grove of oak and walnut trees, long since destroyed by the southward march of asphalt. Our nearest neighbour on the north was fifty yards away, and across from us was a country meadow that ticked with crickets in the summertime and turned yellow with goldenrod in the fall. Living on the edge of town, we rarely heard footsteps at night, or carriage wheels, but the darkness, in every season, was deepened by the lonely sound of locomotive whistles. I no longer wonder, as I did when I was six, that Aunt Mary Van York, arriving at dusk for her first visit to us, looked about her disconsolately, and said to my mother, 'Why in the world do you want to live in this godforsaken place, Mary?'

Almost all my memories of the Champion Avenue house have as their focal point the lively figure of my mother. I remember her tugging and hauling at a burning mattress and finally managing to shove it out a bedroom window onto the roof of the front porch, where it smouldered until my father came home from work and doused it with water. When he asked his wife how the mattress happened to catch fire, she told him the peculiar truth (all truths in that house were peculiar) – that his youngest son, Robert, had set it on fire with a buggy whip. It seemed he had lighted the lash of the whip in the gas grate of the nursery and applied it to the mattress. I also have a vivid memory of the night my mother was alone in the house with her three small sons and set the oil-splashed bowl of a kerosene lamp on fire, trying to light the wick, and herded all of us out of the house, announcing that it was going to explode. We children waited across the street in high anticipation, but the spilled oil burned itself out and, to our bitter disappointment, the house did not go up like a skyrocket to scatter coloured balloons among the stars. My mother claimed that my brother William, who was seven at the time, kept crying, 'Try it again, Mama, try it again,' but she was a famous hand at ornamenting a tale, and there is no way of telling whether he did or not.

My brightest remembrance of the old house goes back to the confused and noisy second and last visit of Aunt Mary, who had cut her first visit short because she hated our two dogs – Judge, an irritable old pug, and Sampson, a restless water spaniel – and they hated her. She had snarled at them and they had growled at her all during her stay with us, and not even my mother remembered how she persuaded the old lady to come back for a weekend, but she did, and, what is more, she cajoled Aunt Mary into feeding 'those dreadful brutes' the evening she arrived.

In preparation for this seemingly simple act of household routine, my mother had spent the afternoon gathering up all the dogs of the neighbourhood, in advance of Aunt Mary's appearance, and putting them in the cellar. I had been allowed to go with her on her wonderful forays, and I thought that we were going to keep all the sixteen dogs we rounded up. Such an adventure does not have to have logical point or purpose in the mind of a six-year-old, and I accepted as a remarkable but natural phenomenon my mother's sudden assumption of the stature of Santa Claus.

She did not always let my father in on her elaborate pranks, but he came home that evening to a house heavy with tension and suspense, and she whispered to him the peculiar truth that there were a dozen and a half dogs in the cellar, counting our Judge and Sampson. 'What are you up to now, Mame?' he asked her, and she said she just wanted to see Aunt Mary's face when the dogs swarmed up into the kitchen. She could not recall where she had picked up all of the dogs, but I remembered, and still do, that we had imprisoned the

Johnsons' Irish terrier, the Eiseles' shepherd, and the Mitchells' fox terrier, among others. 'Well, let's get it over with, then,' my father said nervously. 'I want to eat dinner in peace, if that is possible.'

The big moment finally arrived. My mother, full of smiles and insincerity, told Aunt Mary that it would relieve her of a tedious chore – and heaven knows, she added, there were a thousand steps to take in that big house – if the old lady would be good enough to set down a plate of dog food in the kitchen at the head of the cellar stairs and call Judge and Sampson to their supper. Aunt Mary growled and grumbled, and consigned all dogs to the fires of hell, but she grudgingly took the plate, and carried it to the kitchen, with the Thurber family on her heels. 'Heavenly days!' cried Aunt Mary. 'Do you make a ceremony out of feeding these brutes?' She put the plate down and reached for the handle of the door.

None of us has ever been able to understand why bedlam hadn't broken loose in the cellar long before this, but it hadn't. The dogs were probably so frightened by their unique predicament that their belligerence had momentarily left them. But when the door opened and they could see the light of freedom and smell the lure of food, they gave tongue like a pack of hunting hounds. Aunt Mary got the door halfway open and the bodies of three of the largest dogs pushed it the rest of the way. There was a snarling, barking, yelping swirl of yellow and white, black and tan, grey and brindle, as the dogs tumbled into the kitchen, skidded on the linoleum, sent the food flying from the plate, and backed Aunt Mary into a corner. 'Great God Almighty!' she screamed. 'It's a dog factory!' She was only five feet tall, but her counterattack was swift and terrible. Grabbing a broom, she opened the back door and the kitchen windows, and began to beat and flail at the army of canines, engaged now in half a dozen separate battles over the scattered food. Dogs flew out the back door and leaped through the windows, but some of them ran upstairs, and three or four others hid under sofas and chairs in the parlour. The indignant snarling and cursing of Judge and Sampson rose above even the laughter of my mother and the delighted squeals of her children. Aunt Mary whammed her way from room to room, driving dogs ahead of her. When the last one had departed and the upset house had been put back in order, my father said to his wife, 'Well, Mame, I hope you're satisfied.' She was.

Aunt Mary, toward the end of her long life, got the curious notion that it was my father and his sons, and not my mother, who had been responsible for the noisy flux of 'all those brutes.' Years later, when we visited the old lady on one of her birthdays, she went over the story again, as she always did, touching it up with distortions and magnifications of her own. Then she looked at the male Thurbers in slow, rueful turn, sighed deeply, gazed sympathetically at my mother, and said, in her hollowest tone, 'Poor Mary!'

Only a few months after poor Mary borrowed the neighbours' dogs, she 'bought' the Simonses' house. It was a cold, blocky house, not far from ours, and its owner had been trying to sell it for a long time. The thing had become a standing joke among the Frioleras, a club of young married couples to which the Simonses and my father and mother belonged. It was generally believed that Harry and Laura would never get the big, damp place off their hands. Then, late one dark afternoon, a strange and avid purchaser showed up. It was my mother, wearing dark glasses, her hair and eyebrows whitened with flour, her cheeks lightly shadowed with charcoal to make them look hollow, and her upper front teeth covered with the serrated edge of a soda cracker. On one side of her, as she pressed the doorbell of the Simonses' house, stood a giggling cousin of hers, named Belle Cook, and I was on her other side; we were there to prevent a prolonged scrutiny of the central figure of our trio. Belle was to pose as my mother's daughter, and I was to be Belle's son. Simons had never met Miss Cook, and my mother was confident that he wouldn't recognize me. His wife, Laura, would have penetrated her friend's disguise at once, or, failing that, she would surely have phoned the police, for the weird visitor seemed, because of her sharp, projecting teeth, both demented and about to spring, but my mother had found out that Laura would not be home. When she made herself up, an hour before, I had watched her transformation from mother to witch with a mixture of wonder and worry that lingered in my memory for years.

Harry Simons, opening his front door on that dark evening in the age of innocence, when trust flowered as readily as suspicion does today, was completely taken in by the sudden apparition of an eccentric elderly woman who babbled of her recently inherited fortune and said she had passed his house the day before and fallen in love with it. Simons was a big, jovial, sanguine man, expert at business deals in a lighted office, but a setup for my mother's devilry at dusk. When she praised every room she stumbled into and every object she bumped against – she wouldn't take off her dark glasses in the lamplit gloom – a wild hope must have glazed his eye, disarming his perception. He admitted later, when the cat was out of the bag, that Belle's idiotic laughter, and mine, at everything that was said had disturbed him, especially when it was provoked by my mother's tearful account of the sad death of her mythical husband, a millionaire oil man. But idiocy in a family is one thing, and money is another. Mrs Prentice, or Douglas, or whatever she called herself, was rolling in money that day. She upped Simons' asking price for the house by several thousand dollars, on the ground that she wouldn't think of paying as little as ten thousand for such a lovely place. When she found out that the furniture was for sale, she upped the price on that, too, promising to send her cheque through her lawyers the next day. By this time, she was overacting with fine abandon, but the overwhelmed Simons was too far gone in her land of fantasy for reality to operate. On her way out of the house, she picked up small portable things – a vase, a travelling clock, a few books – remarking that, after all, they now belonged to her. Still Simons' wits did not rally, and all of a sudden the three of us were out in the street again – my mother who had been my grandmother, her cousin who had been my mother, and me. I feel that this twisted hour marked the occupation of my mind by a sense of confusion that has never left it.

My father was home from work when we got back, and he gasped at the sight of his wife, even though she had thrown away her cracker teeth. When these latest goings-on were explained to him, he was all for taking his friend's possessions over to his unsold house and returning them, with nervous apologies. But my mother had another idea. That night she gift-wrapped, separately, the vase, the clock, and the books, and they were delivered to Simons' door the next morning, before he set out for his office, each 'present' containing a card that read, 'To Harry Simons from Mame Thurber with love.' It was not my mother's most subdued performance, but it was certainly one of her outstanding triumphs. The Frioleras laughed about it for years. There had been fifty of them when the club was founded in 1882. At one of their parties fifty years ago – they played pedro and euchre in the winter and went on picnics and bicycle trips in the summer – my father asked his wife, apropos of what prank I do not know, 'How long do you expect to keep up this kind of thing, Mame?' She thought a moment and replied, 'Why, until I'm eighty, I suppose.'

Mary Agnes Thurber, eldest of the six children of William and Katherine Fisher, was eighty years old in January, 1946, and I went to Columbus for a birthday party that brought together scores of her relatives. The day after the event, a columnist in one of the Columbus papers recklessly described her as 'a bit of lavender and old lace.' She was indignant. 'Why, he doesn't even know about the time I threw those eggs!' she exclaimed. I didn't know about it, either, but I found out. At a meeting, a few months before, of one of the several women's clubs she belonged to, she had gone to the kitchen of her hostess' house, carefully removed a dozen eggs from a cardboard container, and returned to the living room to reactivate a party that she felt was growing dull. Balancing the box on the palm of her hand, like a halfback about to let go a forward pass, she cried, 'I've always wanted to throw a dozen eggs, and now I'm going to do it!' The ladies gathered in the room squealed and scattered as the carton sailed into the air. Then it drifted harmlessly to the floor. Lavender and old lace, in their conventional and symbolic sense, were not for Mary Thurber. It would be hard for me to say what was. She never wore black. 'Black is for old ladies,' she told me scornfully.

In 1884, when Mamie Fisher got out of high school, she wanted to go on the stage, but her unladylike and godless urge was discouraged by her family. Aunt Melissa warned her that young actresses were in peril not only of hellfire but of lewd Shakespearean actors, skilled in the arts of seduction, and she pointed out that there was too much talk about talent in the world, and not enough about virtue. She predicted that God's wrath would be visited, in His own time, upon all theatres, beginning, like as not, with those in Paris, France. Mamie Fisher listened with what appeared to be rapt and contrite attention. Actually, she was studying Aunt Melissa's voice, so that she could learn to imitate it.

Deprived of a larger audience, the frustrated comedienne performed for whoever would listen, and once distressed a couple of stately guests in her father's home by descending the front stairs in her dressing gown, her hair tumbling and her eyes staring, to announce that she had escaped from the attic, where she was kept because of her ardent and hapless love for Mr Briscoe, the postman. An entry in her diary of that period, dated Monday, May 14, 1888, would have puzzled the shocked visitors: 'Went over to Flora's to talk over yesterday's visit. I tell you that Ira D. is cute, but I do not like him very well – he is a perfect gentleman, only he will insist on kissing me every time and I will not allow it. I can truthfully say I never kissed a fellow in all my life but once, and that was Charlie Thurber at the depot a few years ago.'

Those of her relatives who drew no sharp line between life and art, the gifted and the mad, and consoled themselves with the hope that marriage would settle her down, could not have been more mistaken. Even the birth of her third son, in 1896, had little effect on her merry inventions, and her aunts must have been relieved when we left Champion Avenue and moved to Washington, D.C., in 1901. They probably thought of Washington, in those years, as a city of inviolable decorum, but it was there that we met a young Cleveland newspaperman named George Marvin, whose gaiety was to enrich our lives. He was a superior wag, with a round, mobile face, a trick of protruding his large eyeballs that entranced the Thurber boys, and a gift of confusion that matched my mother's. Uncivil clerks and supercilious shoppe proprietors in the nation's capital came to regret their refusal to sell Marvin and my mother one dish of ice cream with two spoons, or a single glove for the left hand, or one shoe. The mild, soft-spoken Jekylls from the Middle West would be transformed into Mr and Mrs Hyde, to the consternation of the management. 'Senator Beveridge will hear about this!' Marvin would shout, and they would stalk out of the shoppe, in high and magnificent dudgeon. But it was when we were all back in Columbus two years later that these comics reached their heights. Their finest hour arrived one day at Memorial Hall, during a lecture given by a woman mental healer whose ability and sincerity my mother held in low esteem. She has always been a serious and devoted student of psychotherapy, even when it was known and practised under foolish and flowery names, and she learned long ago to detect tommyrot. Arriving after the lecture had begun, our cutups found an empty wheelchair in the lobby, and my mother, bundled up in it, was rolled down the aisle by her confederate. The lady on the platform had reached a peroration of whoosh, during which she chanted that if you had done it before, you could do it again, whatever it was, and other candy-coated inspiration to that effect. At the peak of this marshmallow mentation, my mother leaped from the chair, crying that she had walked before and could do it again. Some ten or twenty persons of the two hundred present must have recognized her, but the others were caught between cheers and consternation. The lecturer shouted, 'Hallelujah, sister!' and at this point Marvin increased the confusion by bulging out his eyes, dropping his jaw, and mumbling that what he had done before he was now doing again; namely, losing his grip on reality. The crisis ended when a querulous man shouted, 'Hey, that's my wheelchair!' and the culprits made good their escape.

The career of almost any actress is marked by open dates and, in the end, a long period of retirement. Who heard of the late Julia Marlowe in her last twenty years? But my mother's crowded calendar shows no season of repose, and the biographer is overwhelmed by instances and can only select a few more. There was the time she went back to Washington, in her sixties, wearing a red rose so the woman she was going to meet could identify her; they hadn't seen each other for thirty years. The train being early, or her hostess late, she pinned the rose on a sleeping dowager, twenty years her senior, who was sitting on a bench in the railway terminal, and watched at a distance the dismay of her friend when she finally arrived and the irritability of the sleeper awakened by a cry of 'Why, Mame Thurber, how are you? You're looking just fine.' And there was the occasion, not long ago, when she deflated a pompous gentleman, overproud of his forebears, who made the mistake of asking her how far back she had traced her own ancestry. 'Until I came to a couple of horse thieves,' she said with a troubled sigh. 'Do you mean a father and son?' the shocked man asked. 'Or was it a couple of brothers?' My mother sighed again. 'It was much worse than that,' she said. 'A man and his wife. You see, it runs in both sides of the family.' A hundred other hours and moments I leave to the record of another year.

With all this to take up her time, Mrs Charles Thurber nevertheless managed to run her home like any other good housewife, hovering over the cook when we had one, following the cleaning woman around with pail and cloth of her own, and rearing three sons who were far from being mother's helpers. She was famous for her pastry and, after long study and practice, learned to make the best chocolate creams in the world. Two or three professional candy men tried to catch her secret, watching her at work like a child watching a magician, and with just about as little profit. She made her last twenty pounds of chocolates when she was eighty, and then turned to writing a cookbook of her own recipes.

I found, in going over her letters, that time hasn't dulled their sparkle. In one, dated December 26, 1949, she told, in fine full detail, the story of her 1933 search for Miss Bagley, which has become a family saga. Miss Annette Bagley, known to her intimates as Anna, wandered from her home in England more than sixty years ago to become a home-to-home sewing woman in Columbus. She and my mother became great friends, and then, one morning in the spring of 1895, Miss Bagley, at the age of thirty-four, took a train to Boston, where she planned to open a dressmaking shop. For several years my mother's fond letters were promptly answered, but about the turn of the century, two of them were returned by the Boston post office. Miss Bagley had dropped out of sight, leaving no forwarding address, and it wasn't until 1913 that she was heard from again. The floods of that year had inundated Columbus, and she sent a worried telegram from Boston. My mother replied, by wire, that all her friends were safe, and Miss Bagley apparently received this telegram at the Western Union office in which she had dispatched her own, but a letter my mother instantly sent to the old address was returned, like the others. Twenty silent years went by.

In 1933, Mary Thurber took up the quest again, writing to the postmasters of Boston and surrounding towns, and inventing a story about the settlement of an estate. 'Money,' she wrote me in the 1949 letter, 'always increases people's interest.' It greatly increased the interest of an Anna Bagley in Malden, Massachusetts, who turned out to be the wrong one, and with whom my mother exchanged a brief and cloudy correspondence. Then she came East to take up the search in person. She was sixty-seven and she knew that Miss Bagley, if she was alive, was seventy-two. In Boston my mother set out on the old, dim trail like a trained researcher, looking up outdated phone books and directories at the Chamber of Commerce. The most recent record of Annette Bagley she could find placed her friend in Malden in 1925, so she went to Malden. Miss Bagley was not at the address listed, and the woman who lived there had never heard of her. My mother did what any good reporter would have done: she looked up old residents of the neighbourhood and called on the older druggists and grocers. She learned that Annette Bagley had left that Malden house about seven years before. Someone seemed to remember that the old lady had moved to Everett Street. This street turned out to be only a block long, and my mother rang all its doorbells without success. Nobody knew anything about Miss Bagley. Then a druggist suggested that her quarry might have moved not to Everett Street but to the town of Everett, which is only a few miles from Malden. My mother transferred her pattern of search to Everett, and it was in that Boston suburb that the trail became warm. She found Annette Bagley listed in a three-year-old directory, but the elusive dressmaker was no longer at the address given. Neighbours, however, thought she had not gone far away, so her tracer continued questioning druggists and grocers and elderly people she stopped on the street. At twilight of the second day of her search, she came upon a small dressmaking shop on a side street. 'I looked through the window,' my mother wrote, 'and there she was, sitting and sewing with her back to me.' Thirty-eight years had made a great difference in the two friends, and it wasn't until my mother asked the old lady if she had ever lived in Columbus, Ohio, that Annette Bagley recognized her.

The reason for her years of hiding was simple enough. She did not want her Columbus friends to know that her dream of a big and flourishing dressmaking establishment of her own had failed to come true. 'I took her to dinner in Boston,' my mother wrote, 'and then to a movie. It was hard for her to believe that my oldest son, William, was forty, for when she had seen him last he was only two. I'm not sure about the movie, but I think it was "It Happened One Night," or "One Sunday Afternoon," or something like that.' It isn't often that my memory outdoes my mother's, but I have always remembered the name of that movie since she first told me the story of her celebrated search for Annette Bagley twenty-four years ago. It was called 'I Loved You Wednesday.'

In New York, which my mother visited often, she liked to escape from her sons and see the sights of the city on her own. One morning some twenty-five years ago, she reached the second floor of the famous Wendel house on Fifth

Avenue, but her tour of inspection was interrupted. 'I was just going by and I thought I would drop in,' she told me. On that visit she made a tour of Greenwich Village by herself, but asked me to take her to what she called 'the Tony's' and 'the "21",' whose fame she had somehow heard about. At 'the Tony's' she was fortunate enough to meet one of her idols, the late Heywood Broun, and she enchanted him by casting an offhand horoscope for him that turned out to be a recognizable portrait, done in the bold colours of both virtue and shortcoming. She had always had a lot of fun monkeying around with the inexact sciences (she corresponded with Evangeline Adams, and once had Professor Coué out to dinner at our house in Columbus) and I am sure that she must have dipped into Dianetics. She embarrassed my father one time, in an impish numerology phase, by making him return a set of ominously numbered automobile licence plates and exchange it for a safer one. In 1940, when she entered Columbia Presbyterian Medical Centre for a major operation that she took in her stride, she demanded to know the date of birth of her distinguished surgeon before she would let him operate. He solemnly gave it to her, and was pleased to learn that he had been engaged for thirty years in a profession for which his signs clearly fitted him. Later, he was astonished by her familiarity with medicine and surgery, and told her one day that she had the sound implementation of a nurse. 'Of course,' my mother said, 'I'm Capricorn with the moon in Sagittarius.'

The day she was discharged from the hospital, she decided to visit the World's Fair, and she did, in spite of heat and humidity. In a bus on the way back, she found that she had exceeded her strength, and she asked the bus driver to take her pulse. He took it with one hand, continuing to drive with the other, and reported that it was a little high but nothing to worry about. I am sure she got the bus driver's date of birth. She remembered the birthdays of literally hundreds of men and women. She once sent me a clipping of an Earl Wilson column in which he had given Dorothy Parker's birthday as August 23. 'Dorothy Parker's birthday is August 22nd,' my mother wrote. 'August 23rd is Helen Gude's birthday.' A few years ago I phoned her in Columbus and asked if she remembered her surgeon's birthday. 'Why, certainly,' she said. 'He was born on the 30th of March. My Columbus surgeon is also Aries – April 1st.'

When my mother came to New York in 1947, I found that she had made a date for tea at the Algonquin with an old friend of my father's, Charles Dewey Hilles. She said that she herself hadn't seen him for 'a long time.' Mr Hilles, a celebrated Ohio Republican, died eight years ago, and his long obituaries told of his having been, among many other things, an Assistant Secretary of the Treasury under Taft, Chairman of the Republican National Committee from 1912 to 1916, and a member of dozens of boards of directors. I had the good luck to be asked to the Ohio tea party, along with the late John McNulty, for many years a reporter on Columbus newspapers. We had a jolly time, and various ancient facts and forgotten dates were brought up. It came out that my mother was a year older than Mr Hilles. 'When was it,' I finally asked, 'that you two last met?' My mother thought about this and said, 'Well, Mr Hilles was secretary to the superintendent of the Boys' Industrial School at Lancaster, Ohio. Let me see – yes, it must have been in 1888.' My mother was twenty-two in 1888, and Mr Hilles, of course, was only twenty-one. Now, no elderly man of high and varied achievement likes to be reminded of his juvenile beginnings, and it was obvious to us all that my mother's grasp of her friend's later career was tenuous. McNulty saved the situation. 'Eighteen-eighty-eight,' he said, 'was the year the owls were so bad.' What Mr Hilles must have approached as something of an ordeal turned out to be fun for him. He had said he would have to take a 3.30 train, but he stayed until 5.30. Heywood Broun, on the night my mother read his horoscope offhand, had not only missed one train for Boston, but two.

Mary Thurber died on December 20, 1955, within three weeks of her ninetieth birthday, the oldest and the last of her generation of Fishers. At the funeral the last survivor of the old Friolera Club, founded nearly seventy-five years before, had something memorable to say to me. 'You know,' she said, 'even if Mame had been the first to go, she would have outlived us all.' There is no epitaph she would have liked better than that.

Newspaperman—Head and Shoulders

WHEN I STARTED to work as a reporter on the Columbus *Dispatch* ('Ohio's Greatest Home Daily'), in the summer of 1920, its city editor, Norman Kuehner, was on vacation, and I didn't get my first look at him until one hot Monday morning about ten days later. He lumbered into the city room, a big guy in his middle twenties, wearing a suit too dark for the season, and the disconsolate frown of a hunter who has seen nothing but warblers all day. He had big feet, and his long legs supported a heavy torso that widened into muscular shoulders. He must have worn a size 16 collar, and his large face was loosely built around its most striking feature – a pair of brown eyes, whose expression, I soon found out, could change as swiftly as island weather. They would take on a bland gaze of pure innocence, like a choirboy's, and then, a moment later, burn with scorn or turn as cold as a top sergeant's. He had the aggressive air of a man who would snap 'Buy a watch!' if you asked him what time it was. As he stood at his desk, staring about the room, I noticed that he had unusually restless hands. One day, a few years later, the right one, doubled into a hard fist, probably saved his life when a rewrite man, cracking under the strain of the city editor's baiting – Kuehner was a practised and tireless baiter – attacked him with a sharp spindle, set in a heavy metal base. Kuehner knocked him cold with a straight right to the jaw, putting all his weight behind it.

When he spotted me, that first day, sitting at a desk in a corner, his eyes darkened, and he sauntered slowly over to me with the gait of a traffic cop approaching an incompetent and unattractive woman driver. He stood behind my chair for several moments, not saying anything. I said, 'Good morning,' and he still didn't say anything. I had been rewriting some brief items from the *Lantern*, the daily paper got out by students of journalism at Ohio State University, and when he saw what they were, he swept them on to the floor with one swipe of his big hand, growled 'This isn't a college paper,' and strolled away, with the grace of a wagon. He let me sit at my desk the rest of the day doing nothing.

Norman Kuehner (he pronounced it 'Keener'), son and grandson of German cigar makers, never wanted any part of his family's tedious and confining trade. From the time he was able to spell out robbery and murder headlines, he dreamed of being a newspaperman. As a boy in short pants, he carried a *Dispatch* route after school, and he was scarcely out of the eighth grade, and not yet fifteen, when, in 1909, he got a year-round job as office boy on his favourite newspaper. The gawky youth attacked his work breathlessly, fetching and carrying at a dogtrot, and always wearing a serious scowl, even when he was allowed to post the World Series scores, innings by innings, on an outer wall of the building, with a crowd looking on. One of the editors began calling the solemn youngster Gus, because of his supposed resemblance, in figure and temperament, to Happy Hooligan's morose brother, Gloomy Gus. He took this and all other kidding in his stubborn stride, developing a sardonic tone, a jaunty if callow cynicism, and a sarcastic vocabulary of his own. He soon became adept at the quick insult and the cold rejoinder. A tough front, it seemed to him, befitted a newspaperman, whose opening question to any stranger should be a chill 'What's your racket?' (or whatever the idiom then was), instead of a friendly 'What can I do for you?' A kind of personal carapace began to form because of this studied attitude, concealing a natural warmth and a wide area of sentiment from everybody but his family (he was especially adored by his two sisters) and his few cronies. He disliked being caught by anybody else with his armour down. 'If Gus had been a dog,' one of his old friends said recently, 'he would have bitten off his tail to keep it from wagging.'

The office boy came to work before eight o'clock most mornings, so that he could practise on one of the typewriters, making up news items of his own or rewriting actual ones of the day before, brooding and frowning over the keyboard, and pounding out his hard, blunt sentences slowly. They were figuratively stained with blood, for he was fascinated then, and for ever after, by stories of crime, fire, accident, and violent death. Nothing in nickel novels or in anything else he ever read excited him half so much as the daily routine of a city detective. He took to hanging around the 'cop house' on Saturday nights, picking up pointers from the *Dispatch* man who covered the police station, and now and then riding with the cops in the patrol wagon or a squad car to the scene of trouble, which he hoped would involve shooting. He learned to hit the ground fast, or to take cover behind a tree, when other boys his age were still in high school. Everybody on the *Dispatch* knew about his dream of becoming the paper's police reporter and teased him relentlessly. Then, in true Alger-boy fashion, he made it, before he was twenty years old. The police reporter quit, and Kuehner was told he could take a crack at the job. He kept at it, with lusty success and undiminished ardour, until he was made city editor, a few years later. He got along with the cops, talked their language, and stood up under the heavy banter common to city policemen from San Diego to Bangor. They liked the kid, and found out that he could lead with his left and cross with a fast right, and that he never lagged behind on even the roughest assignment. All policemen like to get their names in the paper, in full and correctly spelled, and Kuehner obliged them: 'The arrest was made by Detective Sergeant Jolas K. Menschkey and Patrolman Wilson G. Shellenbarger.' He was right behind the cops when they smashed down a door, or chased a man into a dark areaway. The young police reporter was usually out of breath, often sleepless, but never bored. He remembered these years fondly all the rest of his life.

Norman Kuehner came up to the city desk the hard way, bringing a curt

philosophy with him. 'You get to be a newspaperman by being a newspaperman,' he told all reporters who went to work for him, with a special emphasis
for college men. 'You can't learn how by studying journalism in college under
a broken-down ex-editorial writer for the Hohokus *Bugle*.' (J. S. Meyers, then
head of the Ohio State Department of Journalism, was, as it happened, formerly a managing editor of the Pittsburgh *Post* and editor of the Pittsburgh
Sun.) Kuehner was by this time the owner of a rare collection of edged in-
flections, falsettos, and mirthless laughs. He stood up straight to talk to reporters and towered over most of them. They all got, in their turn, the full
Kuehner treatment, beginning with a first day of idleness, during which they
were ignored as completely as if they weren't there. Then came the practically
impossible assignments. If a new man handled one or two of these successfully, or came back with honourable scars showing that he had tried, the city
editor softened a little, like an iceberg in April weather. One cub reporter, sent
to get a statement from a hospital patient whose room was closely guarded,
borrowed an interne's white jacket, got hold of a stethoscope, and managed to
reach the patient's bedside before he was unmasked and ejected from the
hospital by way of the laundry chute. Kuehner thought he had made a good
try, and grunted something to that effect. His praise was laconic and slow in
coming, but it was genuine. He could forget, finally and grudgingly, the misses
you made, but he always remembered your triumphs. If he growled 'O.K.,' it
meant that you were doing pretty well. The final accolade came when he
shambled over to your desk, with the look of a man in a dentist's chair, and
said in a low voice, 'Nice goin',' turning away quickly before you could thank
him. He disliked the whole handbook of amenities, and every sign and symbol
of intimacy. He rarely called anybody by his first name, and made up nick-
names of his own for his staff. One man was Farmer, another Parson, and still
another, who had been a lieutenant in the first war, Loot. He had a vast range
of nasty intonations when he yelled at them, and a few friendly and affable
ones. Some of the college men that he rode hard gave up and walked out,
unable to tolerate the Teutonic weight that he constantly gave to 'choinalism'
and 'colletch,' and similar words. He could say 'Phi Beta Kappa' so that it
sounded like a Girl Scout's merit badge. Liking Kuehner wasn't easy, and a
lot of people never managed it, but if you did, the feeling stuck – I don't know
exactly why.

I made the grade with Norman Kuehner (he was Gus only to old-timers)
when I went out one day and brought back a photograph of a boy who had
been drowned. Such photographs had great news value to the city editor. He
had been maliciously hopeful that I wouldn't be able to get a picture. 'This
kid's old man threw our police reporter out of the house on his can,' he had
told me. 'Go out and give him the old college try. They must have told you
how to get around tough characters by talking pretty.' I brought back a group
photograph in which the ill-fated youngster appeared. 'Yeah,' Kuehner said
disconsolately, swallowing the ironic gags he had been thinking up for me,
'it'll blow up O.K.' He stared out of a window. 'What are you – sticky-

fingered?' he asked. I explained that I had not gone to the boy's house but had got the picture from his high-school principal. He gave a short, spastic laugh that started in his belly and died in his throat. It might have meant anything.

For several weeks I had been finding in my assignment box the dullest or the hardest assignments he could put his mind to. The next day, I started out of the office to follow up the story of a train wreck that had occurred north of town the evening before. Kuehner's assistant had stuck the assignment in my box. As I passed the city editor's desk, he growled, 'Where the hell do you think you're going?' I told him. 'Forget it,' he said, glaring slowly round the room. His dark glance lighted on a college man who had started to work only a few days before. 'We'll let the Phi Beta Kappa handle it,' he said, and bawled at him, 'Hey, Phi Beta Kappa, come here!' The torture of the new cub reporter had begun, and mine had ended. Up to that point, Kuehner had called me Hey or You, but he had found out that I had once written a libretto for a campus musical comedy, and he began calling me Author, and kept it up as long as I knew him.

When he was city editor, and even after he became managing editor, he liked to sit up until after midnight seeing the Sunday paper to press and, if he was in an amiable mood, telling yarns to whatever reporter was handling the late watch. If a phone rang Kuehner would shout, 'There she blows!' and scuttle over and answer it, hoping that hell was popping somewhere and that he could rush out and look at a dead body or a burning building. I had thought, during my first few months, that his deep absorption in death was morbid, but I changed my mind about this later on. Kuehner was a man of guts and action, but death did something to him he didn't like, and he was for ever seeking the chance to swagger up to it, with a chip on his shoulder, and stare it coldly in the eye. One night, when he was sitting the watch with a young reporter named George Smallsreed, the one he called Parson, he got the news that a man who had been shot through the head was lying in the emergency ward of the Mount Carmel Hospital. He got in his car with Smallsreed and exceeded the speed limit getting to the scene. Smallsreed knew that Kuehner would have liked nothing better than to see a young reporter turn green, or faint, at the sight of gruesome death, but he managed to get through the ordeal. 'When Kuehner had satisfied his curiosity at length,' Smallsreed told me recently, 'he looked at me innocently with those big brown eyes and said, "Let's go out and get a hamburger, Parson." I went with him, but I didn't eat anything.' One reason Kuehner took young reporters along with him on jaunts of this sort was, I suppose, to find out whether they had what he considered the stuff of a newspaperman in them. To Norman Kuehner no one was a genuine newspaperman if he cringed at the sight of blood or in the presence of human extinction. (Smallsreed turned out to have the stuff of a newspaperman in him, all right. About a year ago, he was made editor of the Columbus *Dispatch*.)

One Saturday night when I was sitting the late watch with Kuehner, I was emboldened for some reason to tell him how I had once run out of front-page copy at three o'clock in the morning when I was getting out the *Lantern*, and was saved by the fortuitous appearance in the night skies of what Professor H. C. Lord, roused out of bed, called the most brilliant aurora borealis seen in Ohio since the Civil War. Kuehner tossed his cigarette to the floor, with one of his slow, deliberate gestures, and ground it out under the heel of his No. 11 shoe. 'God never helped me put this paper to bed,' he said sulkily, 'and nobody is ever going to cover Heaven for the *Dispatch* while I'm city editor.' He had got sore, in his abrupt fashion, because I had brought up the touchy subject of college journalism, and also because I seemed to him to be floating around in the supernatural, a region that made him embarrassed and uncomfortable. I never brought up college journalism again, or the question of providential happenings either, but it was an act of God that gave me the chance, a few weeks later, to write a story for a midnight extra, when the old City Hall in Columbus caught fire during a council meeting I was covering.

The managing editor rounded up the crew that got out the extra, for Kuehner had refused to budge from his bed when I telephoned him, around eleven o'clock. 'Listen, Author,' he snarled, 'you're on an afternoon paper. Remember?' And he hung up on me. The next day, he found out that I had saved from the fire, along with somebody's overcoat and somebody else's watch, a large stack of blueprints, not having stopped to realize that they could be easily reproduced, and his abdominal laughter and his kidding went on for weeks. He kept calling me Chief, and demanding to know why I hadn't saved any used carbon paper or rare old thumbtacks. The City Hall fire never completely burned out in his grouchy elephant memory. He wished he had been on hand when the building started to burn, not only because he enjoyed fires but also because he loved to thumb his nose at danger. During the terrible Ohio floods of 1913, he was at the wheel of the last press car to escape from the rising waters on the west side of town, and he drove it across the Town Street Bridge, up to its hubcaps in water, reaching the other side just twenty minutes before the bridge was swept downstream by the flood. When somebody praised his courage, he dismissed it with an impatient wave of his hand. 'Twenty minutes is twenty minutes,' he said. He was not yet nineteen years old.

About a year after the City Hall fire, the *Ohio State Journal*, the city's morning paper, came out on Sunday with a front-page story about a 'ghostly wreath' that had suddenly and mysteriously appeared on a window pane in the bedroom of a house on Oregon Avenue in which a woman had just died. The *Journal* continued to play up the story, and on the following Sunday published a half page of photographs showing curious crowds staring up at the window, and lines of automobiles passing along the street. The cars came from all over central Ohio, the story said, and as many as five thousand passed the house each day. This was too much for Kuehner. The next morning, he ripped the page out of the paper, sauntered over to my desk, and said, 'I seem to remember that you cover Heaven for us. Get up there and crack that miracle and bring me back the pieces.' The miracle cracked easily enough, for the wreath turned out to be nothing more than an accumulation of iridescent oil, common in the manufacture of certain kinds of glass. This I learned from a representative of the Columbus branch of the Pittsburgh Plate Glass Company, who drove me up to the house in his car. It was early in the day, and no curious people were standing around and no cars were driving slowly by. The husband of the dead woman, his grief obviously lightened by the fame that had fallen upon his house, led us up to the bedroom, where the glass expert inspected the window pane. He told us that this particular formation of oil must have been accidental, but added that artisans could make deliberate designs out of the oil and that he had seen vases of roses, and even Scottish terriers, imprisoned in glass. The owner of the house clung obstinately to the theory of divine manifestation, even after the truth had been explained to him, and he was tight-lipped when he led us downstairs to the door, and the index finger of his right hand pointed solemnly in the general direction of Heaven. He was still standing in the door, with his arm raised on high, when we drove away.

Kuehner displayed the cracked pieces of the miracle prominently on the front page that afternoon, and that was the end of the ghostly wreath and of all the wonders connected with it except one – why the oil, which had always been on the glass, had not been discovered before. Kuehner had an answer for that one. 'Look, Author,' he said, 'you got an old miracle around the house for years, and nobody knows about it, and then there's a death, and somebody spots it, and you tell everybody it's brand-new and you never saw it before in your life. Catch on ?' I asked him what he would have done if it had transpired that the wreath had actually been sent down from Heaven. He never failed to have a fast comeback for everything. 'That would have made it a *Journal* rewrite,' he said sourly, 'and I would have given it a paragraph on page thirty.'

A city editor of the old school, Kuehner had hard and fixed ideas about how a news story should be written. 'Write a flowery introduction in the first paragraph,' he told one cub reporter. 'In the second paragraph, tell who, when, where, what, and how. Then, in as few paragraphs as possible, relate the most important details. Write an equally flourishing conclusion. Spend the next five minutes finding the sharpest pair of shears in the office, and cut off the first and last paragraphs. You'll have a helluva good news story.' He had a noisy antipathy to 'literary' writing, or anything that smacked of style, even in feature stories, and his criticism when he encountered such a monstrosity sounded like the roll of thunder. '*This* story is in *bloom*!' he howled at the author of a flamboyant article, and on another occasion he bawled at a reporter, 'You did this damn story with *feeling*,' giving the word all the force of an obscenity. He liked short paragraphs, hated long sentences, and never used a semicolon in his life.

Kuehner was addicted to the ancient journalese vocabulary – 'declared' or 'stated' or 'asserted' for 'said,' 'assigned' for 'given' (as in 'no reason could be assigned for the deed'), and all the rest, including such headline verbs as 'nab,' 'bam,' 'flay,' and 'flout.' Because of his iron insistence on the old platitudes of the trade, several of us were astonished one Saturday night when he attacked a verb form also disapproved of by schools of journalism but almost invariably used in Middle Western newspapers of that day. The late Arthur Johnson, then editor-in-chief of the *Dispatch*, was having a last look at the proofs of the Sunday paper and came across a man who had 'suffered a broken arm' in an auto accident. 'You don't suffer a broken arm,' Mr Johnson said. 'You sustain a broken arm'. Kuehner gave him a disdainful look worthy of a professor of English, and raised his right arm above his head. 'If you ever break your arm in an auto accident, Johnson,' he said, 'and you can do this with it, you are sustaining a broken arm.' I have no idea where Kuehner found out that small grammatical truth, for he was never known to look up anything in a dictionary.

The use of what Kuehner regarded as unusual or fancy words exasperated him mightily. When a reporter wrote that certain conditions 'obtained,' Kuehner snapped at him, 'What did these conditions obtain? It doesn't say here.' In Kuehner's lexicon, conditions 'prevailed' or 'existed.' On another occasion, a fancy reporter from Otterbein, or Wittenberg, or somewhere, used the word 'vouchsafe' in a story, and Kuehner never let him forget it. If the man went out to interview someone who turned out to be a 'no comment' man, Kuehner would snarl at him, 'What's the matter, wouldn't the guy vouchsafe anything?' The old-fashioned vocabulary of the press and the parlance of the police were enough for Kuehner, and he had no interest in enlarging his own knowledge of words. If he ever read a book after he became city editor, he never mentioned it to me, and he liked to brag that he had not seen a play since he was a little boy. His life outside of working hours was circumscribed by the streets that led from his office to his home.

I was in Norman Kuehner's house only once, during Christmas week, nearly thirty years ago, but I have a lasting memory of the city editor at home. He seemed oddly relaxed, as if the *Dispatch* were a tight collar he had taken off at his front door. His forehead was cleared of its office scowl, and there was a new and amiable note in his voice. Time ticked slowly and pleasantly in Kuehner's living-room and, for the first time in his presence, I did not feel a sense of deadline tension and urgency. For his two young sons, to whom he was intensely devoted, he had decorated the Christmas tree, and he had helped his wife arrange under it a fine old German crèche, some of whose pieces had belonged to early generations of Kuehners. When he looked at it, he wore an unfamiliar smile, as comfortable as a bedroom slipper. This was Norman Kuehner, husband and father, good family man, and considerate host. Every morning after he had breakfast, he put the tight collar back on, gathered up his office scowls and snarls, and underwent the transformation that turned Norman Kuehner, head of the family, into Gus Kuehner, city editor. One morning when he arrived at work, he bumped into a reporter who was leaning over a table, telephoning, with his rear end projecting into an aisle. 'Get you a bed!' snarled Kuehner. 'Get you a bridge!' snarled the reporter. Kuehner was back in his element again, his other element.

The ex-police reporter had no fondness for women on newspapers (he sometimes called them 'slob sisters'), and he wished to God they would stay home and let him alone. As far as he was concerned, one good homicide was worth ten thousand society pages, including Sunday's, and a brisk running gun battle more important than a warehouseful of 'woman's angle' feature stuff. He coldly ignored the fuss that was made when a Columbus girl named Mary Catherine Campbell was elected Miss America at the second Atlantic City Beauty Pageant (she won it again the following year), but he was out in the streets yelling with everybody else in town when the conquering Hank Gowdy returned from the famous 1914 World Series, and he always had space for the exploits of Eddie Rickenbacker after he came home to Columbus from the First World War. He didn't care about games – football, baseball, or any of the others – but he was one of the first to recognize the extraordinary local news value of a youngster named Chic Harley when that All-American half back began to burn up the Western Conference in 1916. Such prominent females as Helen Wills, Gertrude Ederle, Amelia Earhart, and Babe Didrikson left him cold. In his opinion, there hadn't been an athletic gal worth looking at since Annette Kellerman.

He worked at sharpening and tempering small insults that drew tears from one or two of the less hardened women in the office. With four or five pointed words, he could take apart feminine looks, hats, perfumes, or talent. One day, after reading a woman reporter's story in which the salient facts appeared near the end, he stalked over to a male reporter's desk, and snarled loudly, 'Turn this lady story upside down.' The lady in question was not there at the time, but she heard about the incident and wept. 'I love Norman,' she sniffled, 'but he is absolutely unbearable.' On another occasion, he was prowling about the city room in an aggressive mood when he spied a girl reporter, a blue-eyed one named Dorothy, sitting with her legs crossed and one slipper dangling from her toes. He grabbed it off and tossed it out of a window. She went down to the street, one shoe off and one shoe on, and found that the slipper had fallen through the open iron cover of a sidewalk elevator shaft and dropped into a second sub-basement. When she got it and told Kuehner where it had gone, he said, 'Good shot,' without looking up at her. Dorothy didn't cry. The *Dispatch* women, however, didn't bother him half as much as certain Columbus ladies who kept fluttering into the office on dull or hysterical missions and demanding to see the city editor. One of them, a periodic visitor, claimed that she could predict earthquakes by means of griping pains in her intestines. Kuehner used to hide from her in the men's room, gloomily smoking cigarettes until she had gone. Another lady, head of a citizens' committee to bring down the price of milk, kept bothering him until he turned on her once and snapped, 'Don't talk to me, lady, talk to the producers.' She ran a gay arpeggio of giggles. 'You *are* funny, Mr Kuehner!' she cried. 'Just imagine me talking to those cows!' This may have been the first and only time in the life of Norman Kuehner that he was left, for more than three seconds, utterly speechless.

Norman Kuehner got the biggest exclusive news story of his career one day in 1929. He had the title of assistant managing editor then, but he was still a police reporter at heart. Five days earlier, the body of an Ohio State co-ed named Theora Hix had been found on a rifle range five miles north of the city, and Kuehner had followed every line of the murder story in all three Columbus papers. A lot of evidence pointed at James H. Snook, professor of veterinary medicine at the university. The county prosecutor had been unable to break the suspect down, but every time Kuehner's phone rang, he was sure he was going to hear the news that Snook had confessed. He hoped to hell the story would break for the afternoon papers. It was a little past noon, on Kuehner's fateful day, when the *Dispatch* man at the police station phoned him and said, 'Shelly just told me he's going to eat lunch at the usual place to-day. Made quite a point of it.' Shelly was Wilson G. Shellenbarger, an old friend of Kuehner's, who had been a patrolman when young Gus covered the cop house, and was now chief of detectives. The 'usual place' was a restaurant at Spring and High Streets where Kuehner sometimes had lunch with Shellenbarger. He was excited, but he kept his voice low and casual as he said into the phone, 'O.K., I'll wander over there,' and hung up. He stuck some folded copy paper in his pocket and hurried to the restaurant.

When Shellenbarger showed up, he told Kuehner that Snook had confessed a few hours earlier but that the story was going to be held for the morning papers. He explained that William C. Howells, Columbus representative of the Cleveland *Plain Dealer*, had been allowed to visit Snook in his cell that morning, together with another newspaperman. Snook had repeated his confession to them, and Howells had agreed to take the stand at the trial, and corroborate the state's evidence, if the prosecutor would hold the story for the morning papers. Shellenbarger wanted to give his old friend Kuehner a break, and he did. He poured out all the facts in the case, including the details of the long and gaudy affair between the college girl and the professor, that led up to the murder. Half an hour later, Kuehner hurried back to his office with a dozen pages of notes and began to hammer out his story. He was about half finished when the county prosecutor's office phoned to announce that a conference of newspapermen would be held there at three o'clock that afternoon. Smallsreed was sent to represent the *Dispatch*, and told to stick close to the prosecutor until four o'clock. When he got back, at five minutes after four, with an official carbon of Snook's confession, he was handed a copy of the *Dispatch's* late-afternoon edition, which had just hit the street. Kuehner's long and vivid story, interspersed with photographs, covered the whole front page.

Kuehner's big story was unsigned, and there was no mention of Shellenbarger's part in it. It wasn't until two years later that Smallsreed found out who wrote the story and where it came from. Kuehner didn't get any glory at the time, but he had the deep satisfaction of knowing that he had scooped the world on one of the biggest murder stories of the century. The ex-police reporter of the Columbus *Dispatch* had had his greatest hour.

I had left the *Dispatch* six years before the murder of Theora Hix, and my going disgruntled Kuehner, because he felt sure I would end up in New York, and he hated New York. He had a standard lecture that he delivered to all reporters when they started work for him. It was brief and clear. 'If you've got any idea of going to New York to become another Oscar Hammerstein,' he would growl, 'quit now. This is no place for you.' He might have used more aptly, for his purpose, the name of Dana or Greeley or Bennett, but he had a high respect for them, in spite of their unfortunate New York background. To him the name 'Oscar Hammerstein' was derogatory, like Phi Beta Kappa, and he gave it, in a mincing tone, his best disparaging accent. He would turn his sarcasm on New York City at the slightest provocation. Once, when the telegraph editor showed him a full column of stuff sent out by the Associated Press in New York on the death of James Huneker, Kuehner glared at the copy and shouted across the room at the drama editor, 'Who the hell is James Huneker?' The man replied, 'He's a famous figure in the world of art,' and Kuehner bawled, 'What the hell world is *that*?' The death of Huneker got three lines in the paper that afternoon.

I saw Norman Kuehner only once – in 1927 – after I left the *Dispatch*, but I was to hear his voice again the next year, when he called me up in New York. Late one afternoon, the telephone in my office rang, and when I picked up the receiver and said 'Hello,' a big voice, heroically but unsuccessfully trying to disguise itself, growled, 'Why the hell don't you come back home where you belong?' Kuehner had been assistant managing editor of the *Dispatch* for only a few months, and he had reluctantly come to New York to attend a convention of newspapermen. The meetings were over, and he was waiting restlessly in the Pennsylvania Station to take a train back to Columbus. I don't think he had ever been in New York before, and he was anxious to get the hell out. One of the last things he said, before he hung up abruptly, was 'Where do you get your ladyfingers now, Author?' This was a deathless Kuehner gag, going back to the day, seven years before, when he had found out that I often dropped in, after work, at a photographic studio near the *Dispatch* where newspapermen gathered and afternoon tea was served. The male tea drinker, Kuehner stoutly believed, could easily be capable of such other feminine vices as running up a pair of dimity curtains in secret, or playing with embroidery cloths. I explained that New York was far more effete than Columbus, and that I had gone in for *babas au rhum*. He made a critical sound with his lips and put up the receiver.

Exactly ten years later, I got a letter from him, the only one he ever sent me. A lot had happened to Norman Kuehner, I found out, between the day he telephoned me and the day I got his letter. In 1936 the managing editor of the Columbus *Dispatch* gave up his job suddenly for reasons that have never been clear to me. He had got into a melancholy state, lost weight alarmingly, and found it hard to keep his mind on his work. There was a persistent rumour outside the *Dispatch* that the paper had decided its editors should all be college men. It is easy to see how the great disparager of college men on newspapers might have cracked under such a cruel, ironic blow. He got a job in the press department of the Landon headquarters in Chicago during the Roosevelt-Landon Presidential campaign, and once telephoned Smallsreed from Chicago to growl, 'You still working on a newspaper? This is the life, and there's dough in it.' His voice sounded strained and unconvincing. There was only one life for Norman Kuehner, and that was on a newspaper, and all his friends knew it. After Landon's defeat, Kuehner drifted back to Columbus and worked for two years in the Unemployment Compensation Commission, in a building that was near the *Dispatch* and a million miles away. His letter to me, in 1938, contained the names of half a dozen Oscars, or former Columbus newspapermen who had come to New York to work, and he wrote, in his old peremptory manner, 'Contact them and tell them I got to have a job. I'll do anything from turning a lathe to trimming ladies' hats.' He never came to New York again, the New York he despised, because he got a job with the Curtiss-Wright Corporation in Columbus, and he kept it until he died. He worked the 'suicide shift,' from midnight until eight in the morning, and kept at it doggedly for three years. In the summer of 1943, he wrote one of his sisters that he had high hopes of going back on the *Dispatch*. This warmly affectionate letter to 'Dearest Irma' was the last he ever wrote. The suicide shift had worn him out, and he had only four months to live.

On Christmas Day, 1943, I arrived in Columbus, and after I had checked in at the Deshler, I bought a copy of the *Dispatch* at the news-stand and found, in flipping through it in my room, the story of the sudden death, from a heart attack, of Norman Kuehner, at the age of forty-nine. He had been living alone in an apartment for his wife had died the year before, one of his sons was a sergeant in the Army and the other a corporal. Kuehner's body might not have been found for days if he hadn't collapsed while he was filling his bathtub with water. The tub overflowed, and attracted the attention of the people living on the floor below. This was the only item in the story of the death of Norman Kuehner, aircraft worker, that would have interested Gus Kuehner, newspaper editor.

I went to his funeral, and found there only a handful of the hundred men and women who had worked for him or with him. The service didn't take long, and nothing was said about Gus Kuehner, police reporter, city editor, and managing editor. I was driven back to my hotel by a sports-writer named Bill McKinnon, one of Kuehner's oldest and closest friends. McKinnon had sat beside him, thirty years before, in the Apperson Jack Rabbit that tore across the Town Street Bridge up to its hubcaps in water. 'I saw him two weeks ago,' McKinnon told me, 'and he said "I sure would like to get that paper out just once more." ' I don't know exactly what happened to Norman Kuehner, as I have said, and I am sure he wouldn't want me to pry into it. I can hear him saying, in one of his exasperating tones of voice, 'Lay off it, Author. This story's cold.'

I have discovered, in talking to some of Kuehner's old friends and associates, that the anxiety dreams of several of us still centre in the city room of the old Columbus *Dispatch* building. In one of my own recurring dreams, I am pounding away at a story I can't handle, because my notes are illegible and the type bars make no marks at all on the grey copy paper. The hands of the clock on the east wall of the city room, facing the reporters' desks, are frozen at a quarter after one, fifteen minutes past deadline, and there is a large, amorphous figure just over my right shoulder, standing there gloomily, saying nothing – the ghost of Norman Kuehner. Some of us, the ones who liked him, will never get him out of our dark subconscious, or, for that matter, out of our bright and fond memory.

Alarms & Diversions

FOR HELEN

The First Time I Saw Paris

WHAT I SAW FIRST of all was one outflung hand of France as cold and limp as a dead man's. This was the seacoast town of Saint-Nazaire, a long while ago. I know now that French towns don't die, that France has the durability of history itself, but I was only twenty-three then, and seasick, and I had never been so far from Ohio before. It was the dank, morose dawn of the 13th of November, 1918, and I had this first dismal glimpse of *France la Doulce* from the deck of the U.S. Transport *Orizaba*, which had come from the wintry sea like a ship out of Coleridge, a painted ship in an unreal harbour. The moist, harsh light of breaking day gave the faces of the silent staring gobs on deck a weird look, but the unreality was shattered soon enough by the raucous voice of a boatswain bawling orders. I had first heard this voice, strong enough to outshout a storm, snarling commands at 'abandon ship' drill: 'Now, light all lanterns!' and 'Now, lower all lifeboats!' I had been assigned to a life raft that was rusted to the deck and couldn't be budged. 'Now, what's the matter with Life Raft Number Six?' the boatswain had roared. A sailor next to me said, 'She's stuck to the deck, sir.' The boatswain had to have the last word and he had it. 'Now, leave her lay there!' he loudly decreed.

The *Orizaba* had taken a dozen days zigzagging across the North Atlantic, to elude the last submarines of the war, one of which we had sighted two days before, and Corcoran and I felt strange and uncertain on what seemed anything but solid land for a time. We were code clerks in the State Department, on our way to the Paris Embassy. Saint-Nazaire was, of course, neither dead nor dying, but I can still feel in my bones the gloom and tiredness of the old port after its four years of war. The first living things we saw were desolate men, a detachment of German prisoners being marched along a street, in mechanical step, without expression in their eyes, like men coming from no past and moving toward no future. Corcoran and I walked around the town to keep warm until the bistros opened. Then we had the first cognac of our lives, quite a lot of it, and the day brightened, and there was a sense of beginning as well as of ending, in the chilling weather. A young pink-cheeked French army officer got off his bicycle in front of a house and knocked on the door. It was opened by a young woman whose garb and greeting, even to our inexperienced eyes and ears, marked her as one of those females once described by a professor of the Harvard Law School as 'the professionally indiscreet.' Corcoran stared and then glanced at his wristwatch. 'Good God!' he said. 'It isn't even nine o'clock yet.'

The train trip down to Paris was a night to remember. We shared a sleeping compartment with a thin, gloved, talkative Frenchman who said he was writing the history of the world and who covered his subject spasmodically through the night in English as snarled as a fisherman's net, waking us once to explain that Hannibal's elephants were not real, but merely fearful figments of Roman hallucination. I lay awake a long time thinking of the only Paris I knew, the tranquil, almost somnolent city of Henry James's turn-of-the-century novels, in which there was no hint of war, past or approaching, except that of the sexes.

Paris, when we finally got there, seemed to our depressed spirits like the veritable capital city of Beginning. Her heart was warm and gay, all right, but there was hysteria in its beat, and the kind of compulsive elation psychiatrists strive to cure. Girls snatched overseas caps and tunic buttons from American soldiers, paying for them in hugs and kisses, and even warmer coin. A frightened Negro doughboy from Alabama said, 'If this happened to me back home, they'd hang me.' The Folies Bergère and the Casino de Paris, we found a few nights later, were headquarters of the New Elation, filled with generous ladies of joy, some offering their charms free to drinking, laughing and brawling Americans in what was left of their uniforms. At the Folies a quickly composed song called '*Finie la Guerre*' drew a dozen encores. Only the American MPs were grim, as they moved among the crowds looking for men who were AWOL, telling roistering captains and majors to dress up their uniforms. Doughboy French, that wonderful hybrid, bloomed everywhere. '*Restez ici* a minute,' one private said to his French girl. '*Je* returny *après cet* guy partirs.' *Cet* guy was, of course, a big-jawed military policeman set on putting a stop to non-regulation hilarity.

'I do not understand the American,' a Casino girl told me. 'They fight at night with each other, they break mirrors, they become bloody, they say goddamn everybody, and the next day what do you think? They are in the Parc Monceau on all fours giving little French children a ride on their backs. They are marvellous. I love them.'

The Americans have never been so loved in France, or anywhere else abroad, as they were in those weeks of merriment and wild abandon. When, late in 1919, most of our soldiers had sailed back home, *La Vie Parisienne* had a full-page colour drawing of an American officer over whose full-length figure dozens of lovely miniature French girls were rapturously climbing, and the caption ruefully observed: 'The hearts of our young ladies have gone home with the Americans.'

My trunk had stayed on the *Orizaba*. Corcoran and I had been the only two civilians on board, and transports were not used to unloading non-military baggage. All I had was the clothes I wore – my hat had been claimed as a souvenir – and I set about the considerable task of buying a wardrobe, paying what amounted to five dollars for B.V.D.s at the Galeries Lafayette. A suit I bought at a shop deceptively called 'Jack, American Tailor' is packed away in the modest files of secret memory. It might have been made by the American

Can Company. I tried on hats for an hour in a shop on the Avenue de l'Opéra, upon whose civilian stock the dust of four years of war had settled. There were narrow-brimmed hats, each with a feather stuck on one side, that made me look like Larry Semon, movie comic of the silent days, and some that would have delighted that great connoisseur of funny hats, Mr Ed Wynn. They were all placed on my head with an excited '*Voilà!*' by the eager salesman, and they were all too small, as well as grotesque. In one of the famous black, broad-brimmed hats, long and lovingly associated with the painters and poets of Bohemian Paris, I looked like a baleful figure attending the funeral of Art. I nearly broke the salesman's heart when I turned down a ten-gallon white Stetson he had dug up out of the cellar. So I went through that cold, dank Paris winter without a hat.

I had bought a cane, which in Columbus would have identified me as a lounge lizard of dubious morals, and I acquired enough boulevard French to say, '*Où est la Place de la Concorde?*' and to reply to '*Voulez-vous une petite caresse?*' My *tout ensemble* was strange, but not strange enough to deceive doughboys and gobs wandering along the Champs Elysées, homesick and disconsolate after the elation died down. I helped them decipher the small red-and-black French-English dictionaries they carried and told them that, contrary to their invariable conviction, they would not be stuck in 'this godforsaken city' forever. Once I translated, for a puzzled demoiselle, a mysterious note she had got through the mails from a doughboy who had returned to her one day before *cet* guy had partired. It began, 'I am in a place I cannot leave.' I managed to explain to her that her boy had been jailed for being absent without leave. I gathered that he had been, when on the loose, a great lover, fighter and piggy-back rider, like the others. 'I wish to cry on your shirt,' his girl friend told me, and she cried on my shirt. That astonished shirt, stained with Lacrimae Puellae 1919, must have cost a lot, but all I remember is that the amazing French shirt-tail reached to my knees.

When I got to France, the franc was worth almost a quarter, but pretty soon you could get fourteen francs for your dollar, and since prices didn't rise as rapidly as the franc fell, the $2,000 annual salary of a code clerk began to mean something. One amateur speculator among us, certain that the franc would come back with all the resilience of Paris, bought up francs and was wiped out when *la chute* continued. In my nearly forty years off and on in France I have seen this coin of a thousand values vary from 5.30 to 350. 'It will be as worthless as dandelions,' a dour concierge predicted in 1919, but she was wrong.

'Ah, *ces américains*,' sighed a Folies girl one evening. '*Quels hommes!* They are such good bad boys. They wish to spend the night, even the weekend.' She went on to explain how this complicated the economic structure of one in her profession. She was used, in the case of other foreigners, to a nightly transference of paid affections as neatly manoeuvred as the changing of partners in a square dance. 'These Americans are men born to marry,' my informant went on. Many of them – thousands, I believe – did marry French girls and took them home to an astonished Brooklyn, a disapproving Middle West, and occasionally more amiable regions. I read somewhere in 1928 that about 75 per cent of these wartime marriages had ended in the return of the brides to France. One of those who stayed wrote me a letter a quarter of a century ago in which she said, dolorously, 'There is not the life in Detroit. It is not Paris. Can you send me some books in French?' She had married a great big good bad American Army lieutenant. I sent her, among other books in French, the poems of Mallarmé and the book Clemenceau wrote after the war. I often wonder what finally became of another girl who married a sailor and went to live in Iowa, and what they thought of her English out there. She had learned it all from the plays of Shakespeare and it was quaint and wonderful to hear, but definitely not for Iowa. 'How goes the night?' she asked me once, straight out of *Macbeth*, to which I was proudly able to reply, 'The moon is down. I have not heard the clock.' This Gallic Elizabethan had given up working for a few francs a week in a garment factory for a more lucrative and less monotonous career. Once I met her by appointment, and in pursuit of my sociological studies, on the terrace of the Café de la Paix, where, over vermouth cassis, she explained that she was going to meet, in half an hour, an American captain whom she had comforted one night long ago when he didn't have a sou. It seems he had promised to meet her at the café and pay his debt of gratitude, and he had written her from somewhere and fixed an hour. 'He will be here,' she said confidently, and she was right. A quiet, almost shy good bad boy, he slipped her a sealed envelope while I studied the passing throng in which, true prophecy has it, you will see everybody you know if you sit at your table long enough. I still remember that what he ordered was chocolate ice cream.

The City of Light, during most of 1919, was costumed like a wide-screen Technicolor operetta, the uniforms of a score of nations forming a kind of restless, out-of-step finale. The first Bastille Day celebration after the war was a carnival that dazzled the eye and lifted the heart. Chairs at windows of buildings along the route of march cost as much as fifty dollars, and step-ladders on the crowded sidewalks could be rented for fifteen dollars. At night, in a thousand 'tin bars,' as our men called bistros, and in more elaborate *boîtes de nuit*, the Americans often changed the prewar pattern of Paris night life by fighting among themselves, or singly, in pairs, or in groups, the Anzacs, the waiters, the management, the *gendarmerie*, or whoever was looking for action. Chairs and bottles were thrown, and mirrors cracked from side to side. There was a conviction among Americans, more often false than true, that they were always overcharged, and this was the chief provocation for trouble, but high spirits, the irritating factor of unfamiliarity, triple sec, and a profound American inability to pick up foreign languages easily, often led to roughhouse. A civilian I knew who hailed from New Jersey, and constantly and profanely wished he were back there, asked me one morning how to say in French, 'I demand the release of these Americans.' It turned out that no Americans he knew were in durance anywhere. My unilingual companion simply planned to go out on the town that night with some compatriots and wanted to be prepared, in case his detachment was overwhelmed by the authorities in some bar. Like me, he worked at the Embassy, then on the Rue de Chaillot, and he had a code-room pass which he proposed to wave while shouting his command. I told him the French were always aroused, never intimidated, by civilians shouting orders, especially if they flaunted mysterious and doubtful official credentials. He would be taken, I told him, for that most despised of creatures, the *mouchard*, or police spy. Not the next morning, but a few days later, he showed up with bruised knuckles and a swollen jaw. 'You were right,' he admitted meekly.

Paris had been down on her knees, but now she got back on her feet, surely and resolutely, in the noble tradition of the world's most spirited city. Montmartre, when I first walked its deserted silent streets, had seemed down and out for good, but by New Year's Eve, 1918, it had begun to function, and before long the Moulin Rouge and the Chat Noir were gaily crowded again. Excellent food, the great pride of Paris, was naturally slow in reaching the tables of the famous restaurants, but I took an American Red Cross girl to Voisin's not many weeks after I arrived, and it seemed to have gone through the war as if nothing worse than a storm had passed. This was the quietly elegant restaurant celebrated for its calm, almost austere, survival of the Siege of Paris in the war with Prussia, when, undaunted by dwindling supplies, it served up the tender cuts of some of the more edible animals of the zoo. I remember being shown one of the remarkable and touching menus of those war years. I have forgotten just when it closed its doors forever, but in 1938, while accompanying my wife on a shopping trip, I was suddenly overcome by a curious and haunting sense of the past in a woman's glove store. Recognition flowed back like a film developing, and I realized that I stood within a few feet of where the American girl and I had sat for lunch one day. It was like meeting an old beloved friend who has undergone a sorrowful change and no longer knows who you are.

Paris during the months of the Peace Conference would have delighted Hadrian, Playboy of the Roman Empire, who enjoyed colourful spectacles brought together from the corners of the world. When President Wilson drove down the Champs Elysées, more people watched and cheered, more flags were waved, more eyes were bright, than I have ever seen in one place at one time. The way from there had to be down, because there was no higher place to reach, and the international highway of acclaim never runs straight and smooth very far. There had been, even on the day of armistice, voices that did not shout '*Finie la guerre!*' but solemnly warned, '*Maintenant ça commence.*' But these prophets of predicament and peril were lost sight of in the carnival. I didn't hear them myself; I was too busy, between coding and decoding telegraphic messages, watching Premier Paderewski arriving at his hotel, catching glimpses of Herbert Hoover sitting erect in the back seat of his big Cadillac, identifying the impressive head of Lloyd George at one of the restaurants in the Bois de Boulogne. At the Casino de Paris, the famous straw hat and lower lip of Maurice Chevalier, not long before turned thirty, attracted crowds as his rising star dimmed a little the light of the great Mistinguett. He did a wonderful burlesque of an American gob, by turns melancholy and gay, excited and bewildered, taking the edge off Mistinguett's singing of 'For Me and My Gal,' a song the French loved. The Americans, of course, were singing 'Smiles' and 'Hindustan,' and then a song of which someone had sent me a recording from America, 'Dardanella.' I remember taking the Red Cross girl to dinner at Noël Peters, where a trio of piano, violin and cello played many pieces, only one of them American. After brandy I had requested an American song, and the pianist finally dug up the sheet music of 'Goodbye My Bluebell.'

Everybody went out to Versailles, where the famous fountains had been turned on for the first time in years. All kinds of devices were used to get into the Hall of Mirrors. Never had so many fake passes been so elaborately contrived, but few of them worked. And through it all the Battle of Paris went on. Souvenir hunting by Americans reached a high point. They took things out of niches and tried to pry things loose from plinths, to add to the relics of war brought back from the front, including ornamental vases made by French soldiers out of the casings of French .75's. I got one of these at Fort Vaux outside Verdun, which had been stormed and taken and retaken so many times. Verdun had been the farthest north reached by me and another Embassy clerk in the week before Christmas, 1918. We had gone by train as far as the town of Vierzy, where my companion searched vainly for the grave of a friend from Illinois who had been a marine. Another marine from the Embassy guard, talking and dreaming of his ranch in Montana, had gone with us as far as Vierzy, mainly to find an open space in which he could practise firing a Luger he had picked up somewhere, but he would have no part of our plan to walk through the battlefields, day after day, as far as Soissons and Verdun. Up there we paid our way into Fort Vaux and the underground city of Verdun with American cigarettes. I often consume again, in fantasy, the light omelet, *pain de famille*, and good white wine served to us by a young French farmer and his wife who were bravely rebuilding their home in one of those landscapes of destruction so poignantly painted by the late English artist Paul Nash. It took long argument to persuade the couple to take money for the meal.

In our trek through the battlefields, with the smell of death still in the air, the ruined and shattered country scarred with ammunition dumps and crashed planes, we came upon the small temporary cemeteries arranged by the Graves Registration Service, each with a small American flag, such as the children of Paris waved at President Wilson, nailed to a post and faded by the rain and wintry weather. In one of these cemeteries my companion, a Tennessee youth, only a little taller than five feet, began singing 'The Star-Spangled Banner' with his hat over his heart, and went on singing it in a sudden downpour of rain, for the anthem, once started, must be finished. He was loaded down with junk on our way back, most of which he had to abandon. He mourned his failure to wrench an ornamental iron gate from the entrance to a shattered chateau. The only thing I brought back, besides the vase, was the identification papers of an Algerian soldier named A. Mokdad, which were lying on the ground, punctured by two machine-gun bullets. Detachments of French labour battalions were trying to clear up the wreckage here and there, a task that seemed hopeless. But the French soldiers were tough, determined men. By the light of a Very shell one night in Soissons we had seen a company of *poilus* marching through the mud, singing 'Madelon.' In the muzzles of some of their carbines flowers from God knows where had been stuck. The soldiers looked enormous and indomitable, and it is good to know that one or two French painters of the time did justice to their stature, painting them to look like the rocks they were. Contrary to the prewar American notion of Frenchmen as small and dapper, there were scores of d'Artagnans in the armies of France for every Aramis – and he was tough enough himself.

Back in Paris, I made a brief survey of the souvenirs collected by Americans I knew. One man had brought from somewhere a machine gun, which he kept in his hotel room and left there when he went home. Legend had it that the upraised sword of the equestrian statue of George Washington in the Place d'Iéna had been replaced nine times, and one over-enthusiastic vandal had been arrested while attempting to take one of the gilt cherubs from the superstructure of the bridge of Alexandre III across the Seine. A sailor I know collected, with the aid of chisel and screwdriver, ornate locks from old doors and gates, and his trophies must have weighed a good hundred pounds. A doughboy who fancied bronze and marble busts in museums was less successful. It was rumoured, in the days of the Great Hunt, that not more than five servicemen were admitted to Napoleon's tomb at one time. Everybody heard, and retold, the wonderful myth of the bold and enterprising soldier in the Louvre who had got away with the arms of the Venus de Milo and the head of the Winged Victory.

I have nothing tangible to remind me of those tangled days, the Verdun vase and the papers of A. Mokdad having long since disappeared. The vase, wherever it is, must still bear the deathless hammered-out name 'Verdun.' From a separate trip to Rheims I brought back nothing but chill memories that still turn up now and then in nightmares. I see the vacant staring space from which the rose window of the cathedral had been carefully removed in time, and the gaping hole in one wall of the edifice, made by a shell hit. This great city of the Champagne country was all but deserted when I was there, and a walk through its streets was a walk on the moon. The disappearance of one wall had revealed a bedroom that looked like a dismal abandoned stage set. The works of a printing shop, its machines and type, were scattered across a street. The façade of a theatre had been ripped off, revealing a crumbling stage, while empty seats and boxes, unharmed except by weather, gave the beholder the feeling that cast and audience had fled in horror during the showing of some kind of extravaganza in hell. And in Paris, so near in space, seemingly so far away in time, morbid visitors, looking for the effects of war, asked where they could find the church upon which a shell from Big Bertha had made its terrible direct hit.

All of us went to the grand opera many times, my own first visit being to hear 'Aïda' and to see the *haut monde* of Paris once again in evening clothes, glittering up and down the marble staircases between acts. Someone pointed out René Fonck in the crowd, and I still remember the ribbon of the great airman's croix de guerre, as long as a ruler to accommodate all the palms he had won. There is a timelessness about grand opera in Paris, and except for the uniforms, there was no hint that the greatest war in history had come so recently to an end. I paid a dollar that night for a pack of American cigarettes, but this was not my most memorable financial transaction. A week or two after our arrival Corcoran and I had paid a dollar apiece for fried eggs, and almost as much for marmalade.

I sometimes ate with the doughboys, who never got used to French food, and groused about American Army grub. In Verdun one day we ate Army beans and the rest of the rations, using borrowed mess kits. 'Look at them guys eat that stuff,' one private said. 'I'll be damned if they don't like it.' We also liked the wheat cakes with genuine maple syrup served at an Army kitchen set up in the basement of the Crillon, the de luxe hotel in the heart of Paris which had been taken over by the Americans.

I saw no doughboys or gobs at the opera, but they crowded into the cinemas when they opened, to watch the American films of three actors popular with the French – W. S. Hart ('*le roi du ranch*'), Harold Lloyd, known as '*Lui*,' and Douglas Fairbanks *père*, lovingly called 'Doogla' by the French.

When I finally sailed back home, sixteen months had elapsed since the Armistice, and the Brave New World was taking on its disillusioning shape. Theodore Roosevelt had died in 1919, which marked in its way the end of an era, and Woodrow Wilson had come down from his dizzy pinnacle of fame and hope, and was on his way to his own dismayed and frustrated end. Before long a celebrated room was to be filled with smoke out of which a political magician named Harry M. Daugherty would produce the shadowy figure of Warren Gamaliel Harding and the misleading motto of 'Return to Normalcy' in a period of flagpole sitting, nonstop dancing, Channel swimming, ocean flying, husband murder, novels of disenchantment, and approaching financial chaos. I reached New York still without a hat. It was March and blustery in New York, and one of the first things I did was to buy one. It fitted my head, and seemed to my repatriated eye extremely becoming. It wasn't until later that day that I looked inside the hat to see the mark of the maker. I quote from a piece I wrote in 1923 for the Columbus, Ohio, Sunday *Dispatch*: 'Something inside the crown caught my eye. I looked more closely. "*Fabriqué par Moissant et Amour, 25 Avenue de l'Opéra, Paris*," it said.'

Paris, City of Light and of occasional Darkness, sometimes in the winter rain seeming wrought of monolithic stones, and then, in the days of its wondrous and special pearly light, appearing to float in mid-air like a mirage city in the Empire of Imagination, fragile and magical, has had many a premature requiem sung for the repose of its soul by nervous writers or gloomy historians who believe it is dying or dead and can never rise again. Paris, nonetheless, goes right on rising out of war, ultimatum, occupation, domestic upheaval, cabinet crises, international tension, and dark prophecy, as it has been in the habit of doing since its residents first saw the menacing glitter of Roman shields many centuries ago. Recently in the New York Sunday *Times* John Davenport sang sorrowfully of the Paris of today as a dying city, a city of ghosts, but his funeral arrangements were laughed off by, among others, a South Carolina reader who protested, 'It is not Paris but an Anglo-American myth that is dying.'

The Americans and English have never become an integral part of the anatomy of the city, which is forever French. Its visitors come and go, hopeful or despondent, comfortable or uneasy, looking in the wrong places for the pulse of the city, feeling in the wrong places for the throb of its heart. I have been in and out of Paris half a dozen times from 1920 to 1955, and I have had my moments of depression and worry about the great city, but I have never felt that I was sitting up at night with a fatally sick friend. I have seen her moods shift from confidence to despond, for Paris is a lady of temperament and vola- tality, but I have never felt she was mortally languishing, like a stricken heroine of grand opera.

I enjoy arguing with Parisian friends about the true gender of their fair city, pointing out that 'feminine,' in my lexicon, means neither frail nor frivolous, neither capricious nor coquettish, but female, and summing up with this sound paraphrase of Kipling: 'The female of the cities is far tougher than the male.' In my observation, the female of any species is not, in Simone de Beauvoir's pallid phrase, the Second Sex, but the First Sex, of which the Second is luckily born. Frenchmen jump too easily to the inference that 'lady,' when applied to Paris, means *poule de luxe*, or that what we feminists have in mind is the gay figure evoked when Monsieur Chevalier sings '*Paris, elle est une blonde.*' What we really mean is Woman in the sense and stature, the sign and symbol, in which she is represented everywhere you look in Paris, from the celebrated statue of the fighting French woman called '*Quand Même*,' in the Tuileries, to the monumental figure on one side of the Arch of Triumph. Or take the statues in the Place de la Concorde representing eight great provincial cities of France, all of which are depicted as women. Perhaps the finest, that of Strasbourg, was shrouded in black when I first beheld it, but I was happily on hand when the lady was joyously stripped of her mourning after Strasbourg had been restored to France.

Street rioting has broken out in the streets of Paris from time to time, for Paris does not repress her anger any more than she suppresses her desires, and windows are smashed and buildings are burned, and now and then someone is killed. Once in a while the United States has been the object of Parisian wrath – thirty years ago I witnessed a *rixe* or two, but never a real *bagarre* – because of our failure to write off the French war debt. There were those at the time who feared that demonstrators might overturn the statue in the Place des Etats- Unis of Washington and Lafayette shaking hands. It has been marked with chalk, but it will never be overthrown. Not far from these sculptured hands across the sea stands an equally solid monument to the 118 Americans who lost their lives in the service of France during the First World War, sixty-one of them in the Lafayette Escadrille. The granite tribute contains the indestructible names of Raoul Lufbery, Norman Prince, Kiffin Rockwell, Victor Chapman and Alan Seeger.

This is the American quarter of Paris that I knew so well in the months after the Armistice. In front of what was once the chancellery of our Embassy at 5 Rue de Chaillot, a statue of Rochambeau salutes the mounted image of George Washington in the Place d'Iéna not far away. It was indeed *bien américain* the time of my first visit, for Woodrow Wilson lived at No. 11 Place des Etats-Unis, and a short walk from there was the Avenue du Président Wilson and a *pension* filled with Americans from the Embassy. The streets were loud with American voices and bright with our uniforms, and marines sometimes played baseball in the Rue de Chaillot. A bar advertised 'American cocktails' and Yanks sang our war songs, including the one with the line 'I'll bring you a Turk and the Kaiser, too,' which may have inspired the wild notion in some of our men to invade Doorn and bring old Wilhelm back to America as the souvenir of souvenirs. Nearly twenty years ago I made a pilgrimage to the old Yank district, meeting French friends of mine who were still there, and reading the tablet placed near the door of the former chancellery by the Paris Post of the American Legion, a small memorial perpetuating the myth that the late Myron T. Herrick was our Ambassador during the war of 1914–18. Actually he had been replaced in December, 1914, by the late William G. Sharp, who served during all but four months of the war, but has gone unremembered and unmarked. Legend made Myron Herrick our wartime ambassador, and legend, from Barbara Frietchie to Mr Herrick, is more durable than fact.

The last time I saw Paris, or heard and sensed the city, since I was no longer able to see the old landmarks, was in the late summer of 1955, and I didn't get around to the once familiar places which, if you are there and interested in such a ramble, you can find most easily by following the Avenue Kléber out of the Place de l'Etoile toward the Seine and the Eiffel Tower. Here are the permanent pages of history, written in bronze and stone, of America in Paris, and they are worth a morning's walk and an hour's meditation.

The second time I saw Paris, in 1925, she wore a new gown and a different mood. The Americans had taken over the Left Bank from the Deux Magots to the Dome and the Rotonde, and there were almost as many writers and artists as there had been doughboys and gobs. It was the era of Hemingway, Scott Fitzgerald and John Dos Passos in Paris, and over the restless new American hive Gertrude Stein, prophetess of the Lost Generation, presided like a modernistic queen bee. But that is another memory, for another time.

A bientôt.

The Psychosemanticist
Will See You Now, Mr Thurber

I BELIEVE THERE ARE no scientific investigators that actually call themselves psychosemanticists, but it is surely time for these highly specialized therapeuticians to set up offices. They must not be carelessly confused with psychosomaticists, who study the effects of mental weather upon the ramparts of the body. The psychosemanticists will specialize in the havoc wrought by verbal artillery upon the fortress of reason. Their job will be to cope with the psychic trauma caused by linguistic meaninglessness, to prevent the language from degenerating into gibberish, and to save the sanity of persons threatened by the onset of polysyllabic monstrositis.

We have always been a nation of categorizationists, but what was once merely a national characteristic is showing signs of malignancy. I shall not attempt to discover the incipient primary lesion, for I am not a qualified research scholar in this field. Indeed, for having had the impudence to trespass thus far I shall no doubt be denounced by the classificationists as a fractional impactionist (one who hits subjects a glancing blow), an unauthorized incursionist, a unilateral conclusionist, and a presumptuous deductionist. Our national predilection for ponderous phraseology has been traced by one authority as far back as the awkward expression 'taxation without representation' (unjust impost). It is interesting to note that the irate American colonists of that period in our history would be categorized today as 'anti-taxation-without-repre-sentationists.'

Not long ago, for the most recent instance in my collection, Senator Lyndon Johnson was described by a Washington newspaperman as a pragmatic functionalist, a term that was used in a laudatory sense. It isn't always easy nowadays to tell the laudatory from the derogatory at first glance, but we should be glad that this Democratic leader is not a dogmatic divisionary or an occlusive impedimentarian. The most alarming incidence of verbal premalignancy occurs, of course, in this very area of politics, but let us skip over such worn and familiar double-jointedisms as creeping Socialists, disgruntled ex-employees, ritualistic liberals, massive retaliationists, agonized reappraisalists, unorthodox thinkers, unwitting handmaidens (male), to name only a few out of hundreds, and take a look at excessive prewar anti-Fascism, a colossal (I use the adjective as a noun, in the manner of television's 'spectacular') that was disgorged a few years ago. Here the classificatory degradationists brought a time element into what might be called the post-evaluation of political morality. The operation of this kind of judgment during and after the Civil

War would have thrown indelible suspicion upon all the Northern patriots, including Abraham Lincoln, who wanted Robert E. Lee to take command of the Federal Armies in the field. They would be known today as 'overenthusiastic pre-Manassas pro-Leeists.'

The carcinomenclature of our time is, to be sure, an agglomerative phenomenon of accumulated concretions, to which a dozen different types of elaborative descriptivists have contributed – eminently the old Communist intellectuals, with their 'dialectical materialists,' 'factional deviationists,' 'unimplemented obscurantists,' and so on, and so on. Once the political terminologists of all parties began to cross-infect our moribund vocabulary, the rate of degeneration became appalling. Elephantiasis of cliché set in, synonym atrophied, the pulse of inventiveness slowed alarmingly, and paraphrase died of impaction. Multiple sclerosis was apparent in the dragging rhythms of speech, and the complexion of writing and of conversation began to take on the tight, dry parchment look of death. We have become satisfied with gangrenous repetitions of threadbarisms, like an old man cackling in a chimney corner, and the onset of utter meaninglessness is imminent.

The symptoms of this ominous condition show up most clearly in the tertiary stage of 'controversial figure.' The most complicated specimen of this type of modern American is the man of unquestionable loyalty, distinguished public service, and outstanding ability and experience who has nonetheless 'lost his usefulness.' Actually, this victim of verbositosis has not lost his usefulness, his nation has lost it. It doesn't do the national psyche any good to realize that a man may be cut off in the full flower of his usefulness, on the ground that that is not what it is. I trust I have made the urgent need for psychosemanticists apparent, even though I have admittedly become contaminated in the process, and I doubt whether my own psychosemanticist, after treating me, will ever be able to turn to my wife and say cheerfully, 'Madam, your husband will write clearly again.'

Before visiting my hypothetical psychosemanticist for a brief imaginary interview, I feel that I should get something reassuring into this survey of depressing ailments of the tongue. We have, then, cured, or at least survived, various incipient mouth maladies in the past. There was a moment when 'globaloneyism,' growing out of the Timethod of wordoggle, seemed likely to become epidemic, but it fortunately turned out to be no worse than a touch of pig Latin or a slight case of Knock, Knock, Who's There? Congress was not prepared to adopt the telescoping of words, which takes both time and ingenuity, and unless an expression becomes absorbed by Congressionalese, it has little chance of general survival. This brings me to what may easily be the direct cause of my being bundled off to the psychosemanticist's before long: the beating the word 'security' is taking in this great, scared land of ours. It is becoming paralysed. This is bound to occur to any forceful word when it loses its quality of affirmation and is employed exclusively in a connotation of fear, uncertainty, and suspicion. The most frequent use of 'security' (I hate to add to its shakiness with quotation marks, which have taken on a tone of mockery in our day) is in 'security risk,' 'weakest link in our chain of security,' and 'lulled into a false sense of security.' Precision of speech and meaning takes a small tossing around in the last of those three phrases. 'Lulled' is actually what happens to a nation after it has been argued, tricked, manoeuvred, reasoned, coaxed, cajoled, or jockeyed into a false sense of security, but the inflexibility that has descended upon us has ruled out the once noble search for the perfect word and the exact expression. What Eric Partridge calls 'a poverty of linguistic resource' is exemplified by the practically exclusive use of two verbs in any public-forum discussion of national security. It is threatened or it is bolstered; I never heard of its being supported, reinforced, fortified, buttressed, or shored up, and only very rarely is it menaced, endangered, or in jeopardy.

The word 'insecurity,' by the way, seems to have been taken over by the psychiatrists as their personal property. In politics, as in penology, 'security' itself has come to mean 'insecurity.' Take, for example, this sentence: 'He was considered a "maximum security" prisoner because of his police record and was never allowed out of his cell block.' Similarly, 'security data' means data of the kind calculated to scare the living daylights out of you, if not, indeed, your pants off. I could prove that 'maximum,' in the case of the prisoner mentioned above, really means 'minimum,' but I don't want to get us in so deep that we can't get out. The present confused usage of 'security' may have originated with the ancient Romans. Anyway, here is what Cassell's Latin Dictionary has to say about *securitas*: 'I. *freedom from care*. A. In a good sense, *peace of mind*, *quiet*, Cic. B. In a bad sense, *carelessness*, *indifference*, Tac. II. Transf., *freedom from danger*, *security*, Tac.'

A vital and restless breed of men, given to tapping our toes and drumming with our fingers, infatuated with every new crazy rhythm that rears its ugly beat, we have never truly loved harmony, the graceful structure of shapes and tones, and for this blindness and deafness we pay the awful price of continuous cacophony. It gets into language as well as music; we mug melody for the sake of sound effects, and the louder and more dissonant they are, the better we seem to like them. Our national veins have taken in the singing blood of Italy, Wales, Ireland, and Germany, but the transfusion has had no beneficial effect. Great big blocky words and phrases bumble off our tongues and presses every day. In four weeks of purposeful listening to the radio and reading the newspapers I have come up with a staggering list, full of sound and fury, dignifying nothing: 'automation,' 'roadability,' 'humature,' 'motivational cognition' (this baby turned up in a series of travel lectures and was never defined), 'fractionalization,' 'varietism,' 'redesegregation,' 'additive,' 'concertization' (this means giving a concert in a hall, and is not to be confused with cinematization or televisionization). The colloquial deformity 'knowledgeable,' which should have been clubbed to death years ago, when it first began crawling about like the late Lon Chaney, has gained new life in recent months. It is a dented derby of a word, often found in the scrawny company of such battered straw hats as 'do-gooder,' 'know-how,' 'update,' 'uptake' (I recently uptook the iodine uptake test for thyroidism), and others so ugly and strange I can't decipher them in my notes. One of them looks like 'de-egghead,' which would mean to disintellectualize or mentally emasculate – a crippling operation approved of by an alarming number of squash-heads, in Washington and elsewhere.

During my month of vigil and research, I heard an able physiologist who has a radio programme say, quite simply, 'We do not use up all the food we take in.' He wasn't allowed to get away with that piece of clarity, however. 'Ah,' cut in his announcer, for the benefit of those no longer able to understand simplicity, 'the utilization factor!' I turned from this station to a droning psychologist, just in time to hear him say, 'The female is sometimes the sexual aggressor.' Here a familiar noun of mental illness and military invasion was clumsily at work beating in the skull of love with a verbal bung-starter. The sweetheart now often wears the fustian of the sick man and the Caesar. In the evening, I tuned in on one of the space-patrol programmes that gleefully exude the great big blockyisms. 'Your astrogation bank will tell you!' cried the captain of a space ship to another interplanetary pilot, meaning his navigational instruments. In a fairy tale, an astrogation bank would be a 'star panel,' but the quality of fairy tale is nowhere to be found in these dime novels of the constellations.

One Sunday morning, my head aching with 'kiss-close' and 'swivel-chair-it,' meaning, I guess, 'at kissing distance' and 'maul it over in your executive brain,' respectively, I stumbled upon a small radio station that had been captured by a man of God, ominous and squealful, who was begging his listeners to live on their knees, not as slaves but as supplicants. This particular fundamentalist, or maybe it is fundamentalitarian, had probably never heard of the great protest 'I would rather die on my feet than live on my knees.' But these yammering eschatologists, and many of their followers, have even less respect for the glory and grace of English than the unsaved politicians. 'Let us cease to sugar-coat, let us cease to whitewash, let us cease to bargain-counter the Bible!' the speaker implored us. He finished second in vulgarity, I regret to say, to a reverend I had heard earlier in the year, who shouted, 'I didn't cook up this dish, God cooked it up. I'm just dishing it out to ye!' The line between holiness and blasphemy becomes even thinner when some of the lay testimonialists begin ranting. 'I own a shoe store in New Jersey,' one of them confessed, 'but Jesus Christ is my senior partner.'

A recent investigation of the worries and concerns of five thousand selected Americans revealed that we are preoccupied almost wholly with the personal and private, and are troubled only mildly by political anxieties, including the danger of war, the state of civil liberties, and the internal Communist threat. This does not come as a surprise to me, since the nature of our national concern about Communism is proved to be personal by such expressions as 'anti-anti-Communists' and 'anti-anti-anti-Communists.' The first actually means men who are against men who are against Communists, and the second, when you unravel it, means men who are against men who are against men who are against Communists. In these wonderful examples of our love of formidable elaborationisms, concept and doctrine are put aside, and personalities take their place. What we have left is pure personalism – a specific reactionary who is against a specific liberal who is against Senator Malone, let us say. The multiplicity of prefixes, another sign of linguistic poverty, was touched with a fine and healthful irony in Quincy Howe's invention of the phrase 'ex-ex-Communist.' (Many will claim that for their own, but Mr Howe got to it first.) One would think that Americans would be worried, or at least concerned, by a man who may have ceased to be a man who may have ceased to be a Communist, but the Worry Research I have mentioned showed that this isn't so. We are worried about health, family matters and money, and we have no time for a man who may be lying about lying. Incidentally, a fairly new advertising slogan, 'The portable portable,' fits neatly into modern jargon: the typewriter that you can carry that you can carry.

While I was exploring the decline of expression in America, I spent a week in a hospital. Medical science has done much for humantiy, but not in the area of verbal communication. It should undergo a prefectomy, and have some of its prefixes taken out. I should like to see the 'semi' removed from 'semi-private,' a dispiriting word that originated in hospitals; there must be a less depressing way of describing a room with two or more beds. I am also for taking the 'sub' out of 'sub-clinical,' and starting all over again with the idea in mind of making the word mean something. Incidentally, I discovered at the hospital the difference between 'to be hospitalized' and 'to become hospitalized.' The first means to be placed in a hospital, and the second has two meanings: to get so that you can't stand it in the hospital any longer, and to like it so much there that you don't want to leave.

Lying in bed brooding over these matters, I turned on the radio and heard an American describe another American as 'an old-time A.D.A. type of anti-Jeffersonian radical' – a beautiful specimen of bumblery. Sir Winston Churchill, in the exhilarating years of his public life, turned out many phrases as sharp as stilettos – for one example, 'squalid gamin.' But you can count on your fingers the Americans, since the Thomas Paine of 'the summer soldier and the sunshine patriot,' who have added bright, clear phrases to our language. If you can bumble an opponent to death why stab him seems to be the general feeling among our politicians, some of whom have got through the twelve years since the war ended with only five adjectives of derogation: naïve, hostile, unrealistic, complacent, and irresponsible. All these slither easily, if boggily, into bumblery, and the bumbler is spared the tedious exercising of his mental faculties.

The day I got dressed and was about to leave the hospital, I heard a nurse and an interne discussing a patient who had got something in his eye. 'It's a bad city to get something in your eye in,' the nurse said. 'Yes,' the interne agreed. 'but there isn't a better place to get something in your eye out in.' I rushed past them with my hair in my wild eyes, and left the hospital. It was high time, too.

When and if I find a reputable psychosemanticist, I want to take up with

him something that happened to me one night more than two years ago. It may
be the basis of my etymological or philological problems, if that's what they
are – words, especially big ones, are beginning to lose their meaning for me.
Anyway, I woke up one summer night, from a deep dream of peacelessness,
only to realize that I had been startled by nothing whatever into a false sense of
insecurity. I had a desperate feeling that I was being closed in on, that there
was a menace in the woods behind my house or on the road in front of it,
watchful, waiting, biding its time. A few weeks later I bought a .38-calibre
Smith & Wesson police revolver, which startled my wife into a genuine sense
of insecurity. She hid the gun somewhere, and the cartridges somewhere else,
and I still don't know where they are. I have often thought of telling my psychosemanticist about it, and I sometimes have the feeling that I did call on him
and that the interview went like this:
  'Doesn't your wife's hiding the gun worry you?' he asked.
  'No,' I said.
  'It would me,' he confessed.
  'It would *what* you?' I demanded.
  It seemed to disturb him. '*What* would what me?' he asked cautiously.
  I suddenly couldn't think of a thing. I didn't even know what what was, but
I had to say something, so I said something: 'Ill fares the land, to galloping
fears a prey, where gobbledygook accumulates, and words decay.'
  About two years ago a wistful attempt was made by some Washington
bureau to straighten out the governmentalization of English. Directives were
sent to the various departments demanding, among other things, the elimina-
tion of 'finalize.' It was as hopeless as asking a tiny child to drop its popsicle
and bathe the St Bernard. Izationism is here to stay. It appeals to bureaucrats
and congressmen because of its portentous polysyllabification. Politicians love
it the way they love such expressions as 'legislativewise.' Lord Conesford,
stout defender of the Queen's English, recently paraphrased Churchill's
'Give us the tools and we will finish the job' by Washingtonizing it like this:
'Supply us with the implements and we will finalize the solution of the matter.'
  Webster's Unabridged, to my sorrow, recognizes such mastadonisms as
'psychologize' and 'physiologize' and, a prime favourite of congressmen,
'analogize.' It was, however, the physiologist I have already mentioned who
classified those of us who are still up and about as 'the non-institutionalized.'
This is a piece of bungalorum calculated to give even the healthiest men a
sense of monolithic insecurity. 'Non' has an insidious way of creeping into
izationisms. A piece of journalism was described on the air not long ago as
'absolutely non-fictionalized.' This negationization of what once could be
described as verbal communication caused a Scot of my acquaintance to ask
me, 'Have you nothing that is positively American? It seems to me that
everything one hears about in America is un-American.' This abused and im-
precise arrangement of letters seems bound to lose its proud A before long and
to end up as 'Un-american.' President Eisenhower might well add to his
imperatives the necessity to speak and write in such a way that we can be

understood by the English-speaking peoples as well as the other races of a world that stands in grave need of clarity, accuracy, and sense.

The conspiracy of yammer and merchandising against literate speech reached a notorious height in 1956 with a singing commercial for a certain cigarette which we were told 'tastes good like a cigarette should.' I have one or two suggestions for the Madison Avenue illiterates in the grey flannel suits. The first is a slogan for a brewery: 'We still brew good like we used to could.' The second is an ad for some maker of tranquillizing drugs:

Does he seldomly praise you any more? Those kind of husbands can be cured of the grumps with Hush-Up. So give you and he a break. Put Hush-Up in his food. It don't have no taste.

And now, for God's sake, let's go out and get a breath of fresh air.

'There's Something Out There!'

LOCH NESS, FOR THE past quarter of a century one of the most famous places on earth, is a long, narrow slash of deep water cutting diagonally across Inverness-shire in the historic West Highlands of Scotland. Its sombre depths and rugged banks are rich in lore and legend, as befits a former part of the great medieval domain of Macbeth, and the dark dwelling, in this century, of the world's most publicized and controversial aquatic creature, the so-called Loch Ness monster, since 1933 familiarly known to millions as Nessie. After twenty-four years the fabulous riddle of the loch still remains unsolved, still attracts thousands of sightseers annually, fascinates investigators, bemuses scientists, inspires in most of its Scottish hosts a quiet pride of possession, but in others a dour embarrassment. The monster has been seen again this year, the first time on March 11, by a police constable and a schoolmaster, whose experience was reported in the staid pages of *The Times* of London, which had recognized the possible existence of Nessie in December, 1933, seven months after its debut in the picturesque loch-laced region of heath and heather, burn and glen and strath, peat and barley, castle ruins, and ancient forts that once guarded the Great Glen. Loch Ness is also associated with Bruce, Bonnie Prince Charlie and the ships of Cromwell. Johnson and Boswell stopped there on their way to the Hebrides, and Robert Burns visited the loch and described it in verse.

Since the cry 'There's something out there!' was first raised on the lochside in the troubled spring of 1933, the Thing in the Loch has bobbed up month after month (except for a few longer wartime intervals) in the water and in the newspapers and periodicals of six continents. It has been written about seriously, sensationally and sceptically, facetiously, indignantly and even angrily. Cartoonists of many countries have used it for the subject of everything from sardonic silly-season whimsey to savage political satire. Although Nessie has not been, and may never be, 'received into the scientific category of Natural History,' to quote one cautious London zoologist, it has taken a permanent and conspicuous place in the long gallery of weird mysteries and wild alarms that extends from the Beast of Revelation to the flying saucers of the atomic era, and includes such ancient and fantastic British exhibits as the Questing Beast of the Arthurian legends, whose noise was 'like unto the Questyng of XXX coupil of houndes,' and the bunyip of Australia, reputed to seize and carry off wicked adults and incorrigible children. In our time, only Bhanjakris, the Abominable Snowman of Asia, approaches the grotesque stature of Nessie's fame, but the Himalayan mountain monster's scrapbook of press clippings is by no means so thick or varied, even though it was first sighted by Western eyes as long ago as 1899, thirty-four years before Nessie made its advent in the loch. (It became a contemporary of Nessie when it was seen by the Everest Expedition of 1936.)

Fourteen hundred years earlier than Nessie, or five centuries before Shakespeare's gory thane of Glamis and Cawdor murdered his way to royal power, there had been a wondrous tale of some enormous and mysterious animal in the complicated waters of the loch, whose tributaries include eight rivers and forty brooks. One Adamnan, in his Latin biography of St Columba, abbot of Iona, related how that holy man, encountering the dreadful creature about to seize a Pict, raised his hand and commanded, 'Touch not that man! Begone at once!' Whereupon it bewent, sinking tamely to its secret lair at the bottom of the river Ness.

It appears likely that this ancient legend was unknown to the couple who on April 14, 1933, while driving on the north shore of Ness, were attracted by a violent commotion in the loch, and watched a long, dark, humped body travel through the water at high speed and then suddenly dive, leaving in its wake a furious swirl of foam upon the surface. On that now celebrated April day, John Mackay, proprietor of the Drumnadrochit Hotel, was driving his wife home from Inverness on the motor road that runs for thirty miles along the northern bank when Mrs Mackay got what is generally conceded to be the first look at the great phenomenon. Others, to be sure, claim to have been first witness, including the distinguished Sir Compton Mackenzie, who insisted to me in Edinburgh in 1955 that he had glimpsed the thing on April 13. The author of 'Sinister Street' and more than eighty other books, now in his seventies, staunchly contends, against an imposing weight of contradictory evidence, that what he and the Mackays saw was only a large wounded grey seal.

A fortnight after their experience, the Mackays related what they had seen to their old friend Alexander Campbell, water-bailiff of Fort Augustus and local correspondent of the Inverness *Courier*. It was Mr Campbell who dubbed the creature 'The Loch Ness Monster' in his story for the *Courier*. Then, on May 11, 1933, Alexander Shaw and his son Alistair, standing in front of their house a hundred and fifty feet above the water on the south shore, saw something, again long and dark and humped, five hundred yards out, heading toward Urquhart Bay. A dependable count is impossible to obtain, but the monster was reported at least thirty-three times in 1933, and more than twice as often the following year, by which time a regular coach service was running tourists out from Inverness, thousands of motor cars from London, Glasgow, Aberdeen, and Edinburgh drove slowly along both banks, and hundreds of excited picnickers from everywhere thronged the banks in good weather. Trees had been cut down and underbush cleared away in the building of new motor roads, and long areas of the loch, once screened from view, were now visible.

During Nessie's heyday, the six years preceding the Second World War, the crowded hotels and shops of Loch Ness flourished mightily. Every second cottage was turned into a teashop, hotels were full up from Whitsuntide until late October, Bed and Breakfast signs appeared on hundreds of homes, and the loch was restlessly spangled with motor launches, private yachts, rowboats and canoes. By 1936 there was a heavy tangle of traffic from dawn to dusk along the more than sixty miles of new motor roads that encircle the loch. Newspapermen and photographers were assigned to the story singly, and in pairs, and in groups, by the newspapers of the British Isles and the Continent. Millions of words were printed, and the literature of the Loch Ness monster is now vast, unorganized, and bewildering. It takes ten hours to read through the *Daily Mail's* monster clippings. Scores of pamphlets on the subject appeared, and a number of books, including a 221-page volume, 'The Loch Ness Monster' (1934) by the late Lieutenant Commander R. T. Gould, R.N., and 'The Rival Monster,' a 1952 satire by the doubting Sir Compton, in which a flying saucer kills the monster. The latest book, 'More Than a Legend,' by Constance Whyte, was published only last April. The author is the wife of the manager of the Caledonian Canal, whose seventeen locks and the River Ness give the monster's lair access to firths and the open sea at the northeast end.

Twenty years ago, while leisurely touring the British Isles with my wife, I drove up one July evening to a small inn on the lochside. I had not given the monster story any study, or much thought. American newspapers, wary of tall tales since the era of Paul Bunyan and the years of P. T. Barnum, had approached the story lightly, somewhat in the manner of coloured postcards by Tuck in Britain which showed anglers pulling gigantic fish and dragons out of the loch. The New York *Herald Tribune*, in an editorial in 1933, had quickly dismissed the whole business as a tourist trap. Seven years later, Goebbels devoted a double page in the *Hamburger Illustrierte* to Nessie, 'exposing' it as a myth, a summer-season invention of hotels and tourist agencies. He ignored two skilfully faked photographs of the captured monster, which had been published in one of his own Berlin papers in 1934, one of them depicting Nessie being hauled out of the loch and the other showing it on public exhibition in Edinburgh. In 1940 Mussolini's paper *Popola d'Italia* declared the monster had been destroyed by a direct hit 'during the intensified bombing of Britain.' At about the same time a Tokyo journal, unaware of this bravura boast, informed its readers that the Thing was prowling the very heath on which Macbeth had encountered the Weird Sisters.

My wife and I had driven some ten miles of one bank without seeing anything unusual in the water. It was still and warm when we arrived at the inn. Two bagpipers were playing Scottish airs near the water's edge. That night I ventured to suggest to the innkeeper that the monster might have been nothing more than a pair of itinerant musicians who had floundered into the water, bagpipes and all. My host viewed my levity with polite resentment. 'There's something out there, you know,' he said quietly, but with unmistakable conviction. He had never seen the monster himself, but he knew a number of persons who had, one of them a nun, two of them priests. These three had taken their experiences calmly, but had declined to be interviewed by journalists. I was later to learn that a number of other eyewitnesses, mainly residents of Inverness-shire, carefully avoided publicity about what they had seen.

The next morning, up early, we drove almost all the way around the Loch Ness banks, but again saw nothing but boats on the brooding water. 'The loch itself oppresses me as much as it did when I first saw it twenty years ago,' wrote the *Daily Mail's* Percy Cater in 1953. (Two decades earlier he had been the first Fleet Street reporter on the scene.) 'It remains as enigmatic as the face of Mona Lisa. . . . Its surface, suggestive of its sinister deeps, is as forbidding as anything I know. . . . In this harsh landscape it is easy to think of strange goings-on in the loch.'

Ness, one of Scotland's many lochs, is the largest body of fresh water in the British Isles, twenty-four miles long, nearly two miles across at its widest, with a maximum depth of 754 feet. It is estimated to contain 263 billion cubic feet of water, or three times as much as romantic Loch Lomond. In shape it somewhat resembles Bermuda, from St George's to the tip of Somerset, and its area is not a great deal smaller. Situated in the foothills of the Grampians, it is alternately primitive and populated, a holiday resort of villages and hotels and cottages, with long high stretches of green hills that seem wild and remote from civilization. The loch's surface, more than fifty feet above sea level, never freezes over. It changes moods with the weather, from the tranquil blue of the Mediterranean to a dark imitation of the sea. Legend holds that there are vast subterranean caves far below the surface, but divers have never verified this. Not many have been able to descend very far and one, seeking to recover the jewels worn by a woman drowned in the loch, is said to have returned hastily to the surface, gibbering of strange sights and menacing creatures. The loch teems with salmon, trout, eels, and many another living thing. Superstition has also stocked it with kelpies, water beasts out of Gaelic myth, equine in form, reputed to seize and drown swimmers. The loch, according to another legend, never gives up its dead and, despite police records of recovered bodies, this old belief will not die.

Controversy, when I returned to Scotland in 1955, was as strong as ever, and two basic and opposed theories separated the believers from the scoffers: on the one hand, multiple witness, and on the other, mass hallucination. There was also a faction of optical illusionists who based their hypothesis on the strange tricks played upon the eye by the changing moods, the shifting lights and shadows, and the deceptive distances of the loch. Hoax and hysteria had early begun raising their mischievous heads. One day in 1934, the veritable tracks of a hippopotamus were discovered on one bank near the water's edge. Casts of them were hastily made and shipped to the British Museum. They all turned out to be of the same four-toed foot, plainly a hunter's trophy that had fallen into the hands of some practical joker. Now and then strange contraptions were secretly slipped into the loch at night, home-made monsters built of logs or wooden chairs linked to miscellaneous junk with rope or wire. Weird amphibians, spawned in fears and fancies, prowled the lochside at night, one of them resembling an enormous horse with eyes as bright as car headlights.

One morning the skeletal remnants of a voracious beast's midnight meal were found on the shore, but they proved to be butcher-shop bones arranged by a waggish human hand. Despite the exposure of hoaxes, there was a growing belief among crofters and other lochsiders that the monster was in fact an amphibian, with a habit of hunting the woods at night. Mrs Whyte flatly states her conviction that *an Niseag*, as she calls Nessie, does come out of the water and cross the road. She cites the experience of a motorcyclist named Grant, a man of steady nerves and good reputation, who almost bumped into the creature, on a moonlit night in January, 1934, as it 'crossed the road in two bounds and plunged into the water.' He called it an unknown hybrid, fifteen to twenty feet long. Six months earlier a Mr and Mrs Spicer had had a similar encounter in early daylight with a thing that also crossed the road, in front of their car, its long neck, like an elephant's trunk, undulating and forming several arches. Their account had been accepted as bona fide by Commander Gould. Unbelievers promptly named this animal a grey seal, a sea lion, or a walrus, but Grant and the Spicers vehemently insist that what they saw was of loathsome texture and unique slimy appearance, with a small head and curious oval eyes, and their description conforms to that of an English engineer who, about the same period, had watched an enormous hybrid in the water near the shore at dawn.

All sorts of speculations and suppositions have been advanced by those who refuse to believe in an unknown beast: the creature is Sir Compton's amphibious grey seal, or a school of playful salmon (two of the most persistent assumptions), a shark, a killer whale, a giant squid, a diving crested grebe or a green cormorant, an otter with a fish in its mouth, a ribbon fish, a salamander, a romping of boisterous porpoises, a flight of wild geese skimming the loch's surface, even a prehistoric Plesiosaurus which had survived the Mesozoic Age – this was once a long creature with four short legs that could be used for paddles in swimming. Believers in the survival of outsize prehistoric monsters point to a gigantic 'bat bird,' closely resembling a pterodactyl, which explorer Ivan Sanderson beheld a few years ago swooping above an African river, showing the long gleaming teeth of its massive lower jaw.

An oldster claimed that the monster was a German airship that had plunged into the loch in 1918 and kept rising and sinking. One group of theorists stuck to the notion of a long hollow tree trunk, inhabited by underwater creatures, which surfaced when they left it and submerged when they returned from food forays. Others mentioned mirages or the possibility of phenomena caused by subterranean gases, blasting, rock faults, and earth tremors. In November, 1950, the Portsmouth Naval Station's School of Torpedos and Mines 'exploded the myth' with pontifical authority by revealing that a chain of mines had been planted in the loch during the First World War. This pronouncement was soon forgotten with most of the other suggestions, including one about a small boy's pet crocodile which had escaped into the loch many years before. Old wives' tales and those of ancient mariners recalled unexplained disturbances in Ness or other lochs in 1872, 1893, 1903, and 1923.

One candidate for the title of Loch Ness monster which has been curiously neglected is the oarfish (*Regalecus glesne*). It reaches a length of from twenty to thirty feet, can live longer than twenty years, is known to swim occasionally on the surface, and 'when it swims, it throws its elongated body into great serpentine curves.' When the oarfish is excited it raises a crest, or mane, consisting of the anterior rays of its long dorsal fin. It is noteworthy that at least fourteen separate reports have described the loch creature as 'having a mane like a horse's.' A few years ago an alleged oarfish thirteen feet long was pulled out of nearby Loch Fyne. Against the oar's validity as the true monster are its narrowness of body, its silvery colour, and the coral redness of its fins. But the primary argument against the oarfish is its supposed allergy to fresh water. A conger eel can live in either salt or fresh or brackish water, but zoologists doubt that the oar has such a power of accommodation, though none has adduced positive proof. The assumption that Nessie was lochborn is supported by the admitted difficulty any large creature would have in reaching Loch Ness from the open sea. Commander Gould, however, defended the possibility after a careful study of the River Ness, which leads to Beauly Firth. He figured that a sea creature the size of Nessie could manage the passage, at night and unseen, when the water is in spate, in January or February. It was his respected opinion that brought about Nessie's first appearance in *The Times* of London.

Just five years ago a 'wake monster' was added to the lively conjectures of conclusion jumpers. This ingenious conception of Nessie grew out of the loch's most terrible disaster, the tragic destruction of John Rhodes Cobb's celebrated jet-propelled powerboat, *Crusader*, which was streaking at more than two hundred miles an hour over a measured mile on September 29, 1952, seeking a new world's record, when it struck a wave band set up by another boat, nose-dived sharply, and was literally blown to bits like an exploding bomb. Such wave bands, long and narrow, expire harmlessly on beaches, but are reactivated when trapped between sheer cliffs at water's edge on either bank, as is often the case in Ness, and may lash back and forth in antic force for nearly half an hour after the passage of a vessel. The 'wake monster' is worthy of mention as an outstanding instance of the continuing reluctance of sceptics to admit that the Thing in the loch is alive.

We come now, in this court of lore, to the witnesses for the defence of a living Nessie, those orthodox believers, impressively numerous, whose consistent testimony over a period of twenty-four years forms the classic description of Nessie as something strange, enormous, and alive, elongated (from twenty to fifty feet), capable of sinuous, hump-producing behaviour and a surface speed of twenty knots or more, given to unpredictable appearances and reappearances, usually in still, warm weather, and sudden submergings which leave in its wake a foaming agitation.

Well over a thousand persons, according to the *Daily Mail*, have watched, or glimpsed, the wonder in the water, whose recorded appearances have now reached a total of more than three hundred. It has been seen for less than a minute by some observers, for nearly an hour by others, lolling on the surface occasionally, or 'sunbathing,' but for the most part undulating rapidly over the surface of the loch in short spurts, or in cavortings that keep it visible for several hundred yards. Its disappearances have usually been followed by at least one re-emergence. Commander Gould, arriving at his own hypothetical measurements by averaging those of fifty-eight witnesses he interviewed in 1933 and 1934, figured that Nessie is about forty-five feet long. The central part of the body he estimated to be twenty feet in length, with an active ten-foot tail, and a fifteen-foot snakelike neck surmounted by a head resembling that of a sheep or a small horse or cow. Its main body has often been described as being like 'an upturned rowing boat.' (In Britain such a boat is often fifteen feet long.) Nessie is possessed of 'inviolable mutism' – a phrase invented by the late William Bolitho to describe the vocal silence of Harpo Marx. No witness has ever heard it make any sound except that of the swirling waters. In this it conforms to the nature of its famous cousin, the sea serpent. The seal, by the way, is a notorious barker and the porpoise a celebrated chatterbox.

Let us now consider the testimony of three separate eyewitnesses notable for soundness, competence, and reliability – the first of them an experienced skipper in the sturdy tradition of Masefield's 'dirty British coaster with a salt-caked smokestack' – Captain William Brodie of Leith, master of the steam tug *Arrow*. This tug was plying the loch on August 30, 1938, when its captain and its crew, except for one fireman, sighted Nessie. Captain Brodie thereupon entered the following in his log: 'Sighted Loch Ness monster while close inshore about two and a half miles east of Castle Urquhart at 4:40 P.M. . . . In sight again for half a minute 4:50 P.M.' Later in an interview, Captain Brodie said that on its second appearance the monster travelled at great speed near the tug, displaying several humps as against the one or two he had observed first. It could not have been a whale, he said, or any other common creature, and his crew agreed. 'I did not believe in the monster and had not been looking for it,' Captain Brodie insisted. 'There can be no doubt of the monster's existence.'

We come next to Mr Ewan Fraser, former caretaker of Urquhart Castle. Mr Fraser, seventy-three years old, but with the keen vision of the lifetime lochside resident, had spotted the monster in July, 1934, and did not see it again until August 14, 1954. This time he quickly called his neighbour, Maggie Macdonald, and her description of the monster, the standard one, coincided with his. At this very moment, it later transpired, the same manifestation had been watched by a Mackenzie and a Maclean, the latter having viewed it through a telescope.

Our third witness is the County Clerk for Inverness-shire, whose name does not appear in my records for the simple and persuasive reason, I think, that his title carries, for his fellow Scots, undeniable weight and authority. After he had reported seeing Nessie of the classic description in the early summer of 1947, the Inverness County Council on May 3 of that year officially recognized the existence of the monster in the loch. 'Now if an English county clerk had made the report,' said a council member, 'it could be rejected as dubious or unlikely, but when *our* County Clerk says there's something out there, there's something out there.'

It would take a Senate subcommittee investigating unlochian activities a good six months to question all the other witnesses for Nessie. Subpoenas would have to go out to scores of wearers of the tartan, to many a Ross, Cameron, MacFadden, Gray, Campbell, Alexander, Gillies, Graham, Blair, Fraser, Douglas, Gillespie, Scott, and Macdonald. (One Captain John Macdonald, it is true, who had made twenty thousand trips up and down the loch over a period of fifty years as skipper of a MacBrayne steamer, resolutely held out for salmon at play, but he had retired well before April, 1933.) The long panel of witnesses includes the nun, a major general, a rear admiral, a Member of Parliament, three doctors, a water bailiff, three bus drivers, a mining director, a vicar, four priests, and other clergymen, several policemen and teachers, a piermaster, several caretakers of lochside estates, a contractor, a number of businessmen, five workmen, a balconyful of hotel guests, and five woodcutters who, like the workmen and the guests, all saw it at once. No one could estimate the number of foreign visitors who may have watched the marvel in the water. At the end of October, 1934, the visitors' book of one lochside hotel contained the names of guests from New Zealand, Chicago, Siam, the Sudan, Ceylon, Johannesburg, Paris, Ireland, Berlin, Gibraltar, the Punjab, Italy, Sydney, Melbourne, Hong Kong, Hamburg, Canada, Alexandria, South Persia, Tanganyika, Rangoon, Madras, Durban, Amsterdam, Vienna, Detroit, and New Jersey.

Nessie's famous humps, the most consistently reported feature of its morphology, are probably produced by what Commander Gould called its 'flexuous motion.' All observers have seen at least one, and a great majority have reported two or three. One man said he counted twelve, but this may be put down to the expected exaggeration of the overwrought, the romantic, or the untrained observer, one of whom placed the monster's length at ninety feet. The creature's undulations on the surface of the water are characteristic of all reports of sea serpents, whose existence in the salt waters of the world was ably argued by Commander Gould in an earlier book, 'The Case for the Sea Serpent.' Scoffers point to the fact that the body of no such creature has ever been washed ashore anywhere. To this Commander Gould could only advance the probability that these enormous creatures sink to the bottom of the sea after death.

The pictorial record of Nessie, compiled haphazardly through the years, is interesting but disappointing. It comprises a number of hasty snapshots of something dark at a distance, some lengths of movie film, without close-ups or sharp definition, and a wide variety of sketches, made on the spot or drawn later from memory. There is no conclusive or even convincing evidence in any photograph of Nessie's exact confirmation or true scientific category. Most observers did not carry cameras, and those that did were usually too startled to employ them properly or too excited to use them at all. Several golden opportunities to photograph the monster at close range appear to have been lost. A gentleman who swears he saw Nessie swallowing fish like a cormorant forty feet from shore had nothing with him but his retinas, and two priests out fishing in a rowboat, who saw the monster for many minutes less than fifty yards from their boat, had forgotten to bring a camera. The best-known photograph was taken in April, 1934, by Mr Robert Kenneth Wilson, a surgeon of London's West End. It was reproduced in the *Daily Mail*, and hundreds of prints of it have been circulated. A few years ago this picture was admitted as Exhibit A in a B.B.C. television investigation of the case of Nessie, but the 'jury,' after careful consideration in the best tradition of English justice, finally returned a verdict of 'not proven.'

Early on, as the English say, monster hunts were organized, and everybody from a naturalist and big-game hunter named M. A. Wetherell (the man who discovered the hippo's spoor) to a troop of Boy Scouts from Glasgow took a hand. Sir Edward Mountain, insurance magnate, in July, 1934, stationed carefully selected observers at intervals of a mile along that length of bank between Urquhart Castle and Fort Augustus off which Nessie has been most often reported. Four of his men and one woman caught sight of Nessie that summer – one William Campbell saw it twice – and half a dozen photographs were taken, with no outstanding success because Nessie was always too swift or too far away. Captain D. J. Munro, R.N. (Ret.), established four observation posts, three on land and one afloat, manned by watchers equipped with telephoto and movie cameras, range finders, stop watches, and powerful binoculars. He also sold shilling shares, to defray expenses, in what he called Loch Ness Monster, Limited, to be capitalized at fifteen hundred pounds. The record does not show how many shares were sold, but some of his men saw Nessie and one or two were able to snap pictures.

It wasn't long before the Loch Ness Fishery Board, the County Council, the Constabulary of Inverness-shire, and other Scottish authorities became alarmed by announced intentions to trap or kill the loch's mysterious resident, which is reputed to have brought more income to Scotland than any other single attraction except Scotch whisky. Two men threatened to stretch thin wires across the loch in the region of Nessie's favourite haunts, baited with a secret lure. A member of the Overseas Club of London planned to capture it in great nets or shoot it with a harpoon gun. J. E. Williamson, an American, said he would go down into the water and hunt for Nessie in his 'photosphere,' a globe six feet in diameter at the end of a 400-foot steel tube. All manner of hydrophones and other depth-sounding equipment were brought to the loch, after an echo graph of something long, eighty fathoms deep, and presumably alive had been registered upon an asdic screen aboard a trawler. The world was closing in on Nessie. When rumours that a submarine would hunt it down were circulated, and there was wild talk of a mighty, electrified loch-wide wire net, the Loch Ness Fishery Board forbade the use of any nets, and higher Scottish authorities went into action to protect Nessie from capture, or death, or molestation. It had been well-established by now that the fantastic creature was not menacing to man, but afraid of him, a peaceable, even timid animal that wished only to be let alone.

In December, 1933, Sir Godfrey Collins, then Secretary for Scotland, had issued instructions 'Forbidding any attack on the animal if sighted,' but monster hunts with great nets or lethal weapons continued to be talked about. The Brighton Aquarium had offered one thousand pounds for Nessie alive, and Bertram Mills, a circus proprietor, upped this to twenty thousand pounds, Then, in 1938, Sir Murdoch Macdonald, M.P. for Inverness, wrote to Lieutenant Colonel John Colville, Secretary for Scotland, asking that the police be instructed to take 'immediate measures to safeguard the monster.' Thereupon Major A. C. Maclean, chief constable of Inverness-shire, ordered his men to be on the lookout for monster hunters who would deprive Scotland of its famous and harmless attraction. The only case of a leviathan more strictly protected than Nessie was that of Pelorus Jack, a huge grampus which for many years around the turn of the century used to pilot ships regularly through French Pass, Cook Strait, New Zealand. It became a national institution and was protected by a stern Order in Council of the New Zealand legislature.

Commander Gould, not only a naval officer of long experience, but also easily the best-implemented investigator of sea serpents, was not a man to jump to facile conclusions. He made no attempt to classify the loch monster with scientific exactness, but was content to set it down as an anomalous creature of the general nature and morphology of the sea serpent, which had probably fled into the loch from the sea to escape its natural enemy, the whale. In his book on sea serpents, his convincing list of sightings of water animals similar to Nessie by seafaring men, one of them later a commodore of the Cunard fleet, takes in an enormous creature frequently seen off Gloucester, Massachusetts, in 1817 and 1819, another observed in Loch Hourn (1872), and a third in the Kyle of Loch Alsh in 1893. To these Dr Maurice Burton, Deputy Keeper of the British Museum's Department of Natural History, added the lau in his 'Living Fossils' (1954). The lau inhabits Lake Victoria in Africa and is described as being from forty to one hundred feet long, with a thick body, a long neck, and a snakelike head. It has been viewed by officers of the Victoria-Nyanza steamers and explorers of standing.

Dr Burton, bearing in mind the multiple descriptions of Nessie's structure and deportment, visited the London Aquarium one day three years ago to observe the conger eels there, some of them five feet long. His vigil at tankside resulted in positive evidence that congers can swim on the surface, undulating latterly and producing humps that seem vertical, and leaving violent agitations of water when they dive. Sometimes, he found, only the tail was visible above the surface, or the long snake-like neck, or just the central part of the dark body, and Nessie has been seen in all of these postures. Dr Burton ably argues the possibility of a conger attaining giant size.

When Nessie went unsighted from September, 1939, until August, 1940, many scoffmonsters declared this was proof that it had never existed except in the imagination. But no war year actually went by without a report of it in the water, and it was seen eleven times in 1941. The winds of interest and attention had shifted in the weather of war, holiday makers had departed, and only doctors' cars and official vehicles travelled the lochside roads.

Naturalists in Britain, wary of a long tradition of hoaxes, including spurious fossils of 'prehistoric man,' have been disinclined to go out on a limb about the Thing in the Loch, since there is lacking any hide or hair, head or tail, of the enigmatic Whatever-it-is, and therefore many questions as to the monster's origin, ancestry, longevity, feeding habits, and sex life, often propounded, remain scientifically unanswered or even untackled. It is known that the conger, like other eels, is a bottom feeder and not a surface diner. The oarfish, like the sea serpent for which it has often been mistaken, has kept most of its habits a secret. There have been vague plans to introduce an oar into the loch and see what happens, but so far this project remains in what movie men call the talking stage. It may be that Walt Disney, who has twice visited Loch Ness, will give the monster the benefit of one of his thorough and fascinating natural history film documents. His New York office says that such a project is under consideration, but so far has only been roughly blocked out. It should be a notable undertaking, if it comes to pass – the champion photographer of *ferae naturae* versus the champion evader of the camera lens, in the contest of the century.

Whatever the enigma of Loch Ness may be, and whatever happens to it finally, it is assured of a double immortality: an everlasting place in the colourful and gaudy annals of the Scottish Highlands, and a permanent residence in the back files of *The Times* of London and perhaps a thousand other journals around the world. These annals and files are increased and enlivened every year by the addition of some new item: a caretaker claims he saw the monster drooling a blackish oily substance; a sailor asserts that the colour of its serpentine coils is yellowish; a college student insists he clocked it making sixty miles an hour; a posthumous report comes to light of a smaller monster seen one day, ten years ago, trailing Nessie at a distance of two hundred yards. This report of a second monster was made by two ladies of the Fraser family of Fort Augustus, who had requested that nothing be published about their experience during their lifetime, and nothing was.

The famous Riddle of the Loch still baffles investigators, but strange things continue to be found in the waters of the world. The most astounding of these was the 1938 discovery that the Coelacanth, a fish supposed to have been extinct for seventy million years, is still extant, in fine fettle and excellent health. Where it has been all this time is as great a mystery as the origin and nature of Nessie. It serves to indicate a depressing possibility that fish, which preceded man, may yet outlast him on this whirling globe. One far day another Nessie may rise to the sullen surface of the loch, scan the silent banks, and behold no living thing staring back at it – nothing furred, or feathered, or wearing clothes. But there are queer and present dangers to worry about. In this ominous era of guided missiles and unidentified flying objects, the cry most often heard is 'There's something up there!' A few years ago eerie green lights appeared high above Texas, and something large and blue and whirling is said to have pursued automobiles on high roads in Oregon when dusk was falling. Only last April residents of Rhodesia twice saw a flock of flying lizards, each about thirty inches long, perhaps the great grandchildren of Mr Sanderson's gigantic 'bat bird.' And what is that strange object in the sky, high above the housetops there, oblate and luminous, moving so swiftly, whooshing so loudly, headed for Earth?

I don't know the answer to any of the mysteries of air, land, or sea, but the remarkable case of the Coelacanth has aroused hopes that Nessie, or one of its ilk, may yet be caught or cornered and classified. They seem to be as prevalent as witches in many parts of the planet. In addition to Nessie and the lau, there are the Skrimsl of the Icelandic fjords and the Ogo-pogo of British Columbia, and it may be that another country than Scotland will eventually be the first to admit one of these underwater monsters to the scientific category of Natural History. Meanwhile, I am betting on Scotland, for many centuries ago it was written 'In every loch there lives a dreaded beast.' Residents of the banks of all the Scottish lochs now keep a sharp, if furtive, lookout for such wonders of the water, and each loch has its ancient legend of 'a floating island' or some other strange upheaval from time to time. I have little knowledge of what may be in the other lochs of Scotland, but I confidently join Captain Brodie, Ewan Fraser, the County Clerk of Inverness-shire, and almost innumerable others in saying of Loch Ness, with unshakable conviction: There's something out there.

In conclusion, I am happy to be able to report that last-minute researches have definitely established at least one positive identification. The name of the County Clerk of Inverness-shire is Mr J. W. MacKillop.

The Moribundant Life, or, Grow
Old Along with Whom?

THE ENGLISH LADY ON my right at a summer dinner party in London
two years ago lifted her fluent eyebrows in a finely shaded disapproval
of my observation, over the *coupe framboise*, that most of the male
American writers I have known are dead. She had taken it as a bit of gaunt and
sepulchral levity, and she would have slapped my wrist gracefully with her fan
if she had had one. Over the coffee, I persuaded her and the rest of those at
table – there were eight of us – that I was not jesting but, rather, trembling,
whistling in the dark as the moonlight of Jeopardy glinted on the marble and
granite names of so many of my friends and acquaintances, all of them fellow-
wordmen of my own generation. I defined my generation as consisting mainly
of men born in the eighteen-nineties, but with an overlap of several years each
way.

We had got onto the subject of the comparative longevity of writers in
America and those living in Europe when someone mentioned that Laurence
Housman had just celebrated his ninetieth birthday. Someone else then remarked that Bernard Berenson, an American, but of long residence in Italy,
was also ninety. One of the gentlemen present, an English publisher, topped
the others by reminding them that Eden Phillpotts, who was born in the year
Lincoln removed General McClellan from the command of the Army of the
Potomac, was ninety-three and writing television scripts for the B.B.C. The
only elderly men of letters in America that I could think of offhand who were
still alive were Robert Frost, Samuel Hopkins Adams, and Carl Sandburg.
But I could reel off the names of thirty fellow-countrymen whose literary
careers and physical being came to an end in their fifties or forties, and at least
half a dozen upon whom, though still alive, one form or another of writer's
cramp had fallen. I confessed, in the warmth of the wine, that I had recently
frightened myself into a cold night sweat by running the list up to ninety-eight,
including newspapermen and a few editors and publishers who had written
something and died soon after.

The lady on my right – the one on my left was interested mainly in children
under seven – asked me if it was true that Americans can only write in certain
phases of the moon and in odd parts of the house, but before I could attempt
an answer, an anecdote about Gordon Craig drifted on admiring laughter
down the table. It seems it had been decided earlier that year to pay homage
to the memory of Mr Craig on the fiftieth anniversary of the publication of his

first book, whereupon his admirers discovered (I don't know why it surprised them) that he was alive and eighty-three.

Everybody at table knew that W. Somerset Maugham, at eighty-one, was still writing in his villa at Saint-Jean-Cap-Ferrat. A score of other writers, alive at the time and still writing in their seventies and eighties and even nineties, were mentioned, Lord Bertrand Russell, Walter De la Mare, Max Beerbohm, H. M. Tomlinson, A. E. Coppard, Percy Lubbock, St John Ervine, Sir Compton Mackenzie, and A. A. Milne among them. In the two years since that dinner party, a few of these venerable authors have died, but 1955 was the high water mark, perhaps the finest hour of elderly but sturdy English writing.

When I belonged to the English Club as a university freshman, more than forty years ago, we used to think vaguely of English authors as being one with sticks and stones and Tennyson, or as men of a fine *fin-de-siècle* Stevensonian fragility, who faintly called, with the doomed Dowson, for madder music and for stronger wine, and died before the *sommelier* reached the table, upon which lay a lovely lyric inscribed to a damsel of dream and writ in Bordeaux red. I woke up the morning after the dinner party realizing that the British authors who had ceased to be before their pens had gleaned their teeming brains were but drops in a lusty bucket of vast durability. I remembered that the aged Swinburne had given up the ghost only a year before the youthful O. Henry, in 1909, a year also attained by George Meredith, the modernness of whose 'Modern Love' goes back to the first year of the Civil War. It was comforting to contemplate the host of British authors that had easily survived the white plague and the other perils of the strange decade of the Yellow Book and the green carnation. I got out of bed, with some effort at the age of sixty, and went through a few mild setting-up exercises, but it wasn't terribly reassuring to remind myself that I am a stronger man than Aubrey Beardsley was, or that I had lasted eight years longer than Thackeray, who once referred, in his forty-seventh year, to his 'old and decaying carcass.'

A few days later, I tottered over to the British Museum, half expecting to bump into H. Rider Haggard or Wilkie Collins on the way, to look up some more facts and figures on British and American authors. It didn't take me long to expand the list of British men of letters who had gone on a long, long time. Ernest Newman was eighty-seven then, and still writing a weekly column of music criticism. Lord Dunsany was seventy-seven, and capable of denouncing modern poetry in no quavering tones. John Cowper Powys, who I thought had disappeared from the earth about the same time as the Brevoort dining room, was eighty-three, Sir Philip Gibbs was seventy-eight, John Masefield and Oliver St John Gogarty were seventy-seven, E. M. Forster and A. S. M. Hutchinson were seventy-six, Alfred Noyes was seventy-five, P. G. Wodehouse was seventy-four, and Frank Swinnerton was seventy-one. I turned to source books about American literary figures of my sex, and was delighted to find out that quite a few of them, born in the vintage years of the last century, were still above the green quilt. Percy Mackaye, eighty; Upton Sinclair, seventy-seven; James Branch Cabell, seventy-six; Carl Van Vechten, seventy-five; Clarence Budington Kelland and Stark Young, seventy-four; George Jean Nathan, seventy-three; and William Carlos Williams, seventy-two.

After my exploration of living Americans, I looked up the dates of some of the departed, and more or less illustrious, men of letters on our side. I hope that some researcher, with more years left than I have, will some day do a monograph on the curious viability, at home and abroad, of writers born in the eighteen-sixties. Owen Wister ('The Virginian'), born in 1860, lived to be seventy-eight; Hamlin Garland ('Main-Travelled Roads'), 1860, reached seventy-nine; George Ade ('Fables in Slang'), 1866, and Meredith Nicholson ('The House of a Thousand Candles'), also 1866, lived to be seventy-eight and eighty-one, respectively. Booth Tarkington and Edgar Lee Masters, born in the last year of the writer's decade, attained the ages of seventy-six and eighty. There were others out of that special period, too – Finley Peter Dunne and David Graham Phillips – but they didn't do so well, reaching sixty-eight and forty-three, in that order. Violence ended Phillips's life; he was shot and killed one day in Gramercy Park, back in 1911. Born just this side of the viable decade, Gouverneur Morris lived to be seventy-seven, and Rex Beach seventy-two. This list of durables is incomplete, and I have no doubt that Indiana alone, seemingly the state of highest vitality, could add more names to those of Ade, Nicholson, and Tarkington.

I tottered back to my hotel, remembering, on the way, various writers of my own generation, and their youthful ghosts began getting between me and the sun. 'Look out,' a taxi-driver cried as I stepped into the street, 'and you'll live longer!' Look out for what, besides motor cars, I wondered. I began piecing together out of memories of my lost colleagues the perils and threats, the man-traps and the pitfalls that had beset them in their short journeys from light to dark.

When I got back to my hotel, the lady who had sat on my right at dinner was there, looking anxious, and a bit surprised to find me up and about. I tried to look rugged, but she kept regarding me as if I were a flickering match. She had been worrying about my descending flame, she said, and had called to see if I was ready to depart. I told her, in the sitting room of my suite, from which the empty bottles and other debris of the night before had been removed, that I was still holding on, in spite of an ominous, unaccountable sound in my ears after my tenth or twelfth cocktail, something like Reginald Gardiner's imitation of a train, and a disturbing tendency of faces to recede dimly, float past me, accelerating their speed, and then come drifting slowly back.

'You all live too hard,' my companion said, 'as if life were chasing you.' And then she proved that she had been giving the situation of my generation serious thought. 'Even your common idioms are jumpy,' she continued. 'You say "Take it in your stride" and "Knock it off" and "Break it up" and "Drag it out" and "Pipe it down" and "Snap out of it" and "Step on it." Your daily routine is so very like the two-mile-high hurdles of one of your field meets. You speak of the life hereafter, in certain of your titles, as if you were breaking your necks to get there – "Hell-Bent for Heaven," "Heaven's My Destination," and "One Foot in Heaven." And it does seem that you never go to bed. Are you all afraid of the dark?'

'We never take it lying down,' I told her firmly. 'Each generation has its rituals and habit patterns. For us, every night is New Year's Eve, I'm afraid. It isn't easy for a writer's wife, returning home from her mother's early in the morning for another go at her marriage, to tell whether her husband is having a nightcap or an eyeopener, the last drink of the evening before or the first one of the day at hand.'

My friend sighed and made a small, impatient gesture. 'How do your wives stick it?' she demanded. 'And what keeps them ticking?' It was a hard question and I turned it over for several moments. 'We have been accused of making a career of sex, a hobby of drinking, a havoc of marriage, and a tradition of divorce,' I began, 'but the wife of an American writer at least knows what she is getting into. We pick women for our mates who have great constitutional strength and are not twittery, even in the face of a charging rhinoceros. A writer's wife usually lasts until her husband begins addressing her by snapping his fingers or going "Psst!" This is an invariable sign that he is going through what we call change of wife in the male. In such a state the writer husband often uses expressions like "marry-go-round" and "welded blitz." '

My companion's gaze turned a little cold. 'It's all the fault of what you call the Scotch Fitzgerald era,' she said severely.

'Gin,' I corrected her, with an impatient gesture of my own, but she talked through it.

'You are not *really* afraid of the dark. Fitzgerald called the novel he liked most "Tender Is the Night." '

'He also wrote "Taps at Reveille," ' I reminded her, 'and Hemingway wrote "Death in the Afternoon." Vincent McHugh's "Sing Before Breakfast" is, of course, short for "Sing Before Breakfast, Die Before Night." ' My guest's voice turned a little sharp. 'Pity you didn't beat Koestler to "Darkness at Noon," ' she said. I opened a bottle of Scotch, to keep up the reputation of my generation, and ordered tea for my visitor.

On my fourth highball, I began to brag a little about the achievements of Edgar Allan Poe. 'Poe,' I said, 'was perhaps the first great nonstop literary drinker of the American nineteenth century. He made the indulgences of Coleridge and De Quincey seem like a bit of mischief in the kitchen with the cooking sherry. O. Henry picked up the flagon where Poe had let it fall, and passed it on to us.'

'Don't romanticize it,' said my friend. 'There must be other factors than liquor involved in the brevity of your lives.'

I had to think that over for a while before replying. 'Senescence comes up gradually over here,' I began at last, 'but in America it pounces on writers like a catamount. This is another reason for our going through life, such as it is, at a dogtrot. I was once about to hand a quarter to a bewhiskered old scalawag who accosted me on the street when I recognized him; he had been a sophomore at Ohio State when I was a senior. There are many other terrors that should not be overlooked: the impalpable, the imponderable, the personal income tax, the mobile investigatory units of Congress, the bears under the bed, the green men from Mars, the cats sealed up in the walls, the hearts beating under the floor boards, the faces of laughing girls that recede, float past, and come back again.'

On my eighth drink, I tried in vain to think of an evening I had spent with any American writer at the end of which he or I had gone home. I recalled, instead, the night in 1934 when Scott Fitzgerald and I went on from 10 P.M. till eight in the morning, and I sketched in the highlights and the highballs for my shocked companion. 'We were both to blame that night,' I said, 'but it was mainly *my* fault the day in 1936 when Thomas Wolfe came to a cocktail party at my New York apartment. He stayed until nine in the morning, and was thoughtful enough to phone back an hour later to ask if he could return to apologize for having stayed so long. It is possible that our American custom of buying whisky by the case,' I added, 'may have something to do with our late hours.'

Upon this, my companion had a grave question for me. 'Do not an American writer and his wife ever think to leave a party before midnight?'

'I wouldn't exactly say leave,' I told her. 'The process is more often one of being put out. On such an occasion, the writer and his mate take up at home where they left off at the party. This is known as bringing out the jugs with the wife. It is customary, in this ritual, to telephone, at three o'clock in the morning, an old friend and his wife. If, for some reason, they cannot appear, which is most improbable, their would-be host is likely, around five o'clock, to threaten to read aloud to his wife from whatever whisky-stained manuscript he may be working on fitfully at the time. To avert this, it is usually the wife's custom to deride the intelligence or sartorial getup of some girl he was once incredibly fond of in his Greenwich Village years.'

'You may be a lost generation,' my companion sighed, 'but you are extraordinarily evident while you last.' I could tell from the way she accented her key words that she was beginning to feel her third cup of tea. Presently, she took flight on the mothy wings of a new eloquence. 'You are incurably competitive, all of you,' she went on, 'and a constant sense of competition is likely to burn men out in their middle years. You speak of the writing game and the publishing game. You know the score, you are forever throwing your highball past someone, and you say "Keep pitching," instead of "Goodbye." '

I had to cut in on her there. 'You are speaking of our fast ball,' I corrected her, but she motioned for silence.

'I fancy that even your reveries are competitive, that you dream not of the girls you have loved but of how you took them away from somebody else.'

'It's time for a toast,' I told her, 'to Edgar Allan Poe,' and I got up and opened a bottle of sherry and poured her some, after slugging my own next drink. I did not wish to diminish the lady's fascinated dismay. 'Here's to Poe,' I said, 'who found his manuscripts in a bottle.'

She sipped and I gulped. 'Please sit down,' she commanded. 'It takes a great deal out of a man to drink standing up. You always seem to ride pleasure as if it were an unsaddled giraffe. You go about your other relaxations in such a way that they seem the arduous involvement of a husband trying to wash a Venetian blind. It is hard to tell your conformity from your dissent, you hit them both so hard.'

I sat down reluctantly, for I had an urge to pace. 'Some twenty years ago,' I began, 'I composed, with a writer friend of mine, a parody of A. E. Housman that seems to fit in here somehow, if you would care to hear it.'

The lady gestured gracefully for more sherry, and I filled her glass. 'I think,' she said, 'that I can now stand anything,' and I began to recite:

> Loneliest of these, the married now
> Are hung with gloom along the vow,
> And stand about the wedland drear
> Dreaming dreams of yesteryear.
>
> Now, of our twoscore years and ten,
> Forty will not come again,
> And take from fifty springs that many,
> It only leaves us ten, if any.
>
> And since to look at girls in bloom
> Ten small years is little room,
> From out the wedland we will go
> And try to find the mistletoe.

My guest set down her unfinished sherry and rose to her feet. 'Grow your age, to use one of your own idioms,' she said. 'Rise quite above it. If poor, dear Henry James had lived in America, instead of England, we should probably not have had "The Turn of the Screw," to say nothing of the novels of his major phase.'

She was about to start for the door when I proposed another toast, this one solemn and sincere. 'I have decided to write a memoir of our so pleasant, if gruesome, conversation,' I said, 'and it has occurred to me that between the writing and the printing of the piece one or more of those we have mentioned, all in wonder and in awe, may have reached the top of that hill beyond which there is no going.' She picked up her glass again, and I touched it with mine, and gave my toast: 'God rest you tranquil, gentlemen, whom life did not dismay.'

After the lady had gone, I phoned downstairs to ascertain the phase of the moon, and found that it was not good for writing. Besides, there are no odd places to work in the suites of the Stanton Hotel. I decided to lie down, instead. After all, an American writer born as long ago as 1894 cannot get too much rest.

Credos and Curios

They shall have stars at elbow and foot; . . .
And death shall have no dominion.

And death shall have no dominion . . .

DYLAN THOMAS

Thurber and his Circle.

The Notebooks of James Thurber

I EXPLAINED many years ago why my letters will probably never be collected and published under the title 'I Saw It Coming,' or under any other title. Since you have no doubt forgotten what I had to say, I will sketch it in for you briefly. I came back from Europe in 1938 to discover that my friends had not saved my letters – or 'preserved the correspondence,' to use the formal phrase. Oh, they had preserved it in a manner of speaking, but they 'couldn't put their hands on it at the moment.' That is, they didn't have the vaguest idea where it was. I knew where it was then, and I know where it is now. Letters have a way of ending up in attics and warehouses, along with polychrome bookends, masquerade costumes, copies of the *American Mercury* for 1930, and Aunt Martha's water colours of Blois and Chenonceaux. If my friends ever set out to locate my letters, they will come upon old college yearbooks, dance programmes, snapshot albums, and the works of John Fox, Jr, and probably lose interest in the original object of their search.

Now, the seventy-one letters written from abroad in 1937–38 were intended as a section of the collected correspondence to be called *Part III : The European Phase*, and their unavailability is regarded by my publishers as a 'major deterrent.' As for *Part I : The Youthful Years* and *Part II : Sturm und Drang (1915–1935)*, God only knows what has become of the letters written during those so important formative periods. There remain the letters written since 1938, and while they are 'as available as hell,' to quote one of my attorneys, their publication would not constitute 'an act of wisdom,' to quote him further. These letters repose in the files of producers, publishers, editors, and agents, and their monotony is another major deterrent, since they all begin with 'As God is my judge' or 'I would rather die than' and trail off into vague hints or open threats of legal action. After reading my carbons of this correspondence, my publishers wrote me as follows: 'I am afraid that we are all of one mind here in feeling that what had every sign of a swell performance has now turned into a rather dark picture. Mr Steckley, of our legal department, is especially distressed, but he is perhaps a bit intemperate in estimating that defamation suits in the amount of $3,000,000 would result from the publication of *Part IV : The Challenging Years*. We hope you may have a jolly fairy tale up your sleeve – something about giants and little princesses.'

The middle-aged, or, as he prefers to be called, mature, writer who realizes that his *Collected Letters* (2 vols., $10) are never going to be brought out sooner or later hits on the idea of gathering together his notes – memoranda, plot outlines, descriptions of characters, and fragments of philosophy – and seeing if he can't do something with them. He is now treading on ground hallowed by the important notebooks of the great masters, from da Vinci to Henry James, but if his invention is running low and his taxes are high, he will go brashly ahead with his ill-advised project. This instantly marks him as a minor author. The notebooks of a major author are always brought out after his death, by a literary executor. If you are a major author, the literary executor will hang around your house, known as 'the estate,' for at least a year, mousing through voluminous papers, collating and annotating, drinking your Scotch with your widow, and sometimes, in the end, marrying your daughter.

There is also the disturbing chance that your executor, while mousing around in your literary remains, may stumble on the Figure in the Carpet, or what he conceives to be the Figure in the Carpet. That is, he may adduce from the notebooks dubious internal evidence supporting the theory that you were homosexual, impotent, or secretly in love with your radio agent's wife. It will be up to your daughter, then, to marry your executor and shut him up, but, if she is a Vassar graduate, she may collaborate with him on a sequel to the notebooks – *The Real John Marcher*, an honest, courageous, and best-selling examination, on behalf of the enrichment of American letters – that will strip you of every last posthumous pride and privacy. If you are a major author, and all this has frightened you, I suggest that you remove from your notebooks everything that might be regarded as evidence of 'the scar'; that is, the early trauma, illness, maladjustment, or inadequacy that led you to become a writer in the first place. Or it might be simpler just to send your daughter to Cornell.

The minor author, known in New York merely as 'a writer' and in Hollywood as 'a word man,' comes to his typewriter with few, if any, notes to guide him. He may jot down a phrase or two on the back of an envelope in a taxi or on a bus, but such notes are usually thrown away as soon as a piece is finished. Even if they were preserved, an accumulation of them over a period of years would scarcely occupy one afternoon of a serious literary executor, who would classify them as 'unr.,' which means 'unrewarding' and suitable only as mementos for hotel maids, assistant gardeners, and third cousins.

If only to justify the title of this essay, I began to poke around one day to see what I could find in the way of memoranda and memorabilia of my own. What I came up with presents a very dark picture indeed, complete with at least seven major deterrents: persistent illegibility, paucity of material, triviality of content, ambiguity of meaning, facetious approach, preponderance of juvenilia, and exasperating abbreviation. There is actually only one notebook, and since it is the solidest, or at any rate the heaviest, item in the collection, we should perhaps glance at it first. It is a notebook I kept, or was supposed to keep, in Professor Weiss's psychology class at Ohio State University in 1913. The first few pages are given over to a description of the medulla oblongata, a listing of the primary colours, the score of the Western Reserve–Ohio State football game that season, and the words 'Noozum, Noozum, Noozum.' (I figured out this last entry after some thought. There was a young woman in the class named Newsome, whom Dr Weiss always called Noozum.) The rest of the pages contain a caricature of Professor Weiss; one hundred and thirteen swastikas; the word 'Noozum' in block letters; the notation 'No William James in library'; an address, 1374 Summit Street; a memo: 'drill cap, white gloves, gym suit. See G. Packer. Get locker'; a scrawl that seems to read 'Orgol lab nor fot Thurs'; and a number of horrible two-line jokes, which I later contributed to the *Sundial*, the university monthly magazine. Two of these will more than suffice:

(1) HE: The news from Washington is bad.
    SHE: I thought he died *long* ago.

(2) ADMIRAL WATCHING ENEMY SINK: Who fired that shot?
    MATE: The ship's cook, sir. He got the range and stove in her side.

No literary executor is going to get his hands on *that* notebook.

I am sorry to say that this rather vacant item is the most orderly exhibit in the pitiful clump of notes I have been able to discover. Most of my other material is written in pencil on sheets of yellow copy paper that have been folded over twice, a practice common with newspaper reporters but highly irritating to literary executors. Let us take the notes in order.

The first sheet, then, bears the following, in pencil, near the top of the upper left quarter: 'Digital. b. donna. stramoneum (Jimson weed). Horn quicksilver. Germander. Aloes. Aloes yourself.' The flippancy of the final phrase, 'Aloes yourself,' suggests that the piece to which this note obviously has reference was not written in a serious mood. Either that or the author's mood changed between the time he made the note and the time he actually wrote the piece.

We come now to the longest of the notes, and the only one with a sense of affirmation. There are twenty-five sheets here, one of them stained with cider, perhaps, and all of them folded only once. The pages are not dated; nothing ever is. The chirography has a curious smudged or sat-on appearance; there are only twenty words to a page, and again the author's mood and intent seem ambiguous. The manuscript that grew out of this plot summary was blown out to sea from a Hamilton-bound ferryboat just off Watford Bridge, Bermuda, on April 8, 1947. There was, of course, no carbon copy. Certain editorial symbols have been employed for purposes of clarification, and where words were not clear, they have, quite simply, been guessed at. Question marks have been parenthesized after such words. Perhaps the reader will wish to hazard interpretations of his own. That is his privilege. The notes, in full, follow:

'Middle-aged novelist has been unable to think of anything to write about for eleven years. Name Julian Gordon. Julian picks up copy Harpers Bazaar (sic) at Tass (?) agency, reads swell short story signed Candace Poe. It turns out to be work of Mr Gordon's wife, who's been secretly knitting little plots. He can't stand having his wife writing without help from him. Julian sarcastically says no female writes without using "it was as if" all the time. Real rift begins when he finds her hangout over garage and reads sheet in ivory-coloured typewriter. Tells her at dinner she can't use sentence "The wind ran scampering up the street like a laughing boy." You've got to use either "ran" or "scampered." Rift widens. Cath. says she is going to rename their country place Greensleeves because look nice on station wagon door. He says by God over his dead body. 15 collar 33 or 34 sleeve B. Brothers blue button-down. Sox 11½. (Note: This appears to be a personal memo, without reference to the plot outline.) Julian, who is still on Ch. 6 of novel begun 1936, discovers Cath. has sold several pieces to mags. in one month, and is in correspondence with Cerf, Finkelhoff (?), and Warner Bros. Julian Gordon announces he intends to buy Smith & Wesson .38 police special on ground that everybody under 21 is out to get him. Sees wife thinks he is going crazy, and decides play part of maniac to hilt. Says sees large silver fish float through bedroom. Says hears horns of elfland f.b. Says Louise Glaum (?) keeps phoning. Cath. buys vicious fawn-coloured boxer as protection against J. Wonderful scene in garage studio while cleaning gun and she typing and boxer growling. She certain he intends shoot her "accidentally." Cath. suddenly cries, "Get him, Greensleeves!" She has called boxer Greensleeves, and now sets him on Gordon Julian (sic). Nuts to Gordon nuts to Cath. nuts to you nuts to me.' That is all there is to the only really interesting item in the Thurber collection.

There are a few more odds and ends, or, to be exact, odds and beginnings, but we need scrutinize only three. The first goes, 'The beaver is a working fool, who went to manual-training school.' I have never been able to fit this in anywhere. The second says, 'Guinea pigs fight when empty milk bottles are clicked together.' They do, too. The third reads, 'The American Woman. $1,300 emerald cigarette lighter.' Since the word 'woman' is capitalized, this obviously does not refer to any particular woman to whom I intended to give a thirteen-hundred-dollar emerald cigarette lighter. Furthermore, I haven't got that kind of money. There was probably an idea for a story in this note when I set it down, but I don't see it now. If you do, you can have it – the idea, I mean. The note itself has been destroyed, along with everything else, except the plot outline of *Greensleeves*. I should take a swing at that story again, now that the fawn-coloured boxer is all the rage.

Six for the Road

PROVIDENCE, no less, guided me to a question-and-answer department in a Sunday newspaper some time ago. I say Providence because the problem posed by a worried hostess that day should have been presented to me in the first place, and not to the etiquette editor, whoever she is. She may know more than I will ever know about silverware and napery, what flowers to put in a finger bowl, and how to write a letter of condolence to an estranged niece-in-law, but when it comes to the etiquette of the stirrup cup, or nightcap, she is palpably beyond her depth.

Before I proceed further, it might be well to quote the question and answer that Providence brought to my attention, so you will know what I am talking about. Here, then, they are, in full:

LATE STAYERS

QUESTION: 'We have some very good friends whom we like to see, but they always stay too late in the evening. Is there any way we can avoid this without being rude?'

ANSWER: 'The husband who has to get up early can excuse himself and go to bed, or his wife might say, "John dear, you go to bed – you have to be up early tomorrow morning." The guests will then probably leave. If they do not, the wife will have to sit up with them.'

Now, I have no doubt that these helpful hints will work splendidly in the case of the sherry set, or with the people on the genteel, or Malaga, fringe of our society. They could also be successfully applied to those ladies and gentlemen who take one brandy after dinner and then settle for a single highball in order to have something to hold, rather than to drink, but bringing these rules to bear, say, on the Harry Spencers and *their* circle would be like trying to make quicksilver stick to a window pane.

Let us try the formula on Harry and Joan Spencer at an evening party and see what happens or, to be precise, what doesn't happen. (By evening party, I mean, of course, one that begins in the afternoon and ends in the morning.) On this occasion, the Spencers' victims – or host and hostess, if you insist on being archaic – are Jim and Laura Bloodgood. The Bloodgoods had met the Spencers at a party in Rye two weeks before, and had asked them, along with some of their other friends, to cocktails and a buffet supper. Jim and Laura had been fascinated by Harry's stories and Joan's fresh charm. Jim had been particularly delighted by Harry's Sam Langford anecdotes and by his famous account of his experiences in a camouflage unit during the war.

The night of the Bloodgoods' party is not one of Jim's best nights, as luck would have it. Laura has even tried to get him to call it off, but he won't listen. He insists that Harry Spencer will be good for him, will cheer him up, and he can stand a lot of cheering up. Jim is a publisher, and things have not been going too well. In September, he developed an irritating stomach rash that his young doctor, hivey from an allergy of his own, diagnosed as psychosomatic. The doctor said he didn't think Bloodgood's rash would disappear until production costs eased off a bit.

Early in the evening, when Jim is discussing his ailment, Harry Spencer wows everybody, except his host, with the remark 'The seventy-year itch, eh, Bloodgood?' It is at this point that the high tide of Jim's interest in the Spencers (Joan had led the laughter) begins to ebb. It is to ebb further a moment later, when Harry begins to harp amiably on Jim Bloodgood's sorest point, the failure of a book he had published entitled *They Ain't Nobody Here but Us Chickens*, merrily written by a young woman during six months on a poultry farm with her city-bred French poodle, Franchot. The failure of the book was bad enough, but Bloodgood's rash had spread to his knees when Leonard Lyons revealed that the whole thing was a hoax, perpetrated by one Paul Niely, a junior at Purdue.

When this story about the book is brought up at the party, Harry Spencer refers to it as *They Ain't Nobody Here but Us Nielys*, and Bloodgood's ankles begin to itch. He is so miserable at the sudden spread of his rash that he doesn't even listen to Spencer's celebrated rendition of the Gettysburg Address in Negro dialect ('All men are cremated eagles,' etc.), but this recitation brings John Greenleaf Hanty, formerly of the *Old Masses*, to his feet in scowling but silent rebuke. The Hantys leave, and then the Johnsons, and then the Merrills, and at twelve-thirty Dora Gardner wakes the sleeping Fred and *they* go. Only the Spencers are left. Joan is sitting on the arm of Harry's chair, kissing him on the forehead and coaxing him to do his shaggy-dog story. They had missed the hostess's low and pointed 'Heavens, is it *that* late?' when the Gardners left.

Jim Bloodgood decides to let fifteen minutes ride without offering to make another drink, but he doesn't know the Spencers. 'Hey!' cries Harry. 'How's about the first of a long series of wee doch-an-dorises?' 'That goes double Scotch for me!' laughs Joan. They both clap hands. Bloodgood does not move or say anything, but Laura, with a small sigh worthy of an actress, makes two short ones. 'Well, the shorter the quicker,' says Harry. 'But the larger the sooner,' comes back Joan. This is clearly, from their exaggerated laughter, a bit of dialogue they do together at all late parties. They have a stock of small, cryptic family jokes, and they are now reminded of their favourite, a lot of deadpan double-talk about 'the honourable cat.' After five minutes, this really gets to Jim Bloodgood. He stands up. 'I don't know about putting the honourable cat out,' he says, 'but I got to go to bed. Hard day at the office tomorrow.' Laura comes in fast with 'Yes, you *must* get to bed, dear. You have *such* a hard day at the office tomorrow.'

Let us now observe carefully the effect of this strategy on the Spencers. They exchange winks. Can it be that they have something up their sleeves, something rehearsed for just such a situation as this? 'Lie down here, Jim,' says Harry, 'and we'll throw something over you.' The Spencers, side by side, stand in front of the sofa, their glasses raised on high, ready to throw something – but you get it, and so does Bloodgood. 'I got to go to bed, goddam it, it's late,' he says, itching. 'Without a posset?' demands Harry roguishly. He turns to Joan. 'Where's the posset?' he asks. 'I don't know, sir,' says Joan. 'I'll see. Here, posset, posset, posset! Here, posset, posset, posset!' She walks around snapping her fingers, until she comes to the bar. 'Here's the posset,' she says, grabbing up the Scotch bottle. 'Give it to me!' snarls Harry, taking the bottle. He pours huge slugs into his glass and Joan's. 'That'll teach it a lesson,' he says grimly. Jim Bloodgood quickly says goodnight, leaves the room, and stamps up the stairs. Laura Bloodgood sinks back in her chair. There is nothing that can save *her*. Not now.

The Spencers suddenly propose a group of toasts: to the late Admiral Sigsbee on his birthday, to Tyler, Rudolph, and James, to the discovery of tungsten in New Mexico, to the honourable cat, and, in mock tears, to the brave men of the sheriff's posset. Harry and Joan are magnificent together when they are buzzed, and they know it. Each appreciates the other's quick ad-libbing, fertile invention, and rich fantasy. They don't need an audience, and they are now practically unaware of their hostess. They just leave her sitting there.

'The first of a series for the road,' Harry tosses at Laura Bloodgood in one of his rare, fleeting recognitions of her presence. He has a store of these multiple-nightcap gags, including a wee doch-an-Dora, Dorothy, Dolores, and so on. Laura, stranded in that lonely chair, abandoned by her husband, and getting no help from me, is in for at least two more long and frantic hours. Joan insists that Harry do his talking-horse routine (the one that takes at least as long as the 'Rhapsody in Blue'), but he refuses unless she will do the apache dance with him. So she does.

This is the Spencers' masterpiece and, like almost everything else they do together, it is divided into several parts, and can run from ten minutes after two until a quarter of three. I myself have known the Spencers for a long time, and I can think of no way to break it up now that Bloodgood has gone to bed and plumped the problem in his wife's lap. Harry and Joan interpret the dance as it would be done by a Supreme Court justice and his wife, then by an arthritic psychiatrist and his amorous patient, and finally by a slain dowager and her butler, the slayer. In this finale, which is pretty rough on Joan and the furniture, the weary hostess is forced to take part. She can't get out of it, because the dancers need an assistant for this one, to play the cop. You see, Harry has just shot Joan, and he knows that a policeman (Laura Bloodgood) has heard the shot and is peering through a window. Laura doesn't actually have to go outside the house to peer through a window, but she does have to stand up. She has to stand up and peer for about eleven minutes, the way a cop would, while

Harry, with the limp Joan in his arms, dances and dances, to make the cop believe that the dead woman is not only alive but having the time of her life. I have seen this dance some thirty-odd times, and it can be terribly effective, especially when the inert Joan's flying arms and legs manage to knock over everything that isn't built in, during the wild climax of whirls that finally convinces the cop that everything is O.K.

The panting, flushed Spencers at last sit down. Laura collapses. 'I think,' says Harry, 'that calls for a drink.' 'I'll make it,' says Joan to Laura. 'You sit where you are.'

The hostess now begins to talk rapidly, before Harry or Joan can think of some pantomime that requires the throwing of books or the juggling of Spode. She remembers something that Dora Gardner whispered to her over the coffee, about the time Harry tossed Dora's sister-in-law in the air (the one with the weak vertebra) to dramatize some point in one of his acrobatic narratives. Now, right here Mrs Bloodgood is going to have to be extremely careful – in the topic she selects, I mean. I assume, naturally, that she is smart enough not to mention cats – she must realize the routine *that* will get her back into.

Oh, they go finally, of course, but I am afraid I cannot claim credit for that. The problem is really beyond my powers, much as I would like to solve it on behalf of the Bloodgoods and all the other ladies and gentlemen who are prisoners in their own living rooms whenever the jolly voices of Harry and Joan are heard at the front door.

I have thought of one thing, though. I have thought of a way to get back at the Spencers. I have been asked to dinner at their house next Thursday, and in preparation for the event I have learned by heart 'Hiawatha,' all the White Sox infields since 1894, a series of thirty-two card tricks, and an interminable *pas seul* that narrates all the major sieges of history from the Bastille to the Alamo. It has wonderful parts in it for Harry and Joan. They have to go upstairs and stay there, to represent the neutral countries.

I know what you're saying. You're saying it won't work. You know what I think? I think you've got something there.

Afternoon of a Playwright

I CALLED the other afternoon, at the laudanum hour, upon Bernard Hudley, the dramatist, and found him, to my astonishment, somewhat less despondent than he had been on my previous visit some months before. 'What's the matter?' I asked anxiously. 'Can I do anything to depress you?'

He didn't answer, but sat staring at a blank piece of paper in his typewriter.

'I am trying to outline a drawing-room comedy of horror,' he said finally, 'but a note of hope, even of decency, keeps creeping into it.'

'That's too bad,' I told him. 'What's the time of the play? Maybe that's where the fault lies.'

He pulled the paper out of the typewriter, tore off a piece, and began chewing it. 'It's set in Tanganyika, 600,000 years ago,' he said. 'I want to show that mankind came to an end that year, and that we do not now, in fact, exist. But 600,000 years ago doesn't seem gloomy enough, somehow.'

I thought about his problem for a moment, and then said, 'I think I see what's the matter. Why don't you make it 598,000 B.C.?'

His eyes lighted gloomily. 'You may have something ghastly there,' he admitted.

'But I don't think they had drawing rooms in those years,' I told him.

'This is not an ordinary drawing room,' he snapped. 'I call it a drawing and quartering room.'

'Now you're being your old self again,' I said. 'Who are you using for characters?'

'Devils and demons,' he said, 'all of them possessed by human beings. I like that part of it all right, but there's nowhere to go from there except up, and you know how I hate up. The first act is terrifying enough to suit me, but I don't know what to do about the second act yet.'

I lit the wrong end of a filter cigarette and handed it to him. 'What's the scene of the second act?' I asked.

'A combination madhouse and brothel,' he said. 'A convention of clergymen has taken it over for the weekend. You see what I mean by the note of hope creeping in?'

'I do indeed,' I said. I got up, walked to the bar in the corner of the room and picked up a bottle.

'Not that one,' he said quickly. 'That's poisoned. Take the one on the right.' I knew Hudley well enough to figure that the bottle on the right was the poisoned one, so I poured a drink from the one I had selected.

'Damn your intuition!' he snarled. 'You're worse than Myra. She has lost her sense of smell completely, but I still can't fool her about those bottles.' His wife, Myra, walked into the room at that moment, wearing dark glasses and showing her lower teeth.

'Bad afternoon,' I said. 'I hope you're feeling awful.'

'Bad afternoon,' she said, and then to her husband, 'It's time for you not to take your thyroid pills.' He didn't say anything.

'You two have been married for three weeks now,' I said. 'What's the matter?'

'Oh, we have tried everything,' she said, 'but something always goes right. You know how things are nowadays.'

He looked gloomier than ever. 'Now Myra's having an affair with a police lieutenant,' he told me. 'She always picks the wrong man, someone that can't run away with her.'

Myra laughed – at least I think it was laughter, although it sounded more like pieces of iron falling into a bathtub. 'Bernard wants the girl next door, but she's too old for him,' Myra said. 'She's nine.'

'And not getting any younger, I suppose,' I put in, unable to think of anything else.

Suddenly, from somewhere in the house, there were two pistol shots in rapid succession.

'This house is the noisiest place this side of hell,' growled Hudley.

'Who's shooting who?' I asked as casually as I could.

Myra took a drink straight from the bottle from which I had poured mine. 'Either my sister has shot her lover, or vice versa,' she said.

'Well, don't go and find out,' her husband croaked. 'I've no time for details. Maybe I ought to go back to that play about the Wright brothers at Kitty Hawk.'

'Why did you drop it in the first place?' I asked him.

'It got cheerful on me,' he said. 'I call them the Fright brothers and made the setting Night Hawk. They both crack up on their first flight, and that prevents the development of the airplane.'

'I see,' I said. 'It *is* cheerful. That would, of course, have prevented the invention of the modern bomber and all the other deadly warplanes.'

Myra sat down in a chair and began reading a copy of a magazine called *Horrible Love Tales*. I began to feel, for some reason, a little nervous. 'What became of the play you were working on last year called *The Explosion*?' I asked.

'Couldn't find a producer,' Hudley grumbled. 'They all said it needed development, that it was too short.'

'What did they mean?' I asked.

Hudley ate another piece of paper, and said, 'The curtain goes up on an empty stage, and before any character appears the whole damn set blows up. It seemed gruesome enough to me, and definitely unique.'

Myra gave her iron laugh again. 'Gruesome, hell!' she said. 'Most hilarious play he ever wrote. You don't see anybody get killed, and, furthermore, the audience could leave the theatre and go to the nearest bar and have a good time.'

'There ought to be a law against people having a good time,' I said, and stood up. 'Bad bye.' I bowed to both of them, and backed out of the room toward the front door, so that I wouldn't be stabbed or shot in the back.

As I went down the front steps of the Hudley house, a man in the uniform of a police lieutenant came up to me. It was Myra's lover. 'Somebody reported hearing shots in there,' he said, and added, hopefully, 'Did she get Hudley this time?'

'No,' I told him. 'Mrs Hudley's sister shot her lover, or he shot her. We were pretty busy discussing modern plays and nobody had time to look.'

'You better come back with me, Mac,' he said. 'Maybe I can pin it on you. I love to pin crimes on the wrong man.'

'You ought to be a playwright,' I told him. 'You seem to have a natural talent for the modern drama.'

He led me back into the house and, when we got to the living room, both Hudley and Myra were lying on the floor. They had bored each other to death in my absence.

'Always business.' The lieutenant laughed horribly. 'I never have a cheerless moment.' He went to the telephone and called the police station. 'Let me have Police Inspector Rawlings,' he said, and then, 'What do you mean, he isn't there? Gone out of town? How long will he be gone? Two days? Good.'

'You said good,' I told him. 'That's bad.'

'We all make mistakes,' he snarled, and he dialled another number. 'Is this Inspector Rawlings' house?' he said into the receiver. 'Let me talk to Mrs Rawlings.' There was a pause, and then he said, 'Eleanor? I've just found out your husband is out of town for two days. Put on something uncomfortable. I'll be right over.' He hung up and started out of the room. As he stepped over what I had thought was Hudley's dead body, the playwright deftly tripped him, causing him to fall and break his neck.

'Somebody will have to call Mrs Rawlings,' I said, and Myra sat up, with the eager look of a little girl at a circus. 'I'll handle that,' she said brightly, as she went to the phone.

'I think I know what do do with the clergymen in the brothel,' I told Hudley.

'It better be awful,' he snarled.

'It is,' I said. 'Why not make them all insane? Then you could call the play *Too Many Kooks Spoil the Brothel.*'

Hudley and Myra pulled guns on me at the same moment, but before they could fire their little son walked into the room and got both of them with a double-barrelled shotgun. 'Dad wouldn't let me have the car tonight,' he explained. 'And Mom wanted me to do my homework.' Suddenly he drew a knife and threw it at me.

'Wake up! Wake up!' said my wife's voice, from the next bed. I woke up groggily.

'What became of all the bodies?' I mumbled.

'I don't know and I don't care,' my wife said, 'but you were yelling in your sleep. Don't you *ever* have any pleasant dreams?' I glanced at my wristwatch. It was a quarter after six. I didn't know whether to get up, or try to go back to sleep. It was nightmare either way.

'You want a drink?' I asked my wife, but she was asleep again. I dressed and went downstairs, and poured myself a stiff drink of straight whisky. I raised the glass and said to the vanished figures of my nightmare, 'There's no place to go but down.' Then I downed the drink. An hour later I was feeling much worse. I had picked the wrong bottle, the unpoisoned one.

The Other Room

THE bar of the Hôtel Continental in Paris is large and comfortable, and never too crowded, especially in October, when the American invaders are beginning to thin out, and it is presided over by an efficient and amiable waiter named Jacques. He had just brought drinks for my wife and me and an English painter we know. You can lean back in the Continental bar, drinking for pleasure, slowly, in the European manner, without the urge to see how soon you can reach the point when you no longer know you're drinking in the American manner.

An American woman, at a near-by table, was explaining to a friend the reason for her dermatitis, insisting that it had been caused by aluminium pots and pans.

'My allergist says I have an emotional conflict or something,' she said. 'Doctors always say there's something the matter with you, but it's almost always something you use around the house, or wear, or eat. Of course, I'm terribly high-strung, I know that,' she said, 'but it isn't that. If it was I'd know it.'

The Continental bar, like any other place where Americans gather, is used largely for the exchange of symptoms, complaints about French coffee, and the enumeration of hotels and restaurants on the Continent and in England which one should, at all costs, avoid.

We were waiting for three persons to join us, all of them compatriots of ours – one a twenty-two-year-old American girl, the daughter of friends of ours back home, and the other two a man and his wife, friends of friends of ours, neither of whom we had ever met. We had got, a few days before, the usual note from somebody in New York, saying that she had instructed the Barretts to look us up at the hotel, and, in the unfailing routine of such matters, they had telephoned and we had made a date for drinks, hoping they would not recite too many symptoms or complaints before we could get rid of them.

The painter was telling us about his own favourite hotel, a mythical composite one, invented in the imagination of a friend of his, and called the Hôtel Pas-de-Calais-et-Pas-de-Confort, when a nine-year-old girl, unmistakably American, and loose momentarily from her parents, materialized at my elbow. She had dashed into the bar to look at the television set near the door leading into the dining room.

'It's in French,' she said. 'It ought to be in English. Why isn't it in English?' I explained to her that it was not in English in the same way that television in America was not in French, but she was unconvinced and clearly unimpressed by my knowledge of such things. The small interruption annoyed me, because

I had been on the point of describing my own favourite French hostelry, the Hôtel-de-l'Univers-et-de-Massachusetts.

'Tell me a story,' commanded the little girl. 'My name is Eunice.' She squirmed into a chair and stared at me.

'Well, did you ever hear of the Teapot Dome scandal?' I asked.

'I don't think I like it,' she said. 'What is it?'

'You surely know what a teapot dome is,' I said. She got up, frowning, stood on her toes a moment, and sat down again. 'Yes,' she said.

I began to drink faster, in the American manner, and said, 'A scandal is when a teapot dome doesn't obey its parents, but runs in and out of bars, and won't eat anything for bekkus except lint and buttons. Well, this particular teapot dome was –'

A large woman, obviously the child's mother, loomed up suddenly out of nowhere, like a pirate ship. 'We never say bekkus to Eunice,' she said. 'She loathes it.'

'I loathe it,' said Eunice.

'Sorry,' I said. 'It has been so long since I was a little girl I have forgotten.'

'Now, now,' said my wife. 'You were going to be nice this evening.'

'For a change,' our painter friend asked, 'or just as a noble experiment?'

'Well!' said the ignored mother, and she dragged the little girl away.

'What happened to the Teapot Dome scandal? You can't just leave it hanging there, you know,' said the painter, but I left it hanging there, for my wife said, 'Here's Linda now.'

Linda Gray, fresh-looking and pretty, with the eyes of an angel, said she was sorry she was late, but I reminded her that American girls were always late, and she was introduced to our English friend.

'Mr Middleton would like to paint you, I am sure,' I said.

'I am a gifted man,' Middleton said, 'but not that gifted. The portrait of this lady would require something more ethereal than paint.'

My wife asked Linda what she would like to drink, and she asked for a Coca-Cola. 'I have had an adventure,' she said. 'Not a very pleasant one.'

'I hope it isn't too racy,' I said. 'My wife has led a cloistered life, and believes that the storks find babies under cabbage leaves.'

'Oh, it wasn't like that,' Linda said, with a slight *frisson*. 'I had just turned away from the window of a shop on the Rue de Rivoli when this American – he must have been about sixty – spoke to me. It's terrible, or sad, or something, but it's usually an American, a middle-aged American, who speaks to us girls on the street, not a Frenchman or any other foreigner.'

'What did he say?' my wife wanted to know. Linda paused a moment. 'He said "*Combien pour toute la nuit?*"' she said.

'He *must* be at least sixty,' I said. 'That goes back to the battle of Paris in the First World War. I know all the verses.'

'You would,' my wife said.

'I used to sing them with the fellows,' I said, 'but I never said them to the girls.'

'I just looked at him,' Linda said, 'and told him, 'I am an American girl.' I really put my best Sunday virtue into it. Funny, he seemed to look at me and past me too. It was odd, and gave me the shivers a little. Then he said something I didn't understand and walked away.'

'Travel is broadening, but disillusioning,' said Middleton.

'I know the type,' I said, 'for I make a study of morbid things. He probably hadn't made a pass at a woman for twenty years back home. Over here, on summer holiday, they get away from their wives, who are out shopping, and the devil takes hold of them. He was probably just trying to recapture his lost youth. Paris has a strange effect on the middle-aged American male, something like the loss of inhibition that takes place on shipboard. Of course, it happens to the American woman, too, sometimes. I knew a cruise director, once, who told me that he had had affairs with women on ships who wouldn't have spoken to him on land.'

'Human nature, as Montaigne or somebody said years ago, is capable of curious behaviour,' Middleton put in. 'The dark unfathomed caves of notion, to coin a phrase – a rather pretty phrase, if I may say so.'

'My God, there he is now!' said Linda. The man she was looking at had just come into the bar and begun looking around. He was sixty, all right, with a familiar harried look, and the sagging shoulders of a man who has sat for years at a desk.

'I hope it isn't Barrett,' my wife said, but it was Barrett. He headed straight for our table, walking with a slight limp.

'In the midst of life we are in *worse* than death,' Middleton said.

'I'd better go,' Linda said. 'I'd better go.'

'He won't remember you,' I told her. 'Don't recognize him.'

'If he could forget this girl's eyes,' Middleton said, 'he is something less than normal.'

I said, 'Are you Mr Barrett?' before he could say anything, but managed to keep both hands busy, one holding my drink, the other my cigarette. I didn't know what to say, but I had to say something.

'You been behaving yourself, Mr Barrett?' I asked.

'Have to,' he said. 'Got the little woman with me, you know.' We managed the introduction somehow. Barrett recognized Linda, there was no doubt about that. He was for three seconds a statue in bronze, a frightened statue, a little tired, a little older than the man who had walked into the room. My wife did her best to cover it over with roses, asking where Mrs Barrett was, and how she was, and how long they were going to stay, and how our mutual friends in New York were, trying to bring some ease to the bronze figure of a trapped, middle-aged, middle-class American man, whose lack of social resource was as evident as wind on a prairie.

Jacques appeared, and more drinks were ordered, and the ease that Jacques invariably brings to a table of Americans helped a little to break the tableau and the spell.

'I'll have a Scotch and soda, this time,' Linda said.

'Do that twice,' Barrett said, and it seemed to me I had known he was going to say just that. Middleton sat studying us all as if he were about to sketch in a composition, a conversation piece.

Barrett sat down stiffly and uneasily on the edge of a chair, the unhappiest man I had seen that summer – or any other summer, for that matter. I felt enormously sorry for him.

'Were you in the First World War, the war the French still call "*La Grande Guerre*"?' I asked, and he sat back a little and came as close as he could to relaxing.

'I was there, Charley,' he said, almost as if to himself. 'This is the first time I have seen Paris since those days. I was at Fère-en-Tardenois, and I got shoved around up there. It was pretty rough going.'

'Never rougher anywhere,' I agreed. 'I knew two guys who were there,' and I told him their names, but I don't think he was listening. 'Yeah, sure, yeah, sure,' he said. 'The Heinies knocked off a lot of us. It was like fighting in a room. They were on all sides of you. I drove out there the other day, hired a car and drove out there. As I got closer to the battlefield, I got scared, I don't mind saying. I wanted to tell the guy to turn around and drive back to Paris, but I didn't. We came to this sign that says "Fère-en-Tardenois – 14 km."; and it seemed like two hours from there. There's a big American cemetery there now.' He was glad to get the Scotch he had ordered, but his hand shook when he picked it up.

'One of the men I knew was made a sergeant on the field,' I said. 'All the sergeants of his company had been killed. He got out of it alive, but he carried shrapnel with him all his life, and was in and out of hospitals.'

'Yeah, sure,' said Barrett. 'I got some stuff in me, too. I got a silver plate, I got two silver plates.' He touched his right leg and then the left side of his head. 'It seems to me I was always in hospitals, army hospitals, in my twenties.' He gave a troubled sigh. 'What I seem to remember most is hospitals. When I get nightmares, even my office turns into a hospital, even now.'

There was a softening of the tension in the air, a little, I thought, like candle-light replacing the glare of torches. Nobody said anything for a moment except Linda. 'I'm sorry,' Linda said.

'Where is Mrs Barrett?' my wife asked, tactfully shifting gears.

'I don't know,' Barrett said. 'I was to meet her here. She's always on time, she's always ahead of me.'

'Perhaps she left a message for you at the desk,' my wife said. 'Shall I find out?'

Barrett stood up, saying, 'No, no, I'll go out and ask,' and he went out of the bar.

'He's kind of nice,' said Linda, after a long moment. 'He has a nice smile. I wish he had smiled when he spoke to me on the street, but he didn't.'

'I think he needs another drink,' I said. Barrett had finished his drink fast, as nervous men do, and so I signalled Jacques. 'The same again, all around,' I told him.

'I don't know anything about him or his wife,' my wife put in. 'All that Ella said in her note was something about "Please be nice to the Barretts. They have both been through a lot. I'll tell you about it later." Ella signed the letter "Hastily." Everybody is always in such a rush.'

'You never know what the boys who survived Fère-en-Tardenois are going to say or do,' I said, 'or how much they are going to drink. You've either been through a battle like that, or you haven't.'

'I don't think he should have driven up there,' Linda said. 'I don't think it was good for him.'

'I do,' Middleton said. 'Maybe he'll get it out of his nightmares, now. Maybe his office will turn into an office again in his dreams.'

Barrett came back to the table, looking even more tired, and somehow greyer. 'Martha is lying down,' he told us. 'This trip has pretty well tuckered her out. We shouldn't have done that châteaux tour, I guess. It took a lot out of her.' He didn't sit down. 'Well, thank you for the drink,' he said. 'It was nice of you to ask us.'

'You're not going yet,' I told him. 'We've ordered you another drink.' His face brightened a little and, after a slight pause, he sat down again, this time farther back in his chair.

'Tell us some more about the war,' I said. 'Maybe it will get those hospitals out of your nightmares.' He gave us his slow, gentle smile. 'It wasn't so much the battle, or even hospitals,' he began, finally. 'At least, that's what one of the docs in the States told me back in the twenties. It was something that happened in the battle of Paris, I guess. Anyway, this doc said so.' The new drinks arrived, and he picked his up eagerly.

'What was it?' Linda asked.

'Kind of a silly thing, it was,' he said. 'We come from Iowa, you know, Cedar Rapids. I was only twenty-one when I got to France, and I thought it was a million miles from anywhere. You get homesick when you're that young, and are that far away from home. It's worse than the battle. You get through the battle somehow, and you don't think much about it till later in the hospital, or when you fall asleep. They had given me a lot of stuff to make me sleep, and I'd never taken dope before.' He drank some more of his whisky and soda. 'I remember Paris clearer than anything,' he said, 'but I can't remember how I got here, or just when it was. I got out of the base hospital, because I couldn't take it any longer, and I got to Paris. I was AWOL. It's all pretty hazy.'

After this confession, he sat for a long time without saying anything, and we waited.

'I remember walking along the Champs-Elysées,' he began finally. 'I never could pronounce it right.' He was correct about that, but none of us pronounced the words for him. 'Then, there was this girl, this French girl. She wasn't any older than I was. She spoke English, though, and was I glad for that! Well, we sat out in front of the Café de la Paix. We drove there in a taxi. She said she thought I didn't look very well, and she said she thought I should have something to drink. And so we had a couple of drinks. Then she told me about herself. She came from some place in Southern France, and her father was a drunkard, and used to beat up the family on Saturday nights, so she ran away to Paris, and got some work in a garment factory, but all they gave her was a few francs a week, and she saw all these other girls in fur coats and things, and so she took to -- well, making the boys feel better, she called it.' This time, there was an even longer silence, but we all waited politely and attentively.

'I never told Martha about all this,' he took up again. 'But the other day I took a taxi up to the street where this French girl used to have an apartment. I remembered the street, and even the number, I remembered the number, too. They call it Rue Marcadet, and it's up there in Montmartre. I didn't get out of the cab. Maybe I should have, but I didn't get out. I just looked at the building, the windows on the second floor. Nobody there would know about her now. Her name was Françoise, but she told me to call her Frances, and so I called her Frances. She would be sixty now. Doesn't seem possible, but she would be sixty now. Well, like I said, she was only twenty herself then, but there were pictures of guys all over her living room, guys in uniform, guys of all the allied countries. The picture I can't forget was a picture of a young Canadian soldier. She had it framed, and it was sitting on her piano. He was a handsome fella, and he couldn't have been more than twenty himself.' He looked at Linda, as if she were too young to hear the rest of the story, but she said, 'I'm much older than any of you were. I'm twenty-two.'

'Well, of course, I never saw the Canadian boy, but he gets into my dreams, too, kinda banged up, with his uniform all bloody. You see, she found out from a buddy of his later that he had been killed in action. This friend of his brought her this note he had written her, the last note he had ever written, I guess. She showed it to me one day in her apartment – the first and only time I ever went there,' he added hastily. 'I remember what it said, all right, every word of it, though I don't remember things as well as I used to.' He took some more of his drink and set the glass on the table.

'Finish that,' I told him, 'and we'll get another one.'

'No, no,' he said, with his little smile, 'I never have more than two. Well, she had a bottle of port wine at her place, and we sat there drinking this port wine, too much of it, I guess. After a while, she went out of the room into – the other room, and left me sitting there with the whole damn war all around me, it seemed like. This good-looking boy on the piano kept staring at me, and looking sad, and awful young – like that part from "St James Infirmary." '

' "So young, so cold, so fair," ' Linda murmured.

'Yeah, that's it,' Barrett said. He picked up his glass again, and leaned back in his chair, and sighed deeply. 'Well, I sat there, thinking of too many things, thinking of everything, the way it all floods back on you, you know.' We all nodded together. 'I thought of a girl back home in Iowa, who was only seventeen then, I thought of Martha. Then I heard this French girl calling to me from – the other room.' He sat forward again, and seemed to stiffen, and his voice, when he spoke again, seemed very far away. 'Well, I got up and left the place. I guess I kinda ran out on her. It wasn't until I got into the street that I realized I was carrying my glass, and it still had some port wine in it. I put it down somewhere, and went on walking. I must've walked for miles. The next thing I really remember I was back at the hospital. I guess the MP's got me.'

He broke off his recital to finish his drink, and then he stood up. 'After that, for a while, I went into a nose dive, kinda what the docs call nervous prostitution,' he (and Sigmund Freud) said. None of us laughed, or even smiled. 'There were a lot of songs we all sang in those days,' he said, 'some of them, well, kinda naughty, as the ladies say. I was thinking of them today, walking around Paris, I was thinking about a lot of things. Seemed like it was 1918 again, and I was young and back in Paris.' He picked up his glass from the table and drained the last drop, and set it down again. 'This girl, this Frances, gets in my dreams sometimes too. But the door is always locked, or something, or the floor to the other room is gone, like it was blown away.'

'All doors open sooner or later. Maybe this one will now,' I said, trying to be cheerful.

'Well,' Barrett said, 'you've all been very nice to me today, and I appreciate it, and I know Martha will, too. I wish you could meet Martha. She's very sweet. I don't know what I would have done without Martha. She's got me through a lot of things.'

'Oh, we'll see you again,' my wife said, 'and Martha, too. Tell her I'll send her some flowers. How long are you going to be here?'

'Three days,' Barrett said, 'three days, and then we're sailing back on the *Liberté*. I like the French ships, I like France.'

Linda suddenly stood up, and ran, rather than walked, around the table. She was tall, in the manner of American girls of today, almost as tall as Barrett, so she did not have to stand on tiptoe when she kissed him on the forehead. 'I like you, too,' she said, warmly. 'I think you're lovely.' He patted her hand twice, and then said something none of us could understand, and hurriedly walked away.

'I'm sixty years old myself,' I said, 'but mighty spry for a man that age, and I'll be even spryer if we have another drink.'

'I should say we all need what you Americans call a flock of drinks,' Middleton said. My wife called Jacques.

Before we left the Continental bar, all of us except Middleton had reached the point where we weren't quite sure we were still drinking. At that point, I have an inveterate tendency to sing, and my wife sensed this moment had come. 'Not here in the bar,' she said. 'You can sing in the cab on the way to the Chope Danton.' In the cab, I said, 'How about "It's a Long Way to Tipperary," or "Where a Nightingale Is Singing and a Pale Moon Beams"?'

'Not that, not one of *them*,' Linda said. 'I want to hear "*Combien pour Toute la Nuit?*"' And so I sang for her, in fair voice, and on key for once in my life, '*Combien pour Toute la Nuit?*'

The Lady from the Land

A RECENT hostess of mine, who gave an Anglo-American cocktail party for forty persons (at which the customary seventy showed up), had selected for the moist event one of the large rooms on the first floor of a famous London hotel. It was fun, that party, until the woman I shall call the Lady from the Land sat down beside me. Something told me that I was going to be reproved or reproached or upbraided or rebuffed, and something was right. What she had to say, or rather to reiterate, was a complaint about a piece I wrote for *Punch* last year in which I predicted that, if our species didn't look up and behave, the porpoises would come in from the sea and replace us as the chief mammal on earth.

'I don't think God likes you for that,' the lady said. 'She doesn't like people who deride, or degrade, the human species.'

'She?' I asked.

'I've always believed that God is feminine,' she told me. 'As a Woman, She would naturally be interested in Mankind, and would never allow the tortoises to take over, as you call it.'

I choked slightly on the fresh Scotch and soda the waiter had just handed me. 'I did not say tortoises, madam,' I told her. 'I said porpoises.'

She waved this away with an impatient gesture. 'It's the same thing,' she said.

I lit a cigarette and recited 'Listen, my children, and you shall hear of the midnight ride of Paul Revere.'

Our hostess suddenly appeared, carrying a martini, and said to me, in what she intended to be a whisper, 'Don't be profound.' I knew then that the martini was her fourth, and I said to her, 'The girl stood on the burning deck whence all but she had fled.' My hostess fled, but my critic didn't.

'All that you men care about is the sea,' my companion said. 'You hear voices from the sea. I've been doing some research on it, and I know. In *Juno and the Paycock* the Paycock says "The sea is callin' me." Tennyson wrote, "One clear call for me, and may there be no moaning of the bar when I put out to sea." '

'May I –' I began.

'Hear me out,' she said. She took a drink from the waiter's tray and I took two, as she went on talking. 'Robert Adlai Stevenson said –'

'Louis,' I corrected her.

'Don't be rude!' she said. 'I'm no loonier than you are. Stevenson said "Home is the sailor, home from sea." You men often have to be drafted for war, but you run away to sea. You can hardly wait.'

During her lecture I had kept hearing slight hiccups, and realized that a gentleman guest with several sails in the wind had been listening. 'Let's get it right,' he said. 'Stevenson didn't want to be buried at sea. He wrote "Under the wide and starry sky, dig the grave and let me lie. This be the verse you grave for me: here he lies where he longed to be, and he laid him down with a will." '

The intruder began laughing loudly, as he managed to get out of his chair. 'If he laid him down with a will, then he died intestate,' he chortled, and he went reeling away to tell it to somebody else.

'I hate the word "intestate," ' my companion said. 'Why do they have to give old men's diseases such awful names?'

'You are thinking of intestatitis, madam,' I said coldly. 'Intestate means he died without a will.'

'But that man said he died *with* a will,' she said sharply.

I was on the point, I'm afraid, of saying, 'Ah, shut up!' but saved myself just in time, and began on my second drink of the two new ones. She kept right on bickering.

'Your Eugene O'Neill in *Anna Christie* goes on and on about that old devil sea.'

'Davil,' I corrected her, but she said, 'Quibble, quibble.' This time I made her hear *me* out. 'What are you working up to, madam, or away from, may I ask?'

'I'm working up to that silly play by Hendrik Hudson,' she said. 'I mean *The Lady from the Sea*.' I decided to let her make a playwright out of Hendrik Hudson, and just went on drinking. 'Now then, no woman hears the call of the sea. It's just you men. You're all Joseph Conrads and William McFees at heart. I think it's perfectly dreadful that your poet Longfellow, when he wrote about the schooner *Hesperus*, said, "The skipper had brought his little daughter to bear him company." Where was the child's mother all that time?'

'It's an old tradition of the sea that a woman aboard a ship is unlucky,' I told her, 'and it has always turned out that way. You may not know it, but the skipper's wife was aboard the mystery ship, the *Mary Celeste*, which should have been called the *Harry Celeste*, and then nothing would have happened to it.'

'That's right, that's right!' my companion exclaimed. 'Blame everything on us women. You even call your ships "she" so that you can blame it on us when they go down or disappear.'

'If you are writing a monograph about all this,' I said, 'you are wasting your valuable time substituting Scotch for ink.'

I was about to get up and join some people, half of whom were taking Kenneth Tynan apart while the other half kept putting him back together again, when another male guest loomed up in front of me. He held an unlighted cigarette in one hand and a matchbox in the other. 'I've given up smoking,' he said. 'Nobody could make me smoke again, not even my wife when I'm mad at her.' He broke the cigarette in two and tossed it away, and brought out another one, which he put in his mouth. 'You couldn't make me smoke this cigarette, even at gunpoint,' he proclaimed loudly.

I pointed my right index finger at him as if it were a gun barrel and said, 'We'll see about that. Now then, either you smoke that cigarette, sir, or I shall pull the trigger.'

He paused a moment, then lit the cigarette and inhaled deeply. 'You made me smoke,' he snarled. 'Remember that.' And he walked away, inhaling.

This time I took three Scotches from the waiter's tray, put one on the floor near me, and held the other two in my hands. Suddenly another woman was in the chair beside me. She took the highball from my left hand.

'I hear you're crazy about the sea,' she said.

'Crazy is correct,' I told her. 'And it's the only accurate thing I've heard said this evening.'

Her voice became brighter. 'Is it true,' she demanded, 'that if a ship is sinking from too much cargo, they throw the supercargo overboard?'

'That's a lot of jetsam, madam,' I told her. 'They don't have to throw him overboard. He jumps. The sea is calling him.'

At this point my wife appeared, for we had a dinner date. I heard my new companion whisper to her, in a worried tone, 'Your husband thinks that a ship's cargo is human.' And she went away.

'I think we'd better leave now,' my wife said, and I stood up, on a fairly even keel.

'The proper maritime term is shove off,' I told her.

'Why in the world have you been going on about the sea to everybody?' my wife demanded. 'I hope you'll be all right at dinner,' she added anxiously.

As we started out, the Lady from the Land sailed up to us. I finished the drink I was still carrying, and turned upon her. 'Don't kiss me, Mrs Hardy,' I said brusquely.

My wife took my arm and dragged me away, leaving the Lady standing there speechless for once in her life.

'I simply have to have another drink at the bar,' I told my wife on the way out of the hotel, and we went into the bar. This time I had a straight Scotch, and was beginning to relax when my wife abruptly said, 'I can't understand why they have to keep weighing the anchor on a ship all the time. It's made of iron, and I don't see how its weight could possibly change.' I thought that over for a moment, but didn't say anything, because the bartender was listening intently. After all, I do not want to be committed to a mental institution during this visit of mine to the Port of London.

'Down the hatch!' I said, and we finished our drinks and shoved off.

'That woman you called Mrs Hardy is a brilliant writer,' my wife remarked. 'Didn't you know that?'

'Brilliant, but listing heavily – listing heavily to Scotch,' I said. 'She believes that Ibsen discovered the Hudson River. Nobody gets anything right any more. Mrs Hardy goes around telling everybody that I believe the tortoises are going to take over.'

My wife laughed merrily, and then said, 'To-morrow and to-morrow and to-morrow creeps in this carapace from day to day.'

I knew I couldn't top that, so I went on with her to the dinner party in sulky silence.

The Future, If Any, of Comedy or, Where Do We Non-Go from Here?

I CALLED the other afternoon on my old friend Graves Moreland, the Anglo-American literary critic – his mother was born in Ohio – who lives alone in a fairy-tale cottage on the Upson Downs, raising hell and peacocks, the former only when the venerable gentleman becomes an angry old man about the state of literature or something else that is dwindling and diminishing, such as human stature, hope, and humour.

My unscientific friend does not believe that human stature is measurable in terms of speed, momentum, weightlessness, or distance from earth, but is a matter of the development of the human mind. After Gagarin became the Greatest Man in the World, for a nation that does not believe in the cult of personality or in careerism, Moreland wrote me a letter in which he said: 'I am not interested in how long a bee can live in a vacuum, or how far it can fly. A bee's place is in the hive.'

'I have come to talk with you about the future of humour and comedy,' I told him, at which he started slightly, and then made us each a stiff drink, with a trembling hand.

'I seem to remember,' he said, 'that in an interview ten years ago you gave humour and comedy five years to live. Did you go to their funeral?'

'I was wrong,' I admitted. 'Comedy didn't die, it just went crazy. It has identified itself with the very tension and terror it once did so much to alleviate. We now have not only what has been called over here the comedy of menace but we also have horror jokes, magazines known as Horror Comics, and sick comedians. There are even publications called *Sick and Mad*. The *Zeitgeist* is not crazy as a loon or mad as a March hare; it is manic as a man.'

'I woke up this morning,' Moreland said, 'paraphrasing Lewis Carroll. Do you want to hear the paraphrase?'

'Can I bear it?' I asked, taking a final gulp of my drink, and handing him the empty glass.

'Just barely,' he said, and he repeated his paraphrase:

'The time has come,' the walrus said,
'To speak of manic things,
Of shots and shouts, and sealing dooms
Of commoners and kings.'

Moreland fixed us each another drink, and said, 'For God's sake, tell me something truly amusing.'

'I'll try,' I said, and sat for a moment thinking. 'Oh yes, the other day I reread some of Emerson's *English Traits*, and there was an anecdote about a group of English and Americans visiting Germany, more than a hundred years ago. In the railway station at Berlin, a uniformed attendant was chanting, "Foreigners this way! Foreigners this way!" One woman – she could have been either English or American – went up to him and said, "But *you* are the foreigners." ' I took a deep breath, and said, 'I admit that going back to Ralph Waldo Emerson for humour is like going to a modern musical comedy for music and comedy.'

'What's the matter with the music?' Moreland asked.

'It doesn't drown out the dialogue,' I explained.

'Let's talk about books,' Moreland said. 'I am told that in America you have non-books by non-writers, brought out by non-publishers for non-readers. Is it all non-fiction?'

'There is non-fiction and non-non-fiction,' I said. 'Speaking of nonism: the other day, in a story about a sit-down demonstration, the Paris *Herald Tribune* wrote, "The non-violence became noisier." And then Eichmann was quoted as saying, in non-English, that Hitler's plan to exterminate the Jews was nonsense.'

'If we cannot tell evil, horror, and insanity from nonsense, what is the future of humour and comedy?' Moreland asked, grimly.

'Cryptic,' I said. 'They require, for existence, a brave spirit and a high heart, and where do you find these? In our present era of Science and *Angst*, the heart has been downgraded, to use one of our popular retrogressive verbs.'

'I know what you mean,' Moreland sighed. 'Last year your Tennessee Williams told our Dilys Powell, in a television programme, that it is the task of the playwright to throw light into the dark corners of the human heart. Like almost everybody else, he confused the heart, both as organ and as symbol, with the disturbed psyche, the deranged glands, and the jumpy central nervous system. I'm not pleading for the heart that leaps up when it beholds a rainbow in the sky, or for the heart that with rapture fills and dances with the daffodils. The sentimental pure heart of Galahad is gone with the knightly years, but I still believe in the heart of the George Meredith character that was not made of the stuff that breaks.'

'We no longer have Tom Moore's and Longfellow's "heart for any fate," either,' I said.

'Moore and Longfellow didn't have the fate that faces us,' Moreland said. 'One day our species promises co-existence, and the next day it threatens co-extinction.' We sat for a while drinking in silence.

'The heart,' I said finally, 'is now either in the throat or the mouth or the stomach or the shoes. When it was worn in the breast, or even on the sleeve, we at least knew where it was.' There was another long silence.

'You have visited England five times in the past quarter-century, I believe,' my host said. 'What has impressed you most on your present visit?'

'I would say depressed, not impressed,' I told him. 'I should say it is the turning of courts of law into veritable theatres for sex dramas, involving clergymen and parishioners, psychiatrists and patients. It is becoming harder and harder to tell law courts and political arenas from the modern theatre.'

'Do you think we need a new Henry James to re-explore the Anglo-American scene?' he asked. 'Or perhaps a new Noël Coward?'

'But you must have heard it said that the drawing room disappeared forever with the somnolent years of James and the antic heyday of Coward. I myself hear it said constantly – in drawing rooms. In them, there is usually a group of Anglo-Americans with tragicomic problems, worthy of being explored either in the novel or in the play or in comedy and satire.' I stood up and began pacing.

'If you are trying to get us out of the brothel, the dustbin, the kitchen sink, and the tawdry living room, you are probably wasting your time,' Moreland told me. 'Too many of our writers seem to be interested only in creatures that crawl out of the woodwork or from under the rock.'

'Furiouser and furiouser,' I said. 'I am worried about the current meanings of the word "funny." It now means ominous, as when one speaks of a funny sound in the motor; disturbing, as when one says that a friend is acting funny; and frightening, as when a wife tells the police that it is funny, but her husband hasn't been home for two days and nights.'

Moreland sat brooding for a full minute, during which I made each of us a new drink. He took his glass, clinked it against mine, and said, '*Toujours gai*, what the hell!' borrowing a line from Don Marquis' Mehitabel.

'Be careful of the word "gay," for it, too, has undergone a change. It now means, in my country, homosexual,' I said. 'Oh, I forgot to say that if one is taken to the funny house in the funny wagon, he is removed to a mental institution in an ambulance. Recently, by the way, I received a questionnaire in which I was asked whether or not I was non-institutionalized.'

My host went over and stared out the window at his peacocks; then he turned to me. 'Is it true that you believe the other animals are saner than the human species?'

'Oh, that is demonstrable,' I told him. 'Do you remember the woman in the French Alps who was all alone with her sheep one day when the sun darkened ominously? She told the sheep, "The world is coming to an end!" And the sheep said – all in unison, I have no doubt – "Ba-a-a!" The sound mockery of sheep is like the salubrious horse laugh.'

'That is only partly non-nonsense,' he began.

'If you saw the drama called *Rhinoceros*,' I said, 'think of the effect it would have on an audience of rhinos when the actor on stage suddenly begins turning into a rhinoceros. The rhinos would panic, screaming "Help!" – if that can be screamed in their language.'

'You think the Russians are getting ahead of us in comedy?' Moreland demanded.

'Non-God, no!' I said. 'The political and intellectual Left began fighting humour and comedy years ago, because they fear things they do not understand and cannot manage, such as satire and irony, such as humour and comedy. Nevertheless, like any other human being upon whom the spotlight of the world plays continually, Khrushchev, the anti-personality cultist, has become a comic actor, or thinks he has. In his famous meeting with Nixon a few years ago he seemed to believe that he was as funny as Ed Wynn. But, like Caesar, he has only one joke, so far as I can find out. It consists in saying, 'That would be sending the goat to look after the cabbage." Why in the name of his non-God doesn't he vary it a bit?'

'Such as?' Moreland asked.

'Such as "sending the cat to guard the mice," or "the falcon to protect the dove," or most terribly sharp of all, "the human being to save humanity." '

'You and I have fallen out of literature into politics,' Moreland observed.

'What a nasty fall was there!' I said.

Moreland went over to stare at his peacocks again, and then came back and sat down, restively. 'In our age of Science and *Angst*,' he said, 'it seems to me more brave to stay on Earth and explore inner man than to fly far from the sphere of our sorrow and explore outer space.'

'The human ego being what it is,' I put in, 'science fiction has always assumed that the creatures on the planets of a thousand larger solar systems than ours must look like gigantic tube-nosed fruit bats. It seems to me that the first human being to reach one of these planets may well learn what it is to be a truly great and noble species.'

'Now we are leaving humour and comedy behind again,' Moreland protested.

'Not in the largest sense of the words,' I said. 'The other day Arnold Toynbee spoke against the inveterate tendency of our species to believe in the uniqueness of its religions, its ideologies, and its virtually everything else. Why do we not realize that no ideology believes so much in itself as it disbelieves in something else? Forty years ago an English writer, W. L. George, dealt with this subject in *Eddies of the Day*, and said, as an example, that "Saint George for Merry England" would not start a spirit half so quickly as "Strike frog-eating Frenchmen dead!" '

'There was also *Gott strafe Angleterre*,' Moreland reminded me, '*and Carthago delenda est*, or if you will, *Deus strafe Carthage*. It isn't what the ideologist believes in, but what he hates, that puts the world in jeopardy. This is the force, in our time and in every other time, that urges the paranoiac and the manic-depressive to become head of a state. Complete power not only corrupts but it also attracts the mad. There is a bitter satire for a future writer in that.'

'Great satire has always been clearly written and readily understandable,' I said. 'But we now find writers obsessed by the nooks and crannies of their ivory towers, and curiously devoted to the growing obscurity and complexity of poetry and non-poetry. I wrote a few years ago that one of the cardinal rules of writing is that the reader should be able to get some idea of what the story is about. If a poem, for example, is understandable only to its author, then

Max Eastman's phrase, "poets talking to themselves," is not only accurate but alarming in a time like ours.'

Moreland didn't say anything at first, but he made us another and stiffer drink.

'The Communists,' he said, 'may yet turn literature into a phase of modern technology. Some members of the Russian Society of Authors will simply have to push a button, and out will come a novel or a play. Incapable of revision – that is, change, growth, and development – and subject only to mechanistic favourable criticism, obtained by pushing another button in another machine. There is a satire in that for a future writer, if there is going to be a future.'

'Modern psychology and psychiatry have made us all afraid of ourselves,' I said abruptly. '*Angst* is spreading, and with it mental ailments of whose cause and cure, one authority has recently said, we know little or nothing. But the terminology of psychiatry proliferates to the point that almost everybody now seems to think he is schizophrenic, schizoid, or schizo. I expect any day to see the slang word "skizzy" come into common use. A psychologist in America not long ago warned his colleagues at a convention that they were not so much arriving at cures as inventing new terms for the incurable. When neuropsychotic became psychoneurotic, the verbiage was off to a flying start, startling too many people. I heard of one frightened woman who burst into her doctor's office crying, 'I think I have got psychotherapy!" The doctor was able to prove to her quite simply that she did not have that.'

'Are you moving toward some basic conclusion?' Moreland asked.

'I was coming to another subject for present or future satire,' I said. 'That is the subject of the Area Man. We are divided into literally hundreds of Area Men, none of whom knows or cares very much about men in other categories of endeavour or thought. But we mumble along in our multiple confusion. Every man is now an island unto himself, interested in, even obsessed by, his own preoccupation. For example, I was agitated some twenty years ago when I discovered the gulf of ignorance that existed between the ophthalmologist and the psychologist. Each of them is concerned only with his own end of the optic nerve, which happens to join the eyeball and the brain. I have found out that the eye doctors and the mind doctors have developed a great many jokes and anecdotes about one another, without getting together and threshing things out. A certain male adult began seeing double, and he went to a psychiatrist, who decided that the man's problem lay in his inability to make up his mind as to which one of two girls he was in love with. The distracted fellow then called on a great eye man who cleared up the condition with certain eye drops. I told this story to our American humorist S. J. Perelman, and he said to me, "The story is incomplete. Which girl *was* he in love with?" '

'I know of two classes of Area Men that certain authorities are trying to interfuse, as the science fiction writers say,' Moreland told me. 'Lord Hailsham was recently quoted as saying that all good scientists are poets, and Alfred North Whitehead made a strenuous attempt to find the scientist in

Tennyson, Wordsworth, and Shelley. He even wrote, "If Shelley had been born a hundred years later, there would have been a Newton among chemists." '

'Shelley in the bells and grass, Shelley with an apple halfway to his head,' I murmured, but my host went me a couple better.

'My heart leaps up when I behold a test tube in the lab!' he cried. 'And did you once see Shelley plain? And was he stained with chemicals?'

'If Shelley was a scientist, then I am a neuro-surgeon,' I said. 'Any scientist knows that the moth cannot desire the star, for the simple scientific reason that the moth cannot see the star. What the moth desires is the street lamp, the candle flame, the light in the window. Too bad Whitehead did not rewrite the great lyric for the sake of modern science.'

'I weep for the man that wept for Adonais,' Moreland sighed.

We both walked over to the window and stared out at the peacocks again.

'Don't ask me how we are going to get out of the present dehumanization of our species,' I told him, 'because I don't know. I am glad to say, to quote Poe, that it is neither beast nor human, it is neither man nor woman, that wakes me every morning at my quiet hotel in London. It is a blackbird, who begins to sing as the clock strikes five. You see –'

But Moreland wanted to show me that he could quote from the poets, too, and he did so:

> The nightingale has a lyre of gold,
> The lark's is a clarion call,
> And the blackbird plays but a boxwood flute,
> But I love him best of all.

We went back and sat down.

'There is, thank God,' I said, 'no such thing as a deblackbirdization.'

'Would you like to see a world conference of Area Men?' Moreland asked. 'If so, do not expect me to attend. There is enough Babel and Bedlam the way it is, and an organization called the United Notions would get us nowhere even faster than we are now going, which is seventeen hundred miles a minute, I believe. Such a convention might even lead to the First Word War.'

'Well, at any rate,' I said, 'you have suggested good titles for a satire, *The United Notions* and *The First Word War*. There are plenty of ideas lying around, but what we lack is wordmen, as they are called in Hollywood, to write about them.'

'Let's get back to *Angst* for a moment,' my host said.

'On the contrary, let's get away from *Angst* for good,' I objected. 'In a review of what he called unscientific science fiction, Kingsley Amis spoke of "the threadbare convention of telepathy." Now, I have studied and practised mental telepathy for sixty years, and its existence is demonstrable. The present *Angst*, the *Zeitgeist* of the moment, is quite simply, it seems to me, the product of mass mental projection of gloom. I have traced its depressing effects during the past two years. In that period I have got a dismaying increase of letters from friends and strangers of all ages, telling of the onset of *Angst*. They use such expressions as anxiety, nameless dread, and even *heulendes Elend*, which is German for the sobbing miseries. Too many people have now got everything from the galloping jumps to the mumbling crumbles, and they are contagious. I have no doubt that telepathy has become a threadbare convention of science fiction, but it is, alas, a monstrous human fact.'

'Let's go and look at the peacocks again,' Moreland sighed, and we both went over to the window.

'I have a theory of my own about the spread of *Angst*,' Moreland said finally. 'We talk too much about this damnable dehumanization, and the process shows up in too many of the dramas and novels of our day. Love has become a four-letter word, and sex is no longer creative but destructive. We are assured, by some authorities, that the normal is a matter of mass behaviour, but the normal can never be synonymous with the average, the majority, the customary, or the habitual. The normal is that which functions in accordance with its design, and in sex, and its inversions and perversions, however popular, we seem to overlook the design of the morphology and biology of the human being.'

'You are oversimplifying,' I told him, 'but it is refreshing in an age of overcomplication.'

'A long time ago we began calling this century the Age of Anxiety and the Aspirin Age,' Moreland went on. 'Your late President Roosevelt, thirty years ago, said that the only thing to fear is fear itself, thus giving the psychiatrist a new term, phobophobia. President Eisenhower spoke so often about the danger of fear and hysteria that he planted them in the consciousness of his television listeners. And then *Time* Magazine not long ago devoted its cover story to an article called "The Anatomy of *Angst*." How can we mentally jam all this broadcasting of gloom?'

'By rising above it,' I said. 'By the lifting of the spirit, by what Dorothy Thompson called, in her last book, "The Courage to Be Happy." It takes guts to be happy, make no mistake about it; and I don't mean slap-happy, or drink-happy, or drug-happy.'

'We are told that the balance of power in the world, and its maintenance, are realistic, but the realistic is not always the true,' Moreland said. 'The greatest truth of our time is both simple and awful – total war means annihilation, and the Brink of War has become the Brink of Was.'

'I wish I had said that,' I murmured. 'Power, incidentally, also tends to make men stupid. When Mikoyan visited the United States, he asked more than one worker, "Do you want war?" They all said no, but bitter irony would have been the proper weapon, if irony were not so dangerous in this age of non-communication. The answer to Mikoyan should have been, "Yes, of course. I should like to be killed, and have my wife and children killed, and all my friends and neighbours, and my city destroyed." '

'We have come a long way from humour and comedy this afternoon,' Moreland sighed.

'On the contrary,' I said, 'we are just getting around to it. Without satire no civilization can be truly described or benefited. We could name many names, from Voltaire to Swift, before we ran into the modern morbid playwrights and sex novelists, who are more interested in the sordid corners of life than in the human heart.'

'You mean the non-heart,' Moreland said. 'Have you counted the recent books that deal with the human condition, or predicament, or tragedy?'

'Yes,' I said, 'and I even remember when we wrote about the bright human spectacle, and the human comedy. If there is no human comedy it will be necessary to create one. How long can the needle of the human gramophone stay in the rut of *Angst* without wearing out and ending in the repetition of a ghoulish gibbering?'

I glanced at my wristwatch and saw that it was time to go. Moreland took me to the door, and we shook hands. I had a final thought, and said to my host: 'I think we must learn to brighten the human idiom, as well as to make it communicable.'

'I'll let you have the last word,' he sighed.

'All right, then,' I said. 'Life at the moment is a tale told in an idiom, full of unsoundness and fury, signifying nonism. The other day I read a love scene in a story that went like this: "Am I beautiful?" she asked him. "Terribly," he said. And then he asked her, "Do you love me?" "Horribly," she said.'

'Why don't you go home and write something humorous?' Graves Moreland demanded. 'Don't you want to?'

'Frightfully,' I told him, and I wandered slowly o'er the lea, wondering if the modern world had lost a great nuclear physicist when Thomas Gray died in the wrong century.

Brother Endicott

HE MAN stared at the paper in his typewriter with the bleak look of a
train-soaked spectator at a dull football game, and then ripped it out
of the machine. He lit a cigarette, put another sheet of paper in the
wringer, and began a letter to his publisher, without salutation: 'Why you
imbeciles have to have a manuscript three months ahead of publication is, by
god –' And out came that sheet. Somewhere a clock began striking three, but
it was drowned out by a sudden upsurge of Paris night noises.

The street noises of Paris, staccato, profundo, momentary and prolonged,
go on all through the summer night, as if hostile hosts were fiercely taking,
losing, and regaining desperately disputed corners, especially the bloody
angle of the Rue de Rivoli and the Rue de Castiglione, just beneath the windows of the writer's hotel room. Presently he heard the jubilant coming of the
Americans, late but indomitable, sleepless but ever fresh, moving in, like the
taxis of the Marne, from the Right Bank and the Left, shouting, laughing,
amiably cursing, as they enveloped and captured the lobby of the hotel. They
loudly occupied corridors and rooms, leaving the King's English sprawled
and bleeding on the barricades of night. A detachment of foot cavalry trooped
past the writer's door, one of the men singing 'Louise' in a bad imitation of
Chevalier.

American reinforcements kept on arriving at the hotel, and below his window the writer heard a young feminine voice crying, 'For God's sake, Mother,
why not? S'only three o'clock!' Her mother's voice cried back at her, 'Your
father's dead and so am I – that's why not.' There was no report from the
father, and the writer visualized him lying on the sidewalk, his wallet deflated,
a spent and valiant victim of the battle of Paris. The writer emptied a clogged
ashtray into a metal wastebasket, switched off the lights in the sitting room of
his suite and sprawled on one of the twin beds in the other room. 'It may be
the Fourth of July to everybody else,' he said aloud, as if talking to someone he
didn't like, 'but it's just two weeks past deadline to me.' He turned over the
phrase, 'The Fourteenth of Deadline,' decided there was nothing in it, and
was about to take off his right shoe when he heard a knock at the door. He
looked at his wristwatch; it was a few minutes past three o'clock.

The late caller was a young woman he had never seen before. She murmured something that sounded like, 'My husband – I thought maybe –' and he
stood aside to let her in, apologizing for his shirtsleeves. 'I was afraid it was the
fellas looking for a tenor,' he said. 'I'm a baritone myself, but out of practice
and not in the mood.' He put the lights on again in the sitting room, waved

casually at a chair and, just as casually, she sat in it. '*Voici le salon*, as they call it,' he said. 'Makes it sound very proper. What can I do for you? My name's Guy Farland.'

'I know,' she said. 'I've heard you typing at night before. I asked at the desk once, and they said you were here. My name is Marie Endicott.'

He reached for his tie and jacket, but she said, with a faint smile, '*Ne vous dérangez pas*. It's too warm.'

'Before we get around to your problem,' he said, 'how about a drink?' He moved to a table containing bottles and glasses and an ice bucket. She nodded when he put his hand on the Scotch bottle. 'Not too strong, please,' she said. 'A lot of soda.'

'I mix drinks my own way,' he told her, 'and I'm said to be good at it. Besides, this is my castle.' He took her in as he fixed the highball, figured that she was not more than twenty-three and that she had had quite a few drinks already, rather desperate ones, which she hadn't enjoyed much. He set her drink down on a table beside her chair. 'If I were a younger writer I would say, "She looked like a chic luna moth in her light green evening gown, as she stood there clutching a dainty evening bag." But you weren't clutching it, just holding it,' he said. 'And I'm a middle-aged writer, not a young one.'

She picked up her drink but didn't taste it. 'I've read your *Lost Corner* four times,' she said. He went back to mix himself a drink, saying, 'It isn't quite that good. I'm trying to finish another book, but you can't think against this goddam racket. I had got used to the Paris taxi horns and their silence makes me edgy. They have cut out the best part of the noise and left in the worst.'

'The goddam motorcycles,' she said tonelessly. He sat down, and they both listened to the tumult outside the window for a moment. 'The noise has loused me up – I choose the precise word for it,' he said. 'It would certainly rain in Verlaine's heart if he could hear it.' She was looking at him as though he were an actor in a spotlight, and he responded with performance. 'I was thinking how silent Paris must have been the night François Villon vanished into immortality through the snows of yesteryear. If your husband has vanished, maybe I can help you find him. I'm a husband myself, and I know where they go. On the Fourth of July, of course, it's a little harder, especially in a foreign country.' He had left the door to the suite ajar, and they could hear a male quartet somewhere down the hall dwelling liquidly on 'The Sweetheart of Sigma Chi.'

'Edward isn't lost,' she said. 'He's the bass. Edward Francis Endicott.' She seemed to add a trace of bitters to the name. 'Wisconsin Alpha. They're in Rip Morgan's room, with a couple of Americans they picked up at this night-club. Edward and Rip insisted on singing "On Wisconsin" – I don't know why we weren't put out – and these strange men knew the words and joined in, but they are from Illinois, and so then they all sang "Loyal to You, Illinois." Our honeymoon has been like that ever since Edward ran into Rip Morgan in Rome.' She gave the word 'honeymoon' a tart inflection. The quartet down the hall now had 'Dear Old Girl' in full swing, and Farland got up and closed the door. 'They sound a little older than juniors or seniors,' he said, coming back to his chair. She took a long swallow of her drink and set the glass down.

'Edward will be forty-six next week,' she said, in the tone of a patient on a psychiatrist's couch, and Farland leaned back for the flow he felt was coming. 'He still wears his fraternity pin. He wore it on his pyjamas on our wedding night. It's the Nelson Merit Pin. He got it one year for being biggest Boopa Doopa Chi in the whole damn country. He has a smaller one, too. Fraternity is his life. Maybe you've heard of Endicott Emblems, Incorporated. Well, he's the president. They make fraternity pins, and signet rings, and everything. He goes around all the time, even over here, with his right hand out like this.' She separated the thumb and little finger of her right hand from the other fingers. 'He gives everybody the grip, in the American Express and at the Embassy, and everywhere he sees an American man. I don't know much about fraternities. I thought it was something men got over, like football practice. I went to Smith.'

Farland noticed that she kept glancing over her right shoulder at the door. 'Brother Endicott won't break in on us,' he said reassuringly. 'Quartets never notice that wives are missing. As for my wife, she's in Italy.'

'I knew she wasn't here,' Marie Endicott said, and Farland followed her gaze about the room, which must have revealed instantly to his visitor the lack of a woman's touch. There were books and papers on the floor, and that unmistakable masculine rearrangement of chairs and lamps which a man finds comfortable and a woman intolerable. 'Nancy is going to pick up our daughters in Italy – we have two. They are coming over on one of the Export ships because they wanted to see Gibraltar. I don't work at night when Nancy's here. Wives don't think it's healthy.'

'Ellen Morgan went to bed,' said the girl, 'and Edward thinks I'm in bed, too.' She took several long swallows of drink this time, and sat forward in her chair. 'The reason I'm here, the thing is,' she began, with a flash of firmness, and then leaned back with a helpless flutter of her left hand. Farland gave her a cigarette and held a match for her.

'Don't get a blockage,' he said easily. 'I'm the one with the blockage. I was thinking of throwing the heroine of my novel out of a window, but you can't do that in novels, only in real life.' The girl wasn't listening.

'Edward can't stand any foreign country,' she said, 'because it isn't God's country, and they don't use God's money, and you can't get God's martinis, or God's anything.' Her eyes drifted toward an unopened bottle of bourbon on the table. 'Or God's whisky,' she said. 'Bourbon is God's whisky, you know.'

'He must have trouble getting God's ice, too,' Farland put in, 'especially at this hour.'

'They don't supply soap at most French hotels,' she went on. 'In the hotel in Le Havre he called downstairs and said, "Some of you cave dwellers come up here with some soap and make it snappy. Endicott wants soap." He speaks of himself in the third person a lot of the time. He doesn't know any French except "*combien*" and "*trop cher*" and "*encore la même chose*" and "*où est le cabinet?*" He calls terraces sitdowns, and he's terrible about the new franc. He says, "*Pas si* goddam *vite*" to taxi drivers. He learned what he calls dough-boy French from his brother Harry. Harry is much older. He was in the First World War. You know doughboy French? "*Restez ici* a minute. *Je retourner après cet* guy *partirs.*"' She drank some more and went back to brother Harry. 'Harry thinks he's dying.' she said. 'He thinks he's dying of everything, but there isn't anything the matter with him. He ought to go to a psychiatrist, and he actually did once, but the doctor said something like, "If you're not sick, and you think you're sick, you're sick." And Harry slammed out of his office.'

'Nice slamming,' Farland said. 'I think I would have, too.'

The girl in the green dress took in a long sad breath and exhaled slowly. 'Harry carries a little mirror, like a woman, and keeps looking at his mouth, even in public,' she said. 'He thinks there's something the matter with his uvula.'

'I'm sorry you told me that,' Farland said. 'It is the only part of my body I have never been conscious of. Can you die of uvulitis or something?'

'Harry and his wife were over here,' the girl continued, 'but they flew back last week, thank God. He suddenly got the idea in the middle of the night that his doctor had secretly called Irene and told her he was dying – Harry, I mean. "This is my last vacation," he screamed, waking Irene up. She thought he had lost his mind in his sleep. "I'm not going to die in Naples or any other foreign city!" he yelled. "I'm going to die in Buffalo!" *We* live in Milwaukee. It isn't far enough from Buffalo.'

'You were just about to tell me why you came here. I don't mean to Europe, I mean to my chambers, tonight – this morning,' Farland said, but she post-poned the reason for her call with a wave of her hand. He sat back and let her flow on. 'Edward is a collector,' she said. 'Big heavy things, like goal posts. He's football crazy, too. I thought he was really crazy once when we were having a cocktail and he lifted his glass and said, "Here's to Crazy Legs!" That's Roy Hirsch,' she explained. 'One of the Wisconsin gridiron immortals. He also drinks to the Horse. That's Ameche. He's immortal, too.'

'I'm trying to figure out what you saw in Edward Endicott,' Farland said, a flick of impatience in his tone. 'It's supposed to be a human mystery, I know, but there's usually a clue of some kind.'

She gestured with her hand again and frowned. 'He has more drums than anybody else in the world,' she went on. 'He began collecting them when he was a little boy, and now he has African drums and Maori drums and some from the Civil War and one from the Revolution. He even has a drum that was used in the road company of *The Emperor Jones*, and one of the forty or fifty that were used in *Valencia* during a big production number at the Casino de Paris in 1925, I think it was.' She shuddered slightly, as if she heard all the Endicott drums approaching. 'Is collecting goal posts Freudian?' she asked.

Farland decided to think that over while he freshened the drinks. 'I don't think so,' he said. 'Goal posts are trophies, a sign your side won. The Indians had it worked out better, of course. Scalping the captain of the losing team would be much simpler. Where does he keep the goal posts?'

'In the attic,' she said, 'except for the one in the guest room. It belonged to Southern Cal. or S.M.U., or somebody we didn't expect to beat and did.' She managed a small evil inflection on 'we.'

'All right, let's have it,' Farland said. 'Why did you come here tonight? All this is overture, I can tell that.'

She sat forward suddenly again. 'Tom will be here, I mean right here, in your suite, in a few minutes,' she said, hurriedly. 'He sent me a message by a waiter at the nightclub, while Edward was trying to get the little French orchestra to play "Back in Your Own Back Yard." Tom must have followed me there. I had to think quick, and all I could think of was your room, because you're always up late.'

Farland got up and put on his tie and coat. 'I ought to look more *de rigueur* for Tom,' he said. 'You're not constructing this very well. You don't just hit your readers with a character named Tom. They have a right to know who he is and what he wants.'

'I'm sorry,' she said. 'I mean about asking him to come here. He's awfully difficult, but at least he isn't predictable. He loves to sweep everything off the mantlepiece when he's mad, but he doesn't use a straight razor and strop it all the time, like Edward. Tom and I were engaged for years, but he didn't want to get married until he got through his army service, so we broke up about that. Everybody else got married and went to camp with their husbands. They had four million babies last year, the American girls.'

'American girls often marry someone they can't stand to spite someone they can,' he said. 'That's a pretty rough generalization, but I haven't got time to polish it up. Is that where Brother Endicott came in?'

'I don't really know what state Tom is in,' she said. 'He just got out of the service, and I was afraid he would follow me here. It's a long story about how I met Edward. I wanted to come back to Paris. You see, I had spent my junior year here, and I loved Paris. Of course, my mother went completely to pieces. I had a job in New York, but every evening when I got home Mother was waiting for me. Sometimes crocked. She always wanted to have a little talk. We had more little talks than all the mothers and daughters in the world. I was going crazy, and then I met Edward. He seemed so strong and silent and –' She groped for a word and came up with 'attentive.' Farland give her another cigarette. 'He wasn't really strong and silent. He was just on the wagon. Tom hadn't written for months, and I thought maybe he had another girl, and Edward promised to bring me to Paris, and so – I don't know.'

'Paris seems to be full of American girls who are hiding out from their mothers,' Farland said. This caused a flash of lightning in her eyes.

'Mother belongs to the damn lost generation,' she said. 'The trouble with the lost generation is it didn't get lost enough. All the damn lost mothers had only one child,' she went on, warming to what was apparently a familiar thesis. 'They all think their daughters are weak enough to do the things they thought they were strong enough to do. So we have to pay for what they did. I'm glad I missed the 1920's. God.'

'They've stopped singing,' Farland said. 'They must be taking a whisky break. How do I fit into this – for Tom, I mean? I don't want to be knocked cold when he gets here. I seem to be in the middle.'

As if it were an entrance cue, there were two sharp raps on the door. Farland hurried out and opened it. A tall young man breezed past him and into the sitting room. 'Are you all right?' he demanded of the girl.

'No,' Farland said. 'Do you want a drink?'

'This is Mr Farland, Mr Gregg,' said Mrs Endicott. Mr Gregg scowled at his host. 'I don't get this,' he said. 'What is that baboon doing now? Could I have a straight Scotch?' Farland put some Scotch and ice in a glass and gave it to him.

'They're probably running out of whisky,' the girl said. 'I don't want Edward to find me gone.'

'He might as well get used to it,' said Tom. He began pacing. 'I was hanging around out front when you left the hotel,' he said, 'and I followed you to that nightclub. It cost me five bucks for one drink, five bucks and taxi fare to write that note.' He suddenly pulled the girl up out of her chair and into his arms.

'This is pretty damned unplanned,' Farland said.

'I got to have half an hour with Marie. We've got to settle some things,' Tom said peremptorily. 'I'm sorry I was so abrupt.' He held out the hand that swept things off mantelpieces. He had a quick, firm grip. 'I haven't got any plans, except to get her away from that monkey,' he said.

'The law is on his side, of course,' Farland put in, 'and the church and all that sort of thing.' The girl had freed herself and sat down again, and Tom resumed his pacing.

'Do you know the grip?' Farland asked her suddenly. 'I think it may be mine. Don't hit me,' he said to the young man.

'Tom threw his pledge pin across the room at a chapter meeting, I think they call it,' the girl said.

'Somebody said something,' Tom snarled.

Farland nodded. 'People have a way of doing that,' he said. 'Human failing.' He held out his right hand to the girl and she gave him the grip. 'Now I do *this*,' he said, pressing her wrist. 'And I do *this*,' she said, returning the pressure. Each then pressed the other's thumb.

'Don't you wiggle your ears, for crissake?' Tom snarled.

'Brother Endicott,' Farland sighed, 'shake hands with Brother Farland. Pennsylvania Gamma.' He picked up the unopened bottle of bourbon and the ice bucket. 'I think I can promise you your half hour undisturbed,' he said. 'God's whisky and the grip ought to do it, and besides, I know the words of "Back in Your Own Back Yard." I also know the "Darling" song.'

'God,' said Marie Endicott.

Tom stopped pacing and looked at Farland. 'Damned white of you,' he said, 'but I don't know why you're doing it.'

'Lady in distress,' Farland said. 'Cry for help in the night. I don't know much about drums, but I can talk about Brother Hunk Elliot.'

'Ohio Gamma,' said Mrs Endicott bleakly. 'Greatest by God halfback that ever lugged a football, even if he did beat Wisconsin three straight years. Crazy Legs and the Horse don't belong to Boopa Doopa Chi, so they don't rate with Brother Elliot.'

'The protocol of fraternity is extremely complicated and uninteresting,' Farland said.

'Nuts,' snapped Tom, who had begun to crack his knuckles. 'Why doesn't that goddam racket stop?' He suddenly leaped at the open window of the salon and shouted into the night, 'Cut down that goddam noise!'

'Do you want everybody *in* here?' the girl asked nervously.

'I don't see why I shouldn't go down there myself and bust him a couple,' he said. 'I don't see why you had to marry him anyway. Nobody in her right mind would marry a man old enough to be her father, and live in Milwaukee.' He whirled and stared at Farland. 'I don't see what you're getting out of this,' he said, 'acting like her fairy godfather or somebody.'

'I –' Farland began, but Mrs Endicott cut in on him. There was a new storm in her eyes. 'He's done more for me in one night than you have in two years!' she said. 'You never wrote, and when you did, nobody could read it, the way you write. How do I know who you were running around with in Tacoma? You're not really in love with me, you just want something somebody else has not.' Farland tried to get in on it again, but Tom Gregg gave him a little push and turned to the girl again.

'It wasn't Tacoma,' he said. 'You didn't even bother to find out what camp I was at.'

'Seattle, then,' she said. 'Fort Lawton. And everybody else got married. I know ten girls who went to camp with their husbands, and three of them were in Tacoma.'

'We couldn't get married on nothing,' he said. 'I happen to have a job now, a good job.'

'Everybody else got married on nothing,' she said.

'I'm not everybody else!' he yelled. 'I'm not just anybody else, either. "Miss Withrow, I want you to meet Mr Endicott." "How do you do, Miss Withrow. Will you marry me?" "Sure, why not? I think I'm engaged to a guy named Tacoma or something, but that's okay." '

'I'll hit you, I really will!' cried the former Miss Withrow.

Farland hastily put the bottle and the ice bucket on the floor and stepped between them. 'I'm not anybody's fairy godfather,' he said. 'I'm just an innocent bystander. I was about to go to bed when all this hell broke loose, and I'll be damned if I'm going down to that room and sing with a lot of big fat emblem makers if you're going to spend your time fighting.' His voice was pitched even louder than theirs. The telephone rang. Farland picked up the receiver and listened for three seconds to a voice on the other end speaking in French. 'It's the Fourth of July!' he yelled, and slammed down the receiver.

'I'm sorry about this,' Tom said. 'I'm willing to talk it over rationally if she is. I got to fly back to work day after tomorrow.'

'Oh, sure,' said Marie.

'I don't usually lose my temper,' Farland apologized, 'but I'm stuck in a book I'm writing, and it makes me jumpy.' He picked up the bottle and the ice bucket again. 'I'll give you until four o'clock,' he said. 'I'll knock four times, with an interval after the third.'

'You probably haven't got your key,' Marie said. She spied it, put it in Farland's pocket, and kissed him on the forehead.

'Do you have to keep doing that?' Tom shouted.

'I haven't *been* doing that,' Marie said.

'Please!' Farland said. 'I'm tossing her aside like a broken doll, anyway.' He grinned. 'How in hell can I open this door with my arms loaded?' Marie crossed over and opened the door for him. 'For God's sake, don't kiss me again,' he whispered, 'and stop fighting and get something worked out.' He raised his voice and spoke to both of them. 'Goodnight,' he said, 'and shut up.' He stepped out into the hall and the girl in the green dress quietly closed the door after him . . . .

A short, heavy-set man in his middle forties opened the door, and seemed to block the way aggressively until he caught sight of the American face of the visitor and the things he was carrying. 'I heard the Yankee Doodle sounds,' Farland told him, and introduced himself. 'I thought maybe you needed reinforcements.' The room exploded into American sounds, as if the newcomer had dropped a lighted match in a box of fireworks. Somebody took the bourbon from him and somebody else the ice bucket. 'My God, it's real ice!' someone said, and 'Brother, you've saved our lives!'

'An American shouldn't spend this night alone,' Farland said above the hubbub. The biggest man in the room, who wore no coat or tie, but on whose vest a fraternity pin gleamed, held out his hand in three parts. Farland gave him the full-dress grip. 'Ed Endicott, Wisconsin Alpha!' bawled the big man.

'Pennsylvania Gamma,' Farland said.

'For crissake, it's a small world!' Endicott said. 'Rip, shake hands with Brother Farland, give him the old grip. Brother Morgan and I belong to the same chapter. Wisconsin Alpha has two national presidents to its credit,' he told Farland, 'and I was one of them, if I do say so myself. These other poor guys took the wrong pins, but they're okay.' He managed somehow to get his right arm around the shoulders of both the other men in the room. 'This is Sam Winterhorn, Phi Gam from Illinois, and this is Red Perry, also Illini – Red's a Phi Psi. Maybe you heard us doing "Fiji Honeymoon" and "When DKE Has Gone to Hell." Put 'er there again, fella.'

Farland was glad when he was finally given a glass to hold instead of a man's right hand. 'Here's to all the brothers, whatever sky's above 'em,' Endicott said, clinking his glass against Farland's. He took a great gulp of his drink, and it seemed to Farland that his face brightened like a full moon coming out from behind a cloud. 'Endicott is a curly wolf this night, Guy, and you can write that home to your loved ones!' he roared. 'Endicott is going to shake hands with the pearly-fingered dawn this day. Endicott is going to ring all the bells and blow all the whistles in hell. Any frog that don't like it can bury his head in the Tooleries.' Farland managed to get out part of a word, but Brother Endicott trampled on it. 'The girls have gone to bed,' he said. 'Wish you could meet Marie, but we'll be around a couple of more days. Marie's Eastern women's college, but Brenda – that's my first wife – was a Kappa. So's Ellen Morgan, Rip's wife. Brenda hated drums. I got the greatest little drum collection in the world, Guy. Once, when a gang of us got up a storm in my house – this was six-seven years ago – damned if Brenda didn't call the cops! One of them turned out to be real mean with the sticks, but the other guy was a surly bastard. I tried to give him the grip, and he got sore as hell. Don't ever try to give a cop the grip, Guy. They think you're queer. Sons-of-bitches never get through high school.'

Farland put on his fixed grin as Endicott rambled on, moving among the disarranged chairs like a truck. He paused in front of one in which Brother Morgan now lay back relaxed, with his eyes closed. 'Judas Priest, our tenor's conking out,' he said.

' 'Way,' mumbled Morgan sleepily.

'Let him sleep,' said the man named Perry. 'What the hell, we still got a quartet. Anyway, what good's a sleepy tenor unless you're doing "Sleepy Time Gal"?'

' "Sleepy Time Gal!" ' bawled Endicott, and he suddenly started in the middle of the old song, biting a great hunk out of the lyric. The phone rang, and Endicott smote the night with a bathroom word and jerked up the receiver. 'Yeah?' he began truculently, and, as the voice at the other end began protesting in French, he said to the revellers, 'It's one of them quoi-quois.' He winked heavily at Farland and addressed the transmitter. '*Parlez-vous la langue de Dieu?*' he asked. Farland realized he had been rehearsing the question quite a while. '*Bien*, then,' Endicott went on. 'You people ought to be celebrating, too. If we hadn't let Lafayette fight on our side, he would have gone to the goddam guillotine. The way it was, even Napoleon didn't dare lay a hand on him. They cut the head off Rabelais and Danton, but they couldn't touch Lafayette, and that's on account of the good old Thirteen States.' The person at the other end had apparently hung up, but Endicott went on with his act. 'Get yourselves a bottle of grenadine and a pack of cubebs and raise a little hell for Lafayette,' he said, and hung up.

'Not Rabelais,' Farland couldn't help saying. 'Robespierre.'

'Or old Roquefort!' Endicott bawled. 'They all sound like cheese to me, rich old framboise, and they all look alike. Let's hit the "Darling" song again.'

They got through 'Three O'Clock in the Morning' and 'Linger Awhile' and 'Over There' and 'Yankee Doodle Dandy' and 'You're the B-E-S-T Best' and by that time it was ten minutes after four. 'Don't keep looking at your Benrus,' Endicott told Farland. 'Nobody's going anywhere. What the hell, we've got all day.' Rip Morgan's troubled unconscious greeted this with a faint moaning sound. Farland's tone grew firm and terminal, and the Illinois men joined him and began the final round of handshakes. Farland picked up the ice bucket, which had been empty for some time now, and started for the door.

'We'll all meet in the bar downstairs at six,' Endicott commanded. 'Be there!' The two departing Americans said they would be there. 'I'm going to stay stiff till they pour me on the plane,' Endicott went on. Farland's hand felt full of fingers after he had shaken hands again with the Illinois men and they had gone. Brother Endicott, he felt sure, would have his hands full for at least fifteen minutes, putting Brother Morgan to bed. . . .

Farland rapped on the door of his suite three times, paused, and rapped again. There was no response, and he unlocked the door and went in. All the lights in the sitting room were out except one, and he turned it off and began undressing before he reached the bedroom. The battle of the Paris night still went on, and it seemed louder than ever. Farland put on the bottom of his pyjamas, couldn't find the top, said, 'The hell with it,' and went into the bathroom and brushed his teeth. 'Everything happens to you,' he sneered at the man in the mirror. 'What's the matter, don't you know how to duck any more?'

He was about to throw himself on his bed when he noticed the note on his pillow. It read simply, 'You are the B-E-S-T Best,' and it was signed, obviously in Mrs Endicott's handwriting, 'Tom and Marie.' In spite of the noise and his still tingling right hand, Farland fell asleep. When he woke up, he picked up the telephone and called the *renseignement* desk. He looked at his watch. It was nine-thirty-five. 'I want to get a plane out of here for Rome this afternoon,' he said when the information desk answered. 'A single seat. And I don't care what line. There is just one thing. It has *got* to leave before six o'clock.'

The Manic in the Moon

'MOST trains of thought and avenues of conversation lead eventually to the moon nowadays,' a professor observed at a summer party in Connecticut. We had been talking about President Kennedy's gift to Khrushchev in Vienna of a replica of the frigate Constitution, and my companion wondered how many young Americans know that the Constitution was Old Ironsides. At this moment, we were joined by a young female American who said she didn't know, and couldn't care less. I asked her if she had never heard of the line 'Old Ironsides at anchor lay in the harbour of Mahon.'

'No,' she said, 'and I don't want to know where Mahon is, if there *is* a Mahon.' She left us abruptly for the company of less disturbed persons, and the professor said, 'It would have been a clever piece of propaganda if the President had had a paraphrase of that line engraved in tiny words on the prow of the frigate: "Old Ironsides at anchor lay in the harbour of the moon." '

Since we were now launched successfully into space, we went on to discuss the letters published in *Izvestia* from formerly religious readers who had suddenly given up their belief in God because of the flights of Gagarin and Titov. One of these correspondents, I have been told, said that this minute monkeying around in a minuscule corner of the universe (that is my own description of it) proved that science is God, and only Man is truly super and supernal. Why this person had not been saved by the new scientific salvation when the eight-engine bomber was invented, or the H-bomb, I do not know. I don't happen to be a phrenetically religious man myself, but I flatly refuse to accept Gagarin as the Son of a new God. Since the professor had got into paraphrase, I suggested that radio would overlook a good bet if it did not revive the old *Superman* series and change the line 'It's a bird! It's a plane! It's Superman!' to 'It's a bird! It's a plane! It's God!'

To get off the subject of outer space, I remarked that I had had a dream in which the Jehovah of the Old Testament offered me the opportunity of changing species and asked me what species I would choose. I said that I would like to be a warbler, but I couldn't stand the hours.

Charles Wertenbaker (to get back to the moon by a special avenue) coined the paraphrase 'Lo, the poor idiom.' He couldn't have realized that he was dealing in terms of prophecy, since he died before his restless species began taking competitively to outer space in order to explore the neighbourhood of what Alfred North Whitehead called 'a second-rate planet with a second-rate sun,' thus wryly summarizing the Man-shaking discovery of Copernicus that the earth is not the centre of the universe. We all know how Man loves to be the centre of everything, from attention to eternity. What is going on now, or going up, would not surprise Whitehead, who would have been over a hundred this year if he had lived. Man has reached both poles, the top of Everest, the bottom of the ocean, and the end of his mundane tether, and there is no place left for him to go but up.

The poor idiom now stands in danger of being turned inside out and upside down as the result of our compulsion to reach the moon and points beyond. It seems certain that many old familiar expressions and solid clichés will undergo, before long, a complete change in meaning and application. Many phrases connoting soundness and security will, it seems to me, become old-fashioned and even obsolete. 'Both feet on the ground' will no longer indicate, as the century flies on and up, sanity in a man but cowardice, or, at best, apathy. The same will be true of 'down to earth,' 'well-grounded,' 'stands his ground,' and 'it suits me down to the ground.' Conversely, such common usages as 'up in the air' and 'going around in circles' and 'looping' must lose their sense of flightiness and become symbols of flight. These prospective reversals of meaning are likely to contribute to what is already being called the 'space neurosis.' 'The world is too much with us' will not be easy to explain, in a decade or so, to a foreigner striving to learn and make sense out of the New English.

One of the inevitable changes that I view with alarm will be in the area of phrases now associated with nobility of character, gallantry, and beauty. Medical science will not be able to determine for many years, I understand, the effects of space travel on the human mind and organism – effects that may be grave and, for all anybody knows, fatal. Thus, 'light-hearted' may come to mean a cardiac condition, and 'high-minded' may be solely applied to mental states brought about by speed, momentum, and distance from the earth. I deplore the possibility that 'earth goddess' may come to signify a female human being unwilling to accompany her husband into the wild blue yonder, hence maladjusted, behind the times, timorous, and even psychotic. Such a woman will not be, alas, 'out of this world.' I shudder to think that 'starry-eyed' may no longer describe a pretty girl, aglow with love, hope, and wonder, but an ophthalmological ailment similar to glaucoma. And let us pray that 'out of sight, out of mind' will not mean, in the interstellar future, temporarily blinded and demented by soaring too close to the sun.

I can foresee in, say, the year 2000 the kind of phrases the disgruntled wife of an inveterate space traveller will hurl at her husband after he has been rocketing around in the empyrean off and on for a decade or so. I have a premonition that they will include 'Go jump into space,' 'Tell it to the Martians!,' 'Get lost in the stars,' and 'I'm tired of you throwing your weightlessness around.'

An American friend of mine in London, where I recently spent several months trying not to think about the future, staggered into my hotel room one day, asked me for God's sake to give him a drink, and, when I did, began pouring out his fears about the coming ominous effects of space mania upon certain popular songs in which the moon figures as a romantic symbol of love and lovers. 'We can't keep on singing "The moon belongs to everyone, the best things in life are free," ' he babbled, 'if either Russia or the United States plants its flag on the moon first.' What especially worried my friend, he told me on his second drink, was what will happen to the last line of the old ballad called 'I'll Be Seeing You.' I didn't happen to remember that last line offhand, and so he sang it for me: 'I'll be looking at the moon, but I'll be seeing you.' He sang it so loudly and with such a note of terror in his voice that my wife rushed in from the next room and said, 'Are you all right?' We both said 'No,' in unison, and she withdrew and shut the door behind her. 'The women are not worrying enough,' my friend said.

'They're down to earth, that's why,' I told him. 'They have a leg to stand on.' And then I asked, 'What worries you so much about that last line you just sang?'

'I'll tell you what worries me about it,' he said. 'I woke up this morning and found myself singing "I'll be looking at the moon, but I'll be seeing U.S.S.R." Then I got into "I've told every little star just how wonderful U.S.S.R." ' He sat down and put his head in his trembling hands.

'You're going to get the Birch Society after you if you don't look out,' I warned him. 'If you're going to go airminded – that is, space-kooky – for heaven's sake do it patriotically.'

'How?' he demanded.

'Well,' I said, 'take that old Crosby ballad "Moonlight Becomes You." Now, the last line of that goes "Moonlight becomes you so." Why not change that to "Moonlight becomes U.S."? You might also try "I told every milky way all about the U.S.A." '

My moon-struck visitor wasn't listening, though, and suddenly began walking up and down again. 'How do we know stars fell on Alabama?' he demanded. 'Maybe they were thrown there – by a Castronaut!' he yelped. He walked over and waved a finger at me, as if I were to blame for it all. 'Do you know what moonbeams will become?' he said. 'They will become messages beamed at the moon! Even if the moon finally does belong to us, it will no longer be one of the best things in life that are free. It will cost forty-eight billion dollars.'

'Nobody has planted a flag on the moon yet,' I reminded him. 'It still has its place in poetry and romance, and, as a satellite, it still goes on affecting the tides.'

'It affects the tides and the fit-to-be-tieds,' my friend said mournfully.

Before long, he went to sleep in his chair, and for a while I sat brooding about the imminent disfigurations of sense and meaning. 'Inner man' would someday be nothing more than a man inside a space capsule, and 'somebody up there loves me' would be an allusion to a husband, lover, father, or son in orbit.

I went into the bedroom and asked my wife what we should do about my visitor. 'Why don't you call his wife and tell her to come over and get him?' she said. So I telephoned his flat, but his wife was out, and Clara, the maid, answered the phone. Clara is a foreigner who has always spoken an unknown language all her own, but I discovered, to my dismay, that it had become distorted by my space thoughts.

'She has gone to the moonies,' said Clara, 'I mean the movies. Now wasn't that stupnik of me!'

'Get thee to a moonery,' I said, and hung up on her.

'What's the matter with everybody?' my wife asked, meaning me, my space-ridden friend in the next room, and all other men. I thought it over for a moment and then told her.

'Everybody is talking in moon syllables,' I said. 'It's becoming moonotonous. It's a goddam moonstrosity.' I thought that covered it, but my wife, as she so often does, topped me.

'You're moondoggling,' she said. 'Why don't you get your mind on something else?'

When I went back into the living room, my friend was wide awake again and fixing himself a double Scotch and soda. He took up his babbling where he had left off. 'In ten years everything we now say will have a new meaning, or maybe I should say a new mooning.'

'Please don't,' I broke in, but he went right on.

'Footloose and fancy free will become footloose and fanny free, meaning the astronaut can't get his feet on the floor of the spaceship or his bottom on the chair. A fast woman will simply be one who is going at a speed of seventeen hundred miles a minute. If she is in a delicate condition, it will mean she is so far from earth that she weighs less than fifteen pounds.'

I got him to his flat in Russell Square somehow, and turned him over to his wife, who had got back from the moonies. When she had put him to bed and returned to the living room, she pointed nervously at a potted plant on a table. 'Do you know what he calls that?' she quavered.

'I can guess,' I said. 'He calls it a potted planet.' I was right.

'When I got home, I found Clara in tears,' she told me. 'She said you told her to get her to a moonastery.'

'I did not,' I said. 'I would never tell a woman to get her to a moonastery. *You* know that.'

'I don't know what I know. I don't know what anybody is talking about any more.'

My hotel in London is near Green Park, and when I am there in spring and summer I am waked each morning by the gay singing of a blackbird. His song takes my mind off the moony present and the star-crossed future, and back to the tranquil years that W. E. Henley wrote about. The morning after my friend's descent upon me, I began whistling in bed, accompanied by the blackbird's boxwood flute. This woke up my wife, who said drowsily, 'I'm glad you're in a better moon – I mean –'

'I know what you mean,' I told her, 'but for God's sake don't tell me I'm in high spirits. High spirits is what you drink from a flask when you are two hundred and fifty thousand miles from earth.'

'It isn't far enough,' my wife murmured as she dropped off to sleep again. I wasn't so lucky.

When I got back to my home in the United States, I turned to the Oxford English Dictionary and looked up 'moon.' One of the definitions I encountered was 'moonproof: proof against the moon's light or influence.' Obviously, we are going to need moon-proofers as time goes onward and upward. The practice of moon-proofing may even become a branch of psychiatry, like psychotherapy. The expression 'in a moon' once meant 'in a fit of frenzy,' and the moon-proofers will have to get their patients out of that condition.

Paul Nash, the English painter and critic, who died long before the race into space began, once did a collage showing the moon being attacked by a certain European herb with showy flowers, and he called his creation 'Last Night Light and Heavy Hellebores Bombed the Mountains of the Moon.' I found, on looking up the herb in the dictionary, that the powdered root of the white American hellebore is used to kill lice and caterpillars. Now, it happens that lice and caterpillars are not two of my many problems, but I keep thinking about Paul Nash's floral bombers, and I wish he were still on earth to do another, more timely collage, one to be entitled 'Last Night Light and Heavy Moonbores Attacked the Mountains of the Earth.'

What do you say we all sleep outdoors one of these balmy summer nights, braving the agitating effects of moonlight? We might even try to remember the years when tranquillity did not come in bottles but was a simple anodyne of nature, the years when the outdoors at night, under the light of our so disturbing satellite, was serenely known as the Inn of the Silver Moon.